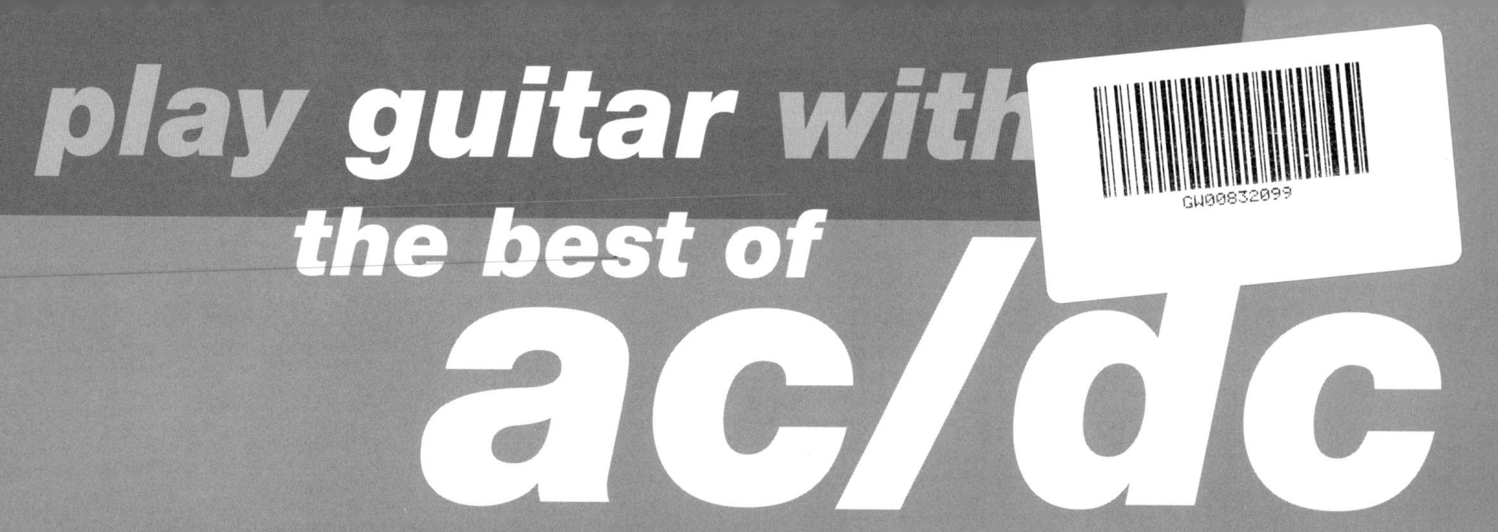
play guitar with
the best of
ac/dc
GW00832099

Published by
**Wise Publications**
14-15 Berners Street, London W1T 3LJ, UK

Exclusive Distributors:
**Music Sales Limited**
Distribution Centre, Newmarket Road,
Bury St Edmunds, Suffolk IP33 3YB, UK

**Music Sales Pty Limited**
20 Resolution Drive,
Caringbah, NSW 2229, Australia

Order No. AM998052
ISBN 978-1-84938-159-8


Printed in the EU

www.musicsales.com

Compiled by Nick Crispin
Music arranged by Arthur Dick
Edited by Tom Farncombe
Music processed by Paul Ewers Music Design

CD recorded, mixed and mastered by Jonas Persson
Additional progamming by Rick Cardinali
All guitars by Arthur Dick
Bass by Tom Farncombe
Drums by Noam Lederman

# play guitar with...
# the best of
# ac/dc

**Wise Publications**
part of The Music Sales Group
*London/New York/Paris/Sydney/Copenhagen/Berlin/Madrid/Tokyo*

***Your Guarantee of Quality***

***As publishers, we strive to produce every book to the highest commercial standards. The music has been freshly engraved and the book has been carefully designed to minimise awkward page turns and to make playing from it a real pleasure. Particular care has been given to specifying acid-free, neutral-sized paper made from pulps which have not been elemental chlorine bleached. This pulp is from farmed sustainable forests and was produced with special regard for the environment. Throughout, the printing and binding have been planned to ensure a sturdy, attractive publication which should give years of enjoyment. If your copy fails to meet our high standards, please inform us and we will gladly replace it.***

# guitar tablature explained

Guitar music can be notated in three different ways: on a musical stave, in tablature and in rhythm slashes

RHYTHM SLASHES: are written above the stave. Strum chords in the rhythm indicated. Round noteheads indicate single notes.

THE MUSICAL STAVE: shows pitches and rhythms and is divided by lines into bars. Pitches are named after the first seven letters of the alphabet.

TABLATURE: graphically represents the guitar fingerboard. Each horizontal line represents a string, and each number represents a fret.

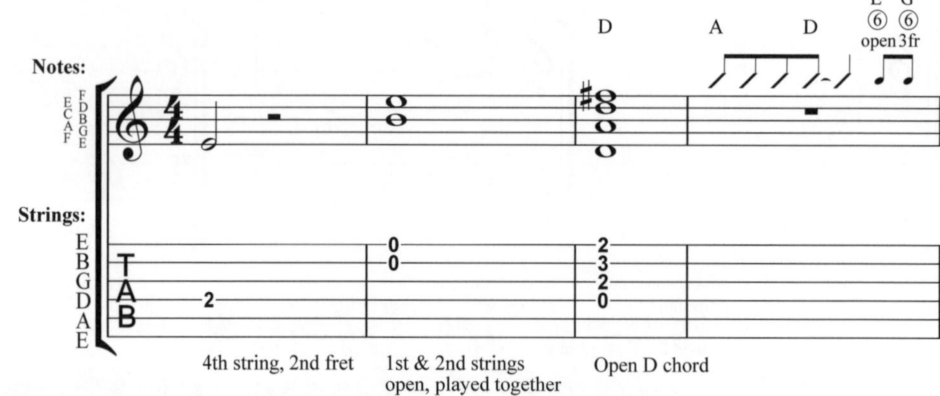


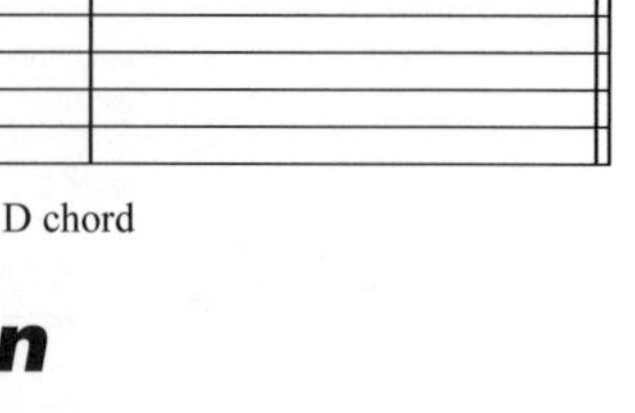

## definitions for special guitar notation

SEMI-TONE BEND: Strike the note and bend up a semi-tone (½ step).

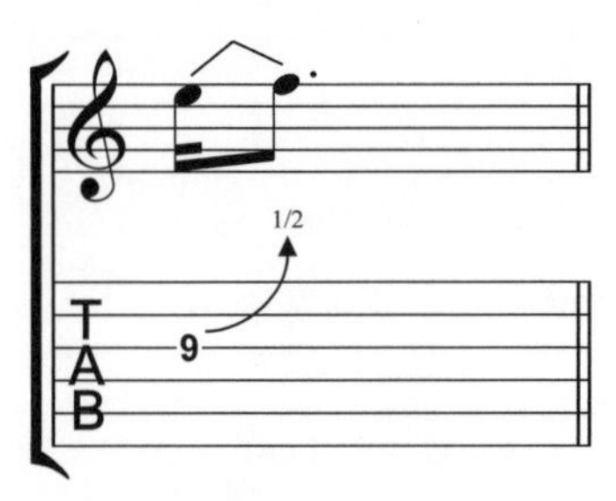


WHOLE-TONE BEND: Strike the note and bend up a whole-tone (full step).

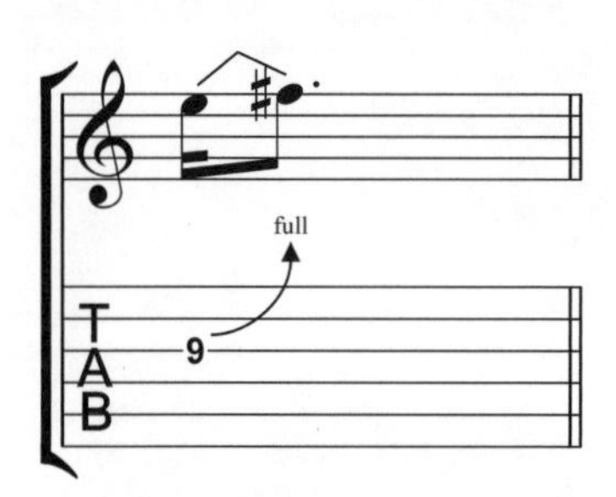


GRACE NOTE BEND: Strike the note and bend as indicated. Play the first note as quickly as possible.

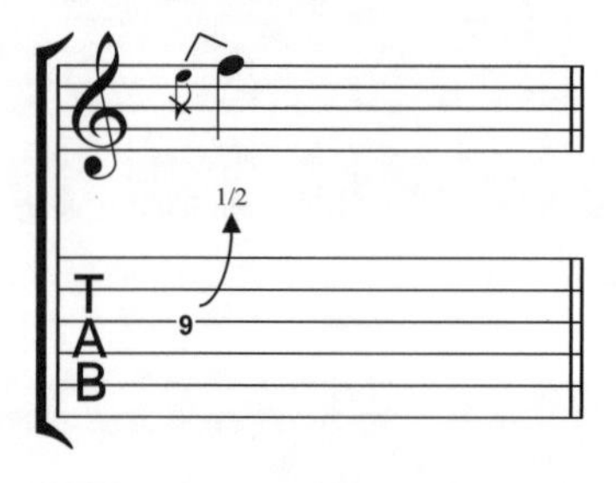


QUARTER-TONE BEND: Strike the note and bend up a ¼ step

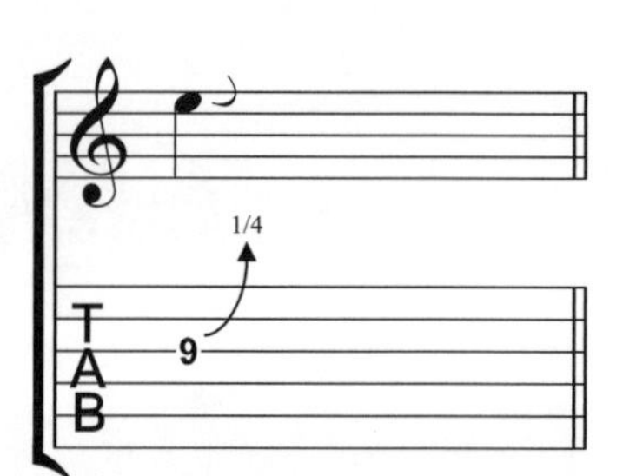


BEND & RELEASE: Strike the note and bend up as indicated, then release back to the original note.

COMPOUND BEND & RELEASE: Strike the note and bend up and down in the rhythm indicated.

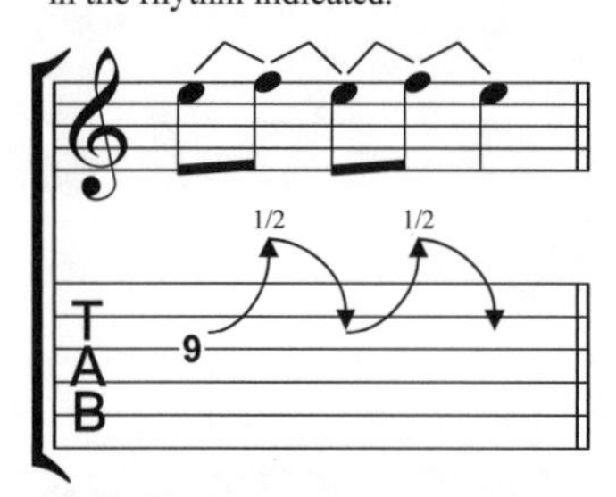


PRE-BEND: Bend the note as indicated, then strike it.

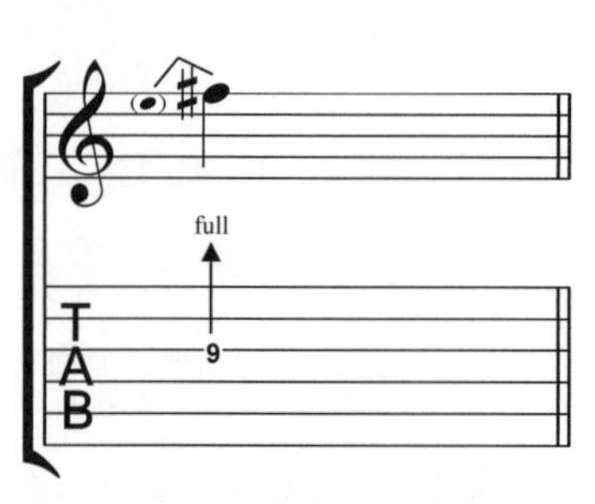


PRE-BEND & RELEASE: Bend the note as indicated. Strike it and release the note back to the original pitch.

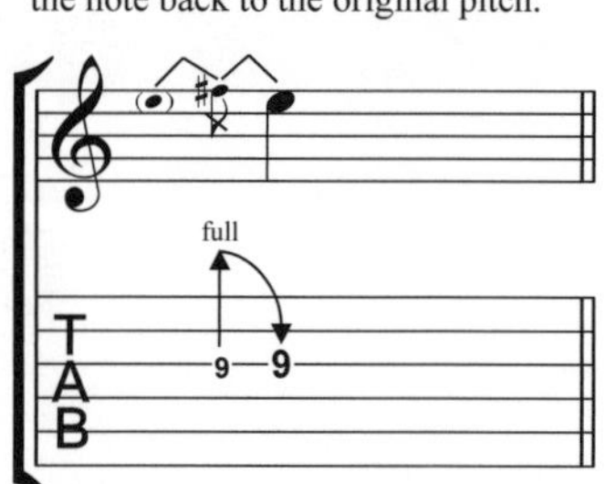


HAMMER-ON: Strike the first note with one finger, then sound the second note (on the same string) with another finger by fretting it without picking.

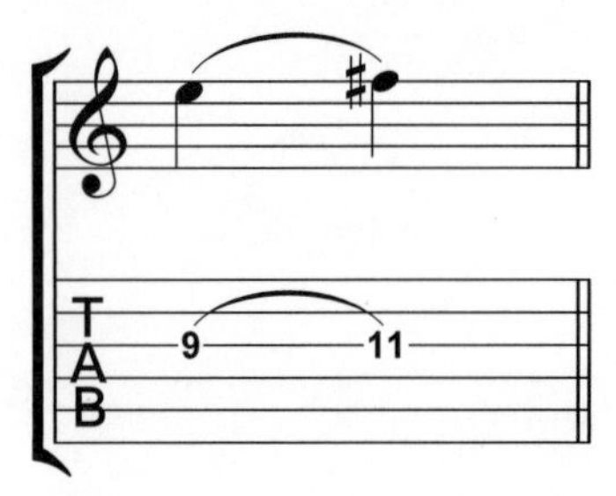

PULL-OFF: Place both fingers on the note to be sounded, strike the first note and without picking, pull the finger off to sound the second note.

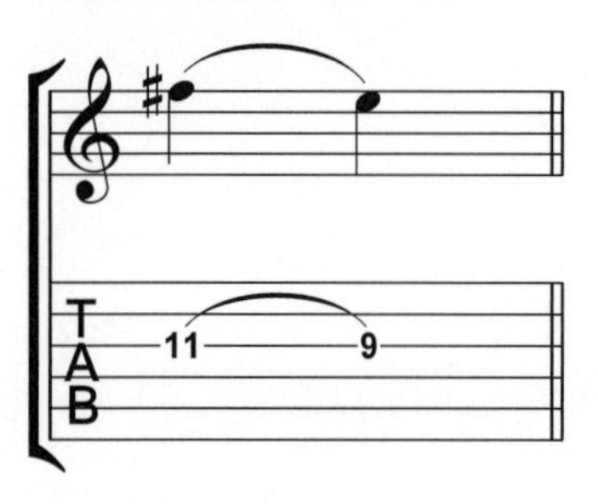

LEGATO SLIDE (GLISS): Strike the first note and then slide the same fret-hand finger up or down to the second note. The second note is not struck.

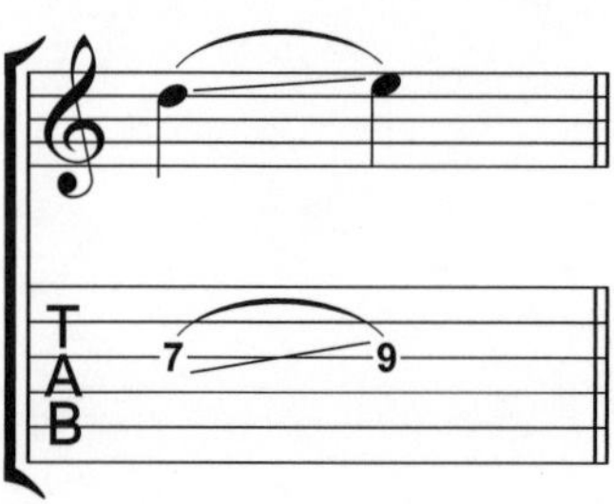

MUFFLED STRINGS: A percussive sound is produced by laying the first hand across the string(s) without depressing, and striking them with the pick hand.

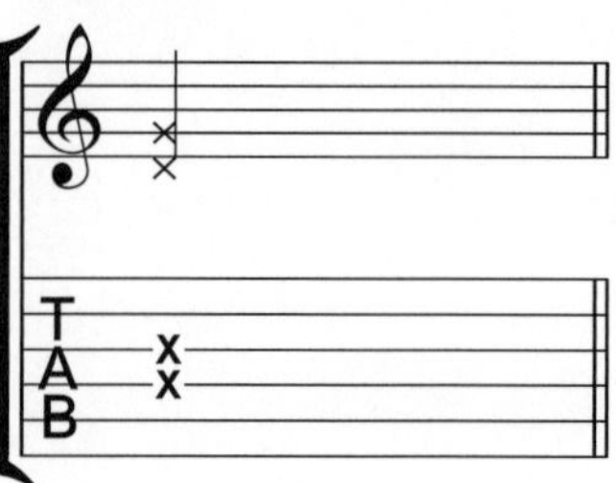

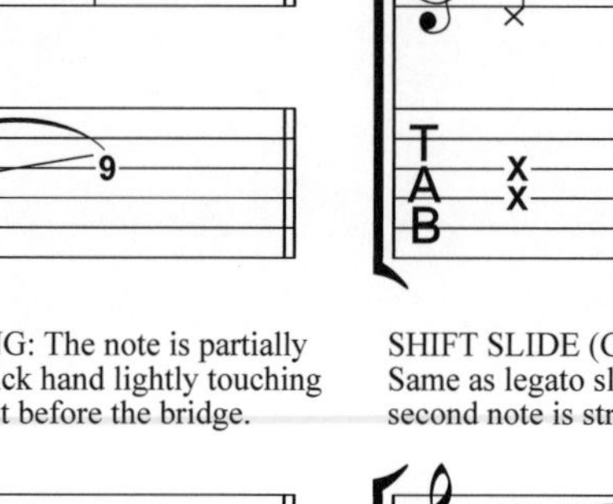

NATURAL HARMONIC: Strike the note while the fret-hand lightly touches the string directly over the fret indicated.

PICK SCRAPE: The edge of the pick is rubbed down (or up) the string, producing a scratchy sound.

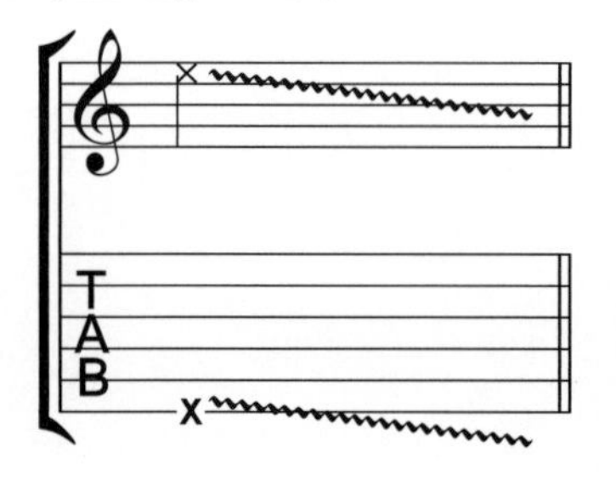

PALM MUTING: The note is partially muted by the pick hand lightly touching the string(s) just before the bridge.

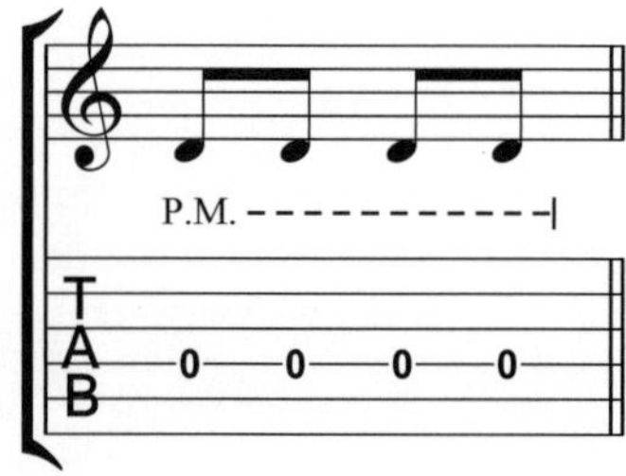


SHIFT SLIDE (GLISS & RESTRIKE) Same as legato slide, except the second note is struck.

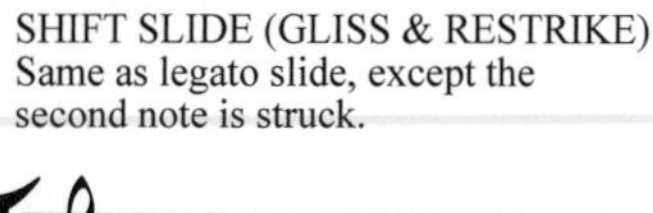

TAP HARMONIC: The note is fretted normally and a harmonic is produced by tapping or slapping the fret indicated in brackets (which will be twelve frets higher than the fretted note.)

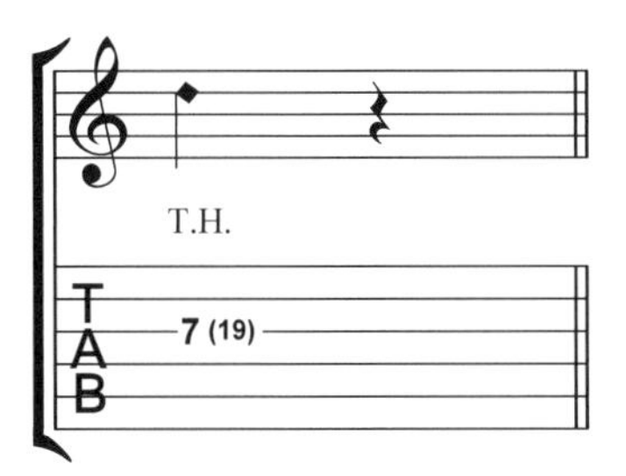


TAPPING: Hammer ('tap') the fret indicated with the pick-hand index or middle finger and pull-off to the note fretted by the fret hand.

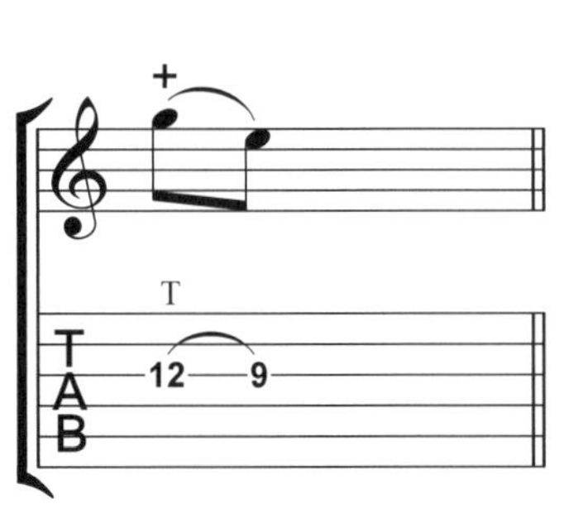


PINCH HARMONIC: The note is fretted normally and a harmonic is produced by adding the edge of the thumb or the tip of the index finger of the pick hand to the normal pick attack.

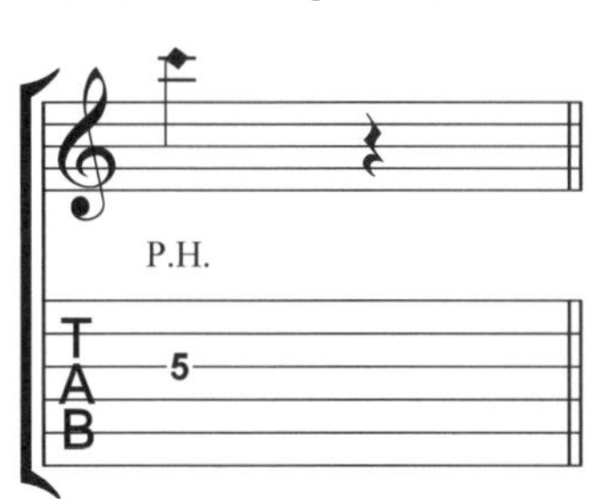


ARTIFICIAL HARMONIC: The note fretted normally and a harmonic is produced by gently resting the pick hand's index finger directly above the indicated fret (in brackets) while plucking the appropriate string.

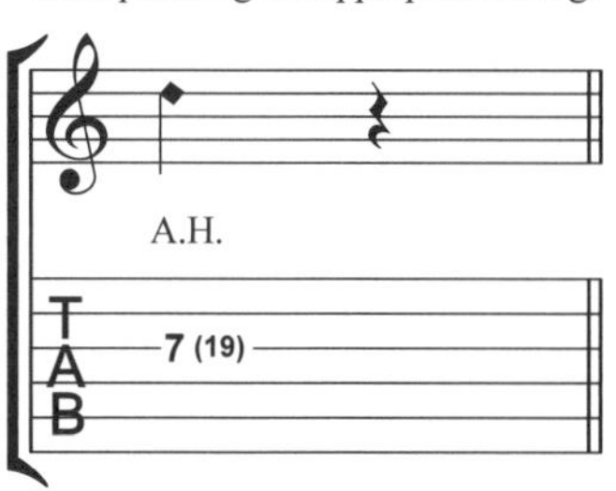


TRILL: Very rapidly alternate between the notes indicated by continuously hammering-on and pulling-off.

RAKE: Drag the pick across the strings with a single motion.

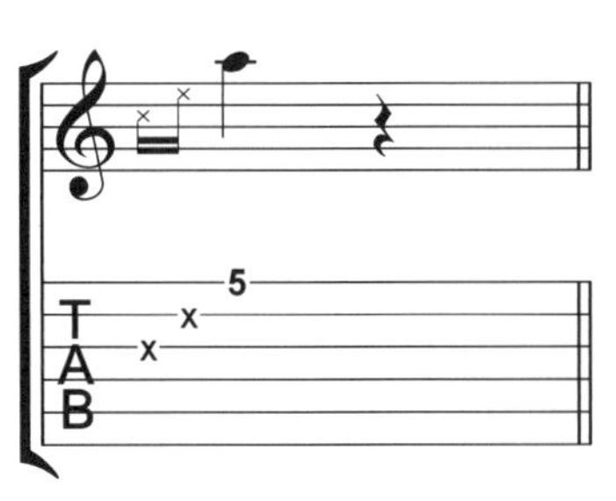


TREMOLO PICKING: The note is picked as rapidly and continosly as possible.

ARPEGGIATE: Play the notes of the chord indicated by quickly rolling them from bottom to top.

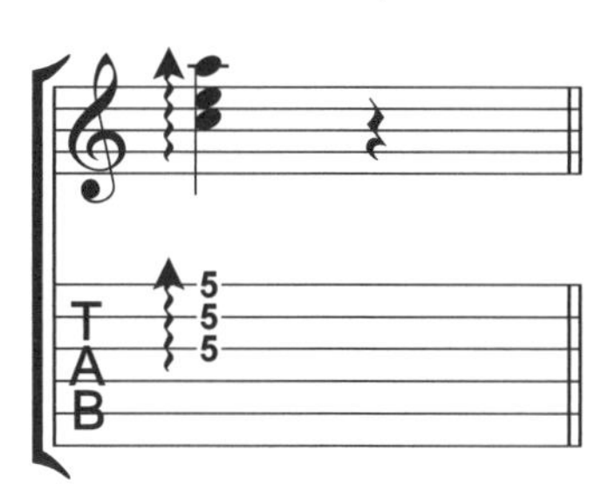


SWEEP PICKING: Rhythmic downstroke and/or upstroke motion across the strings.

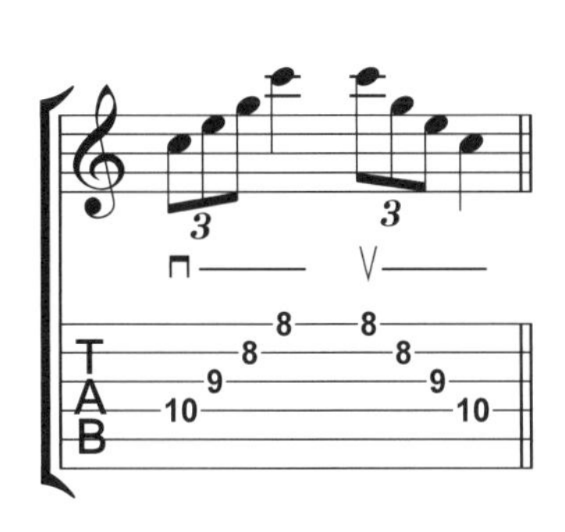


VIBRATO DIVE BAR AND RETURN: The pitch of the note or chord is dropped a specific number of steps (in rhythm) then returned to the original pitch.

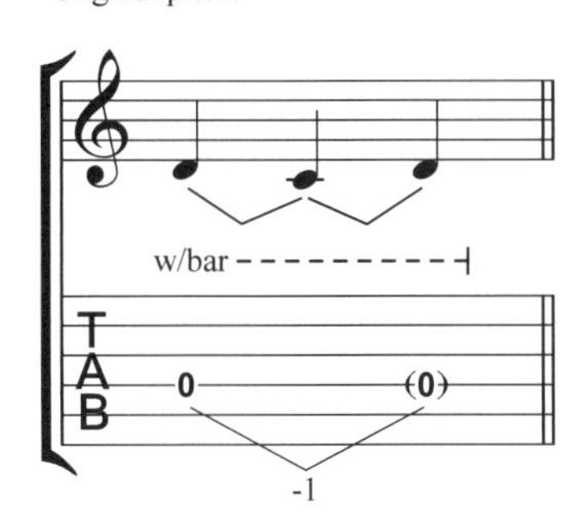


VIBRATO BAR SCOOP: Depress the bar just before striking the note, then quickly release the bar.

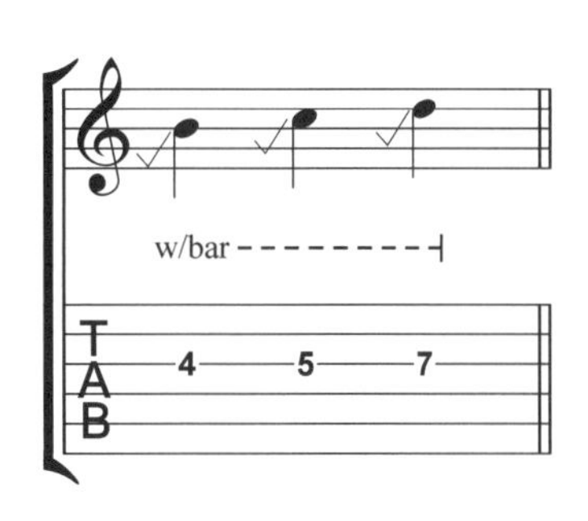


VIBRATO BAR DIP: Strike the note and then immediately drop a specific number of steps, then release back to the original pitch.

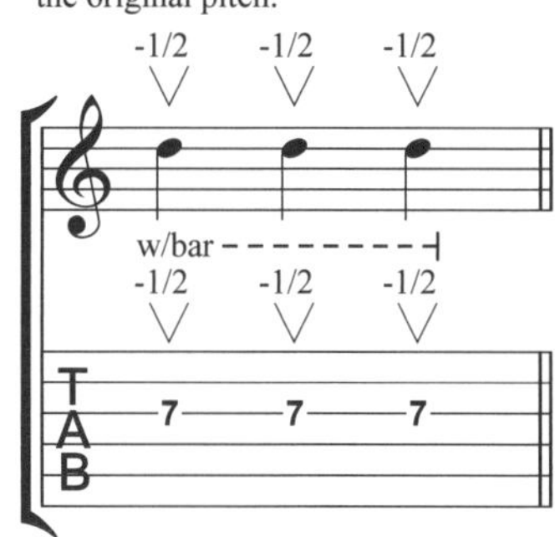


## additional musical definitions

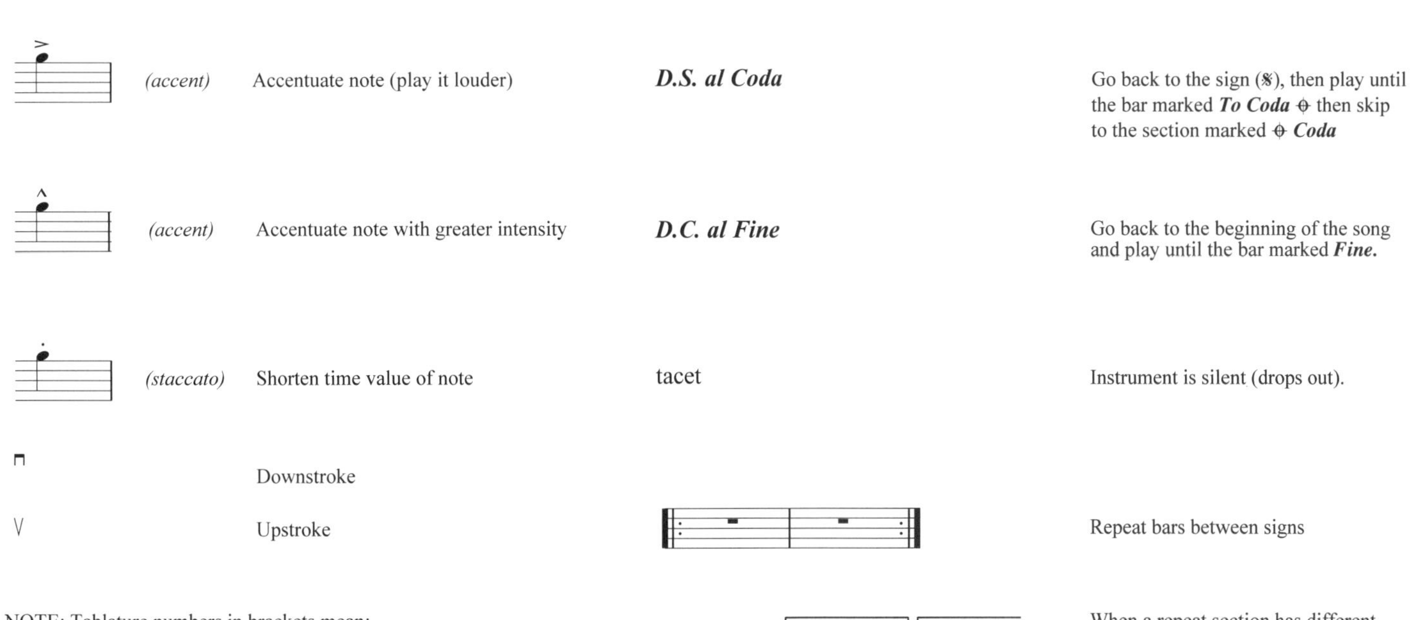

(accent) Accentuate note (play it louder)

(accent) Accentuate note with greater intensity

(staccato) Shorten time value of note

Downstroke

Upstroke

***D.S. al Coda*** Go back to the sign (𝄋), then play until the bar marked ***To Coda*** 𝄌 then skip to the section marked 𝄌 ***Coda***

***D.C. al Fine*** Go back to the beginning of the song and play until the bar marked ***Fine.***

tacet Instrument is silent (drops out).

Repeat bars between signs

NOTE: Tablature numbers in brackets mean:
1. The note is sustained, but a new articulation (such as hammer-on or slide) begins
2. A note may be fretted but not necessarily played.

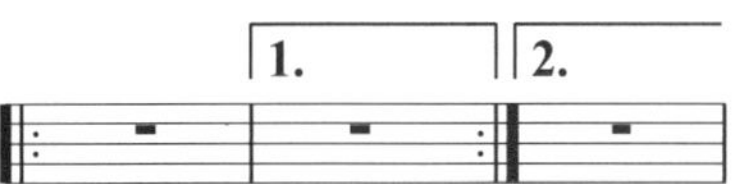


When a repeat section has different endings, play the first ending only the first time and the second ending only the second time.

# back in black

Words & Music by
Angus Young, Malcolm Young & Brian Johnson



***Full performance demo: CD 1 track 1***
***Backing only: CD 2 track 1***

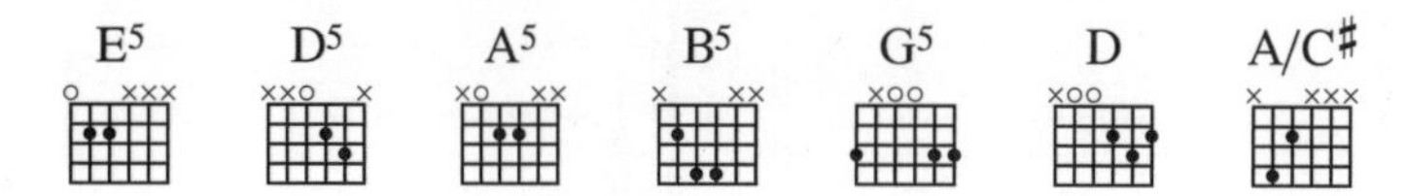


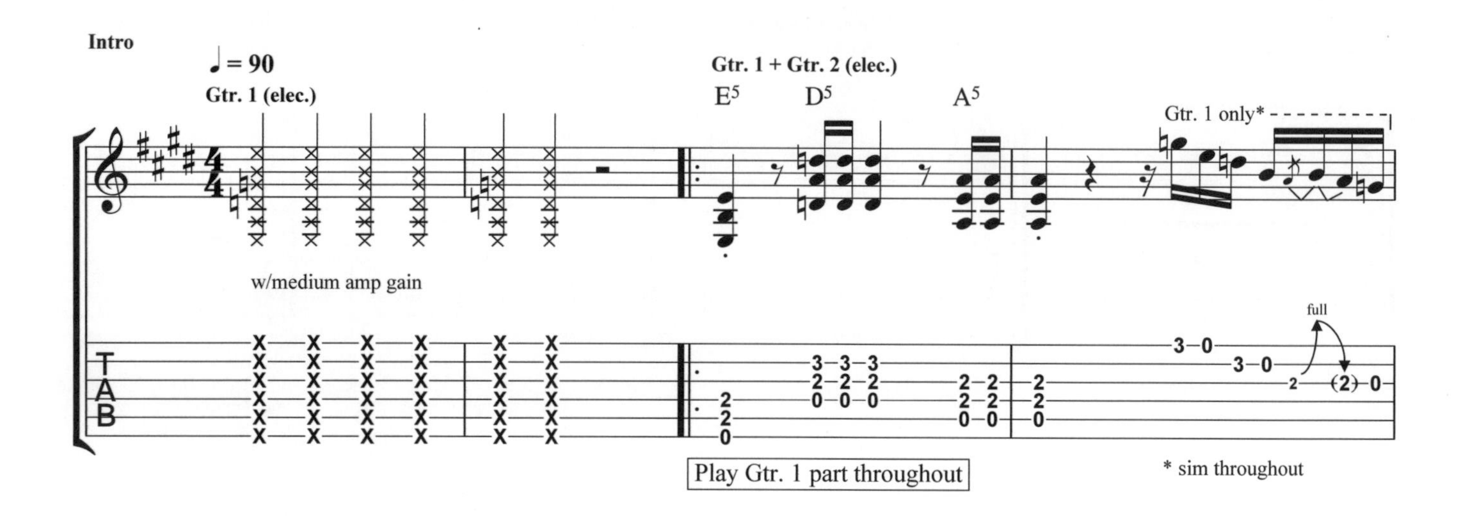


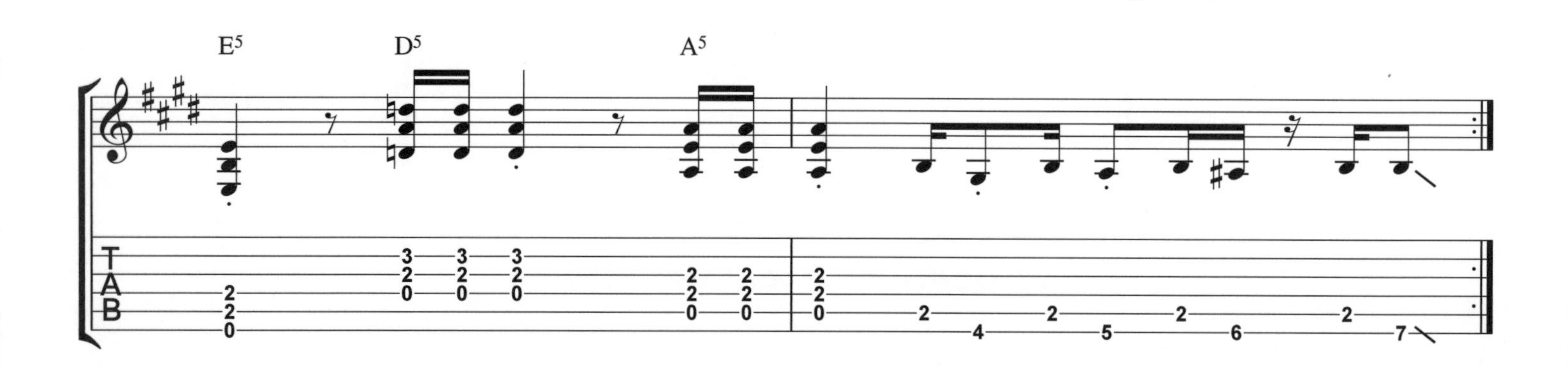


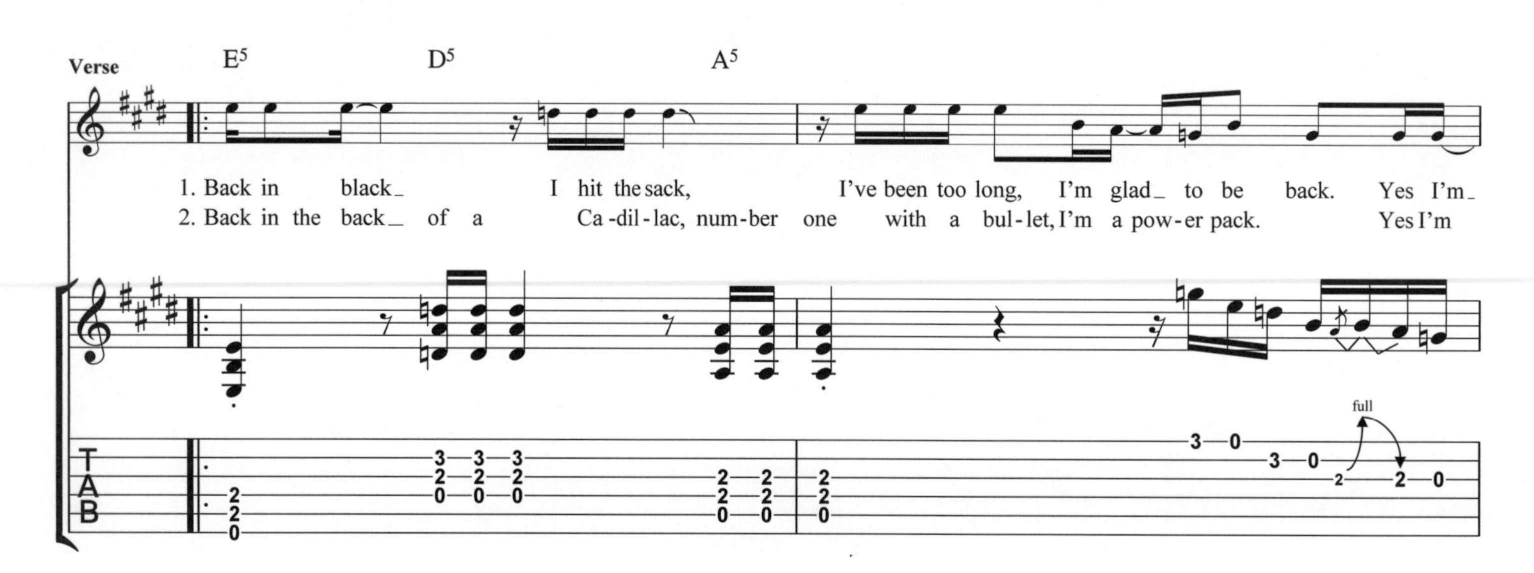

E5 D5 A5
— let loose from the noose that's kept me hang-in' a-bout. — I keep
in a bang, with a gang, they got-ta catch me if they want me to hang, 'Cause I'm
E5 D5 A5
look-in' at the sky 'cause it's get-tin' me high, for-get the hearse 'cause I'll nev-er die. I got
back on the track and I'm beatin' the flack, no-bo-dy's gon-na get me on an-oth-er rap. So
full
E5 D5 A5
nine lives, cat's eyes, a-bus-in' ev-'ry one of them and run-nin' wild.
look at me now, I'm just-a mak-in' my play, don't try to push your luck, just get out-ta my way.
'Cause I'm
Chorus
A5 E5 B5 A5 B5 A5 E5 B5 A5 B5
back, yes I'm back. — Well I'm

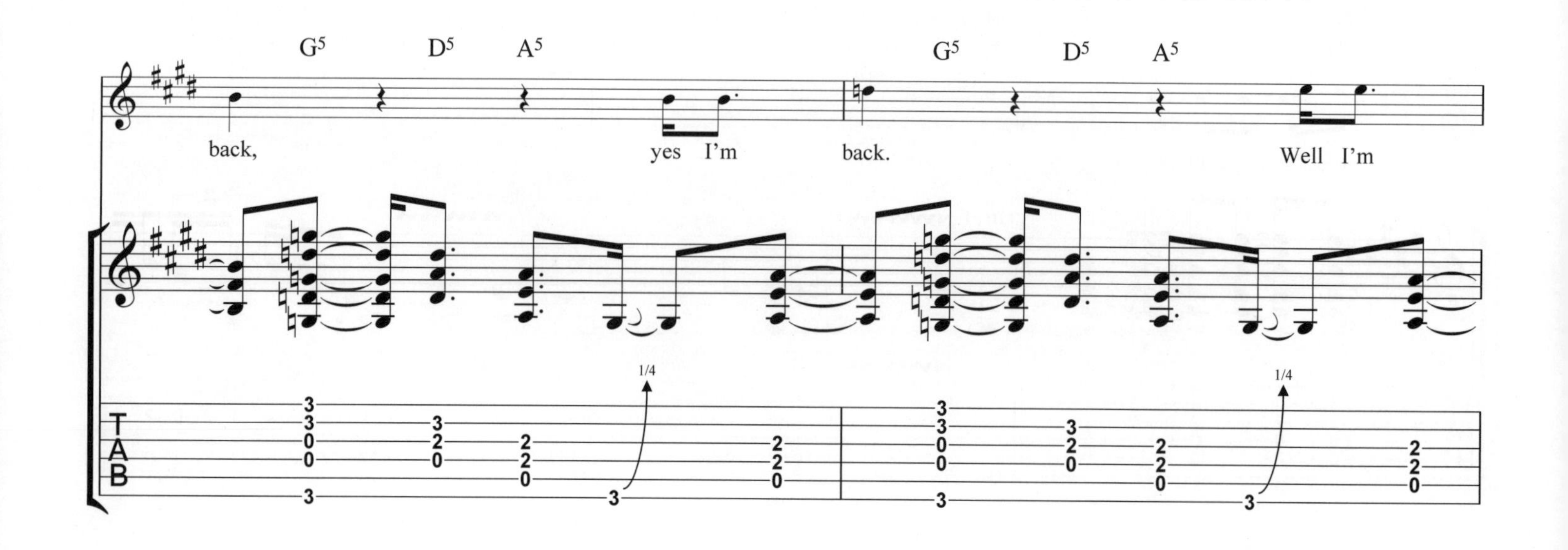
G5
D5
A5
back,
yes I'm
back.
Well I'm
1/4


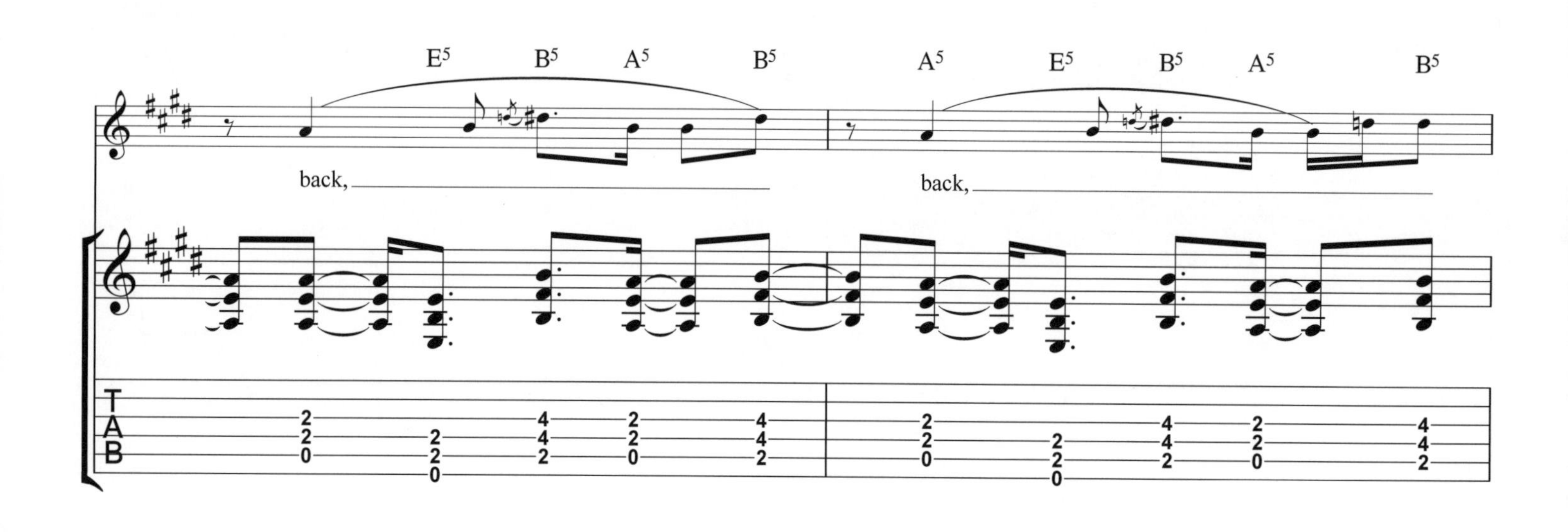
E5
B5
A5
back,

1.
G5
D
back in black,
yes I'm
back in
black.

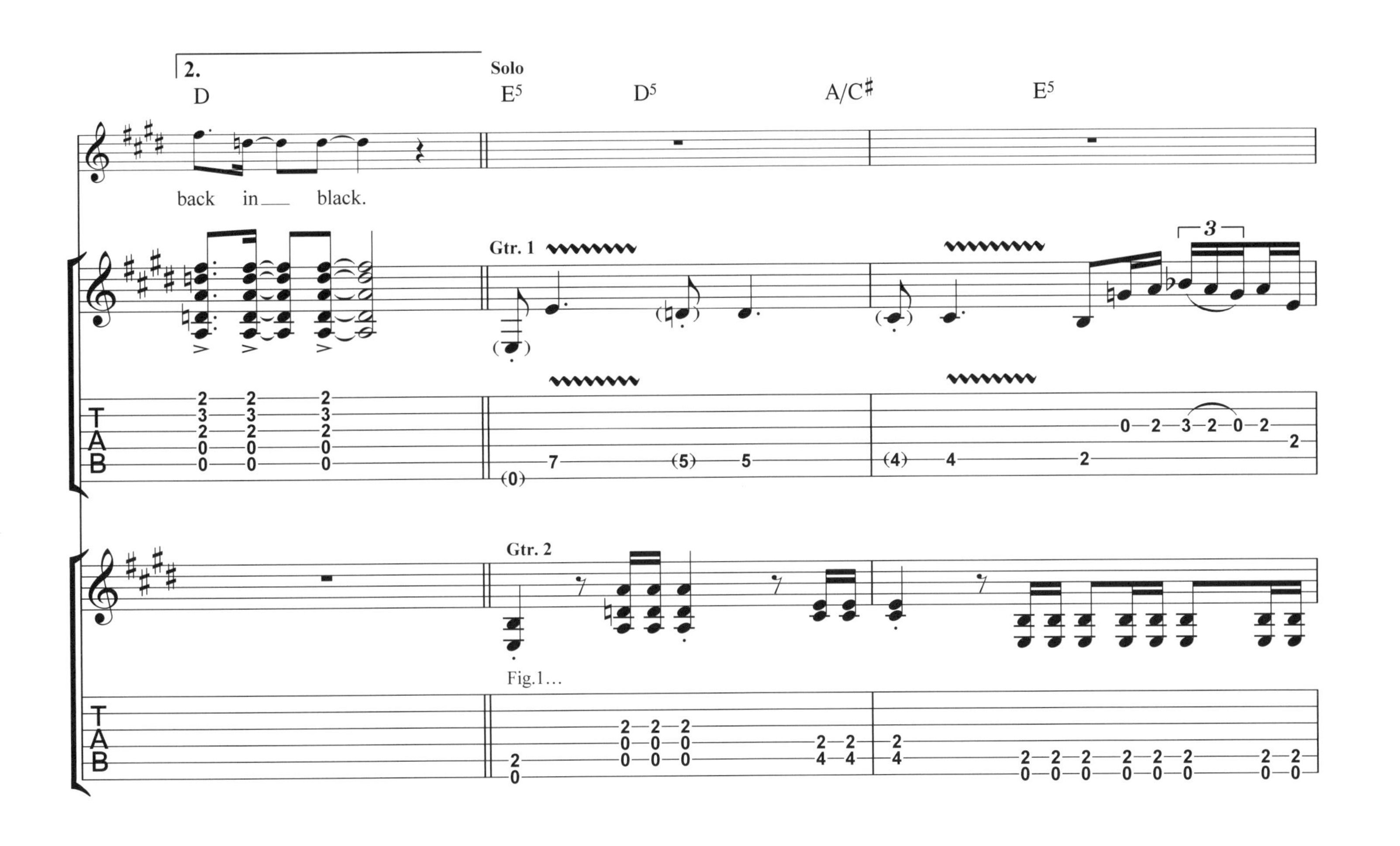
2.
Solo
D
E5
D5
A/C♯
E5
back in black.
Gtr. 1
Gtr. 2
Fig.1…


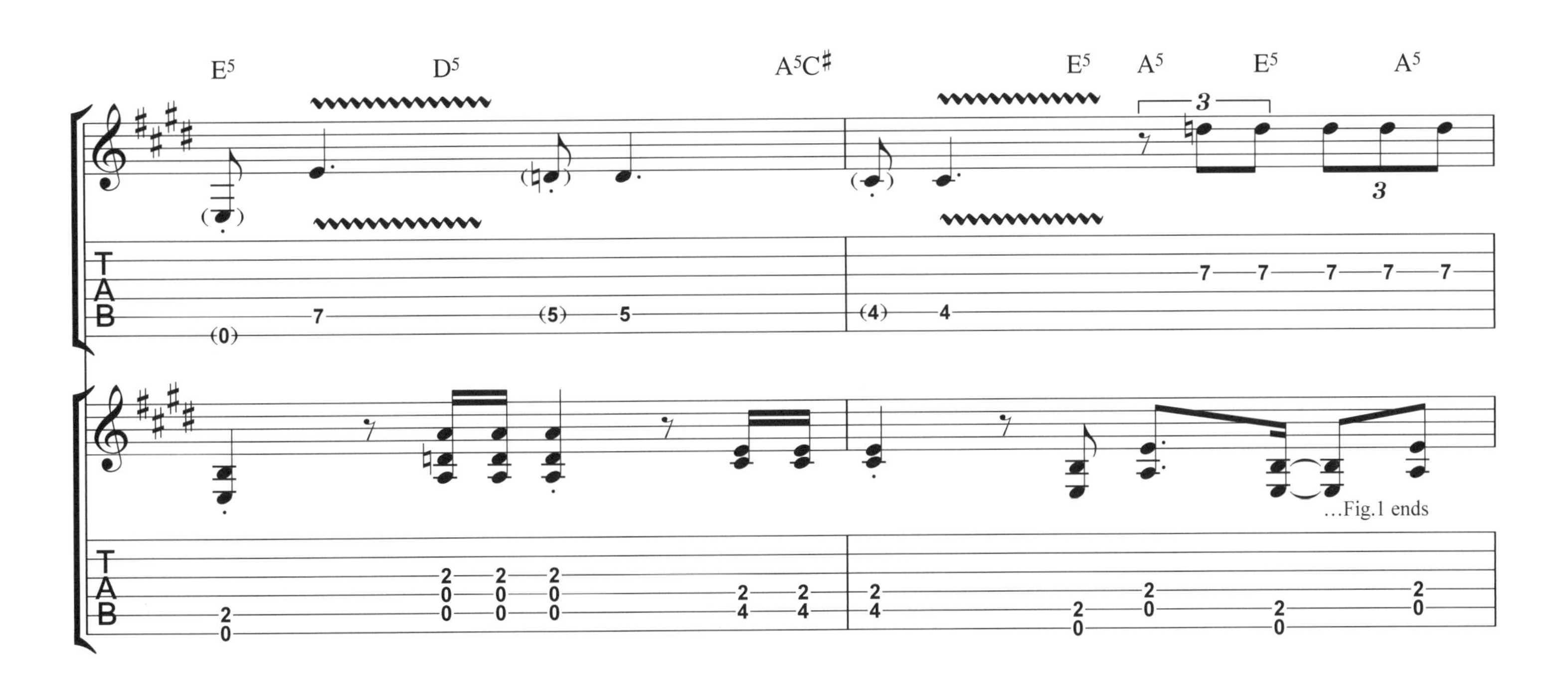
E5
D5
A5C♯
E5
A5
E5
A5
…Fig.1 ends


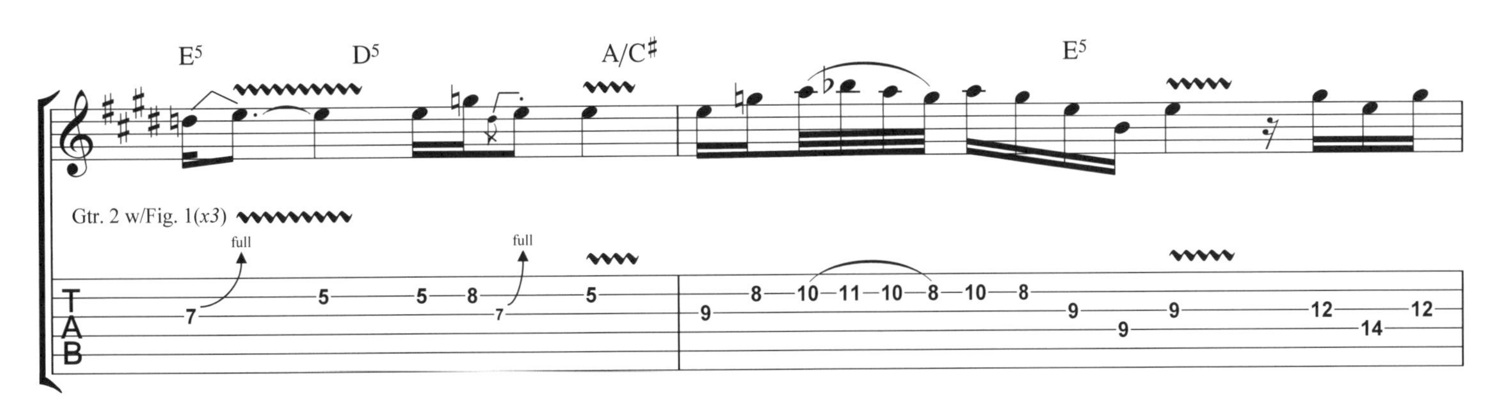
E5
D5
A/C♯
E5
Gtr. 2 w/Fig. 1(x3)
full
full

D5
A/C♯
E5
A5
let ring...
D.S. al Coda
Well I'm

Coda
D
(E5)
back in black.
(Gtrs. 1+2)
1/4
1/4

1/4
1/4

(A5)
1/4
1/4

(E5)
Well I'm
1/4
1/4

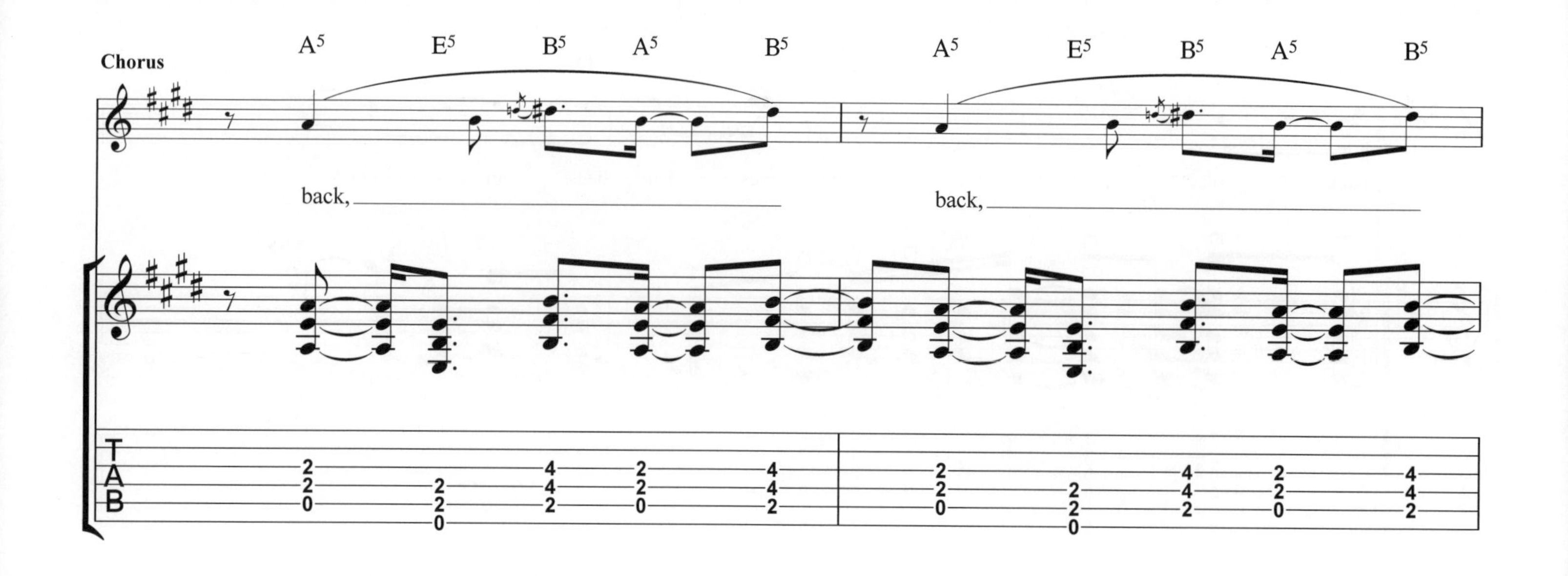
Chorus
A5 E5 B5 A5 B5 A5 E5 B5 A5 B5
back,
back,

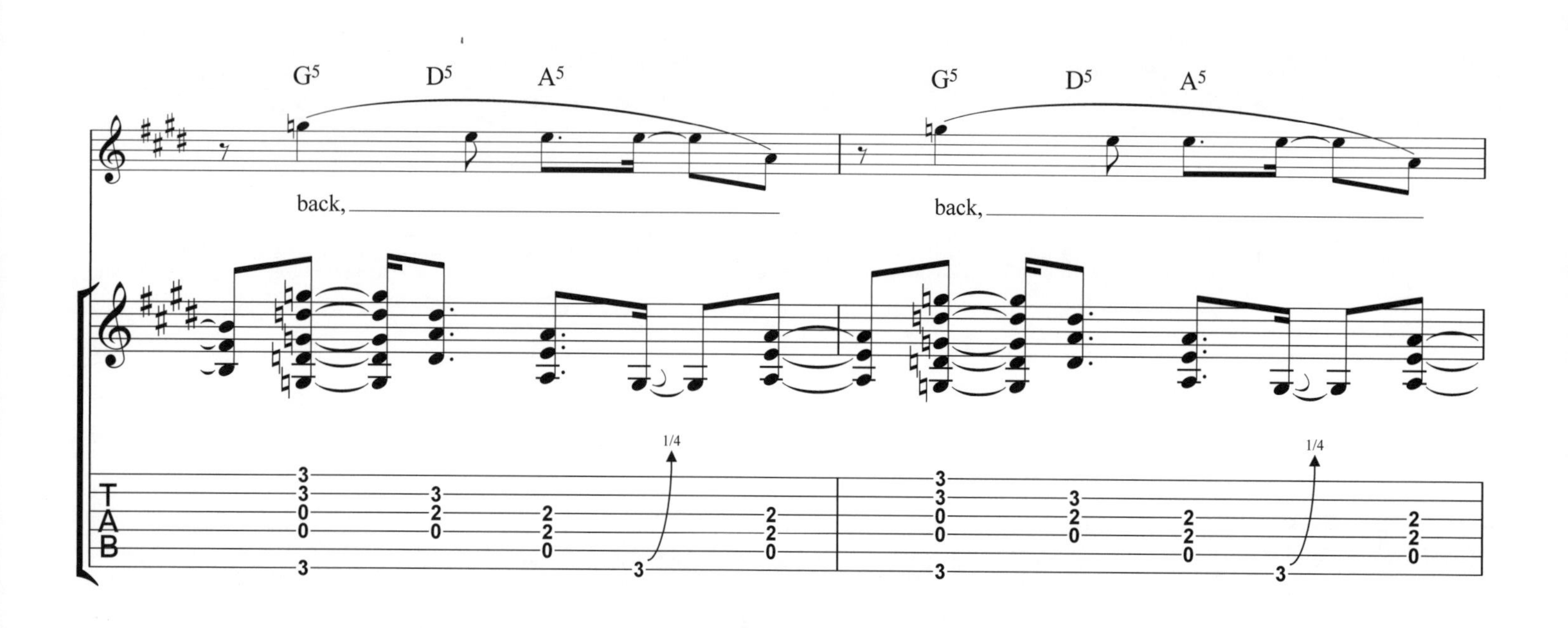
G5 D5 A5 G5 D5 A5
back,
back,
1/4
1/4

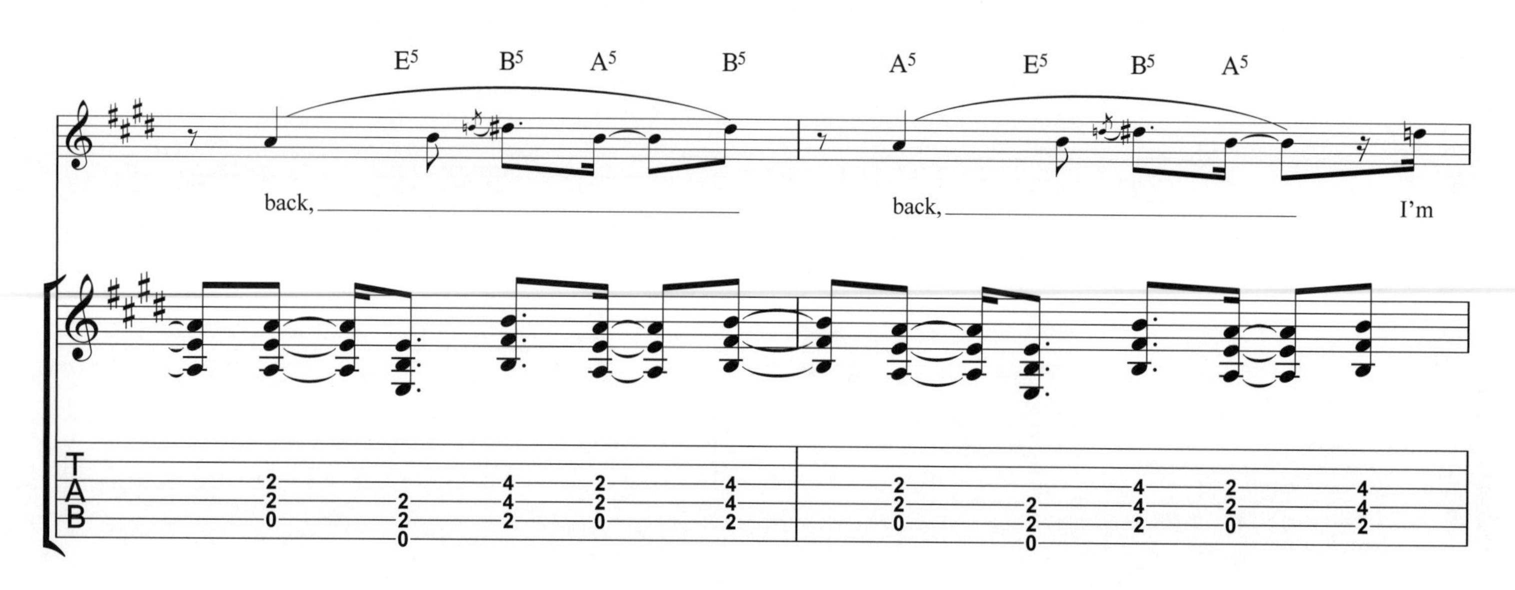
E5 B5 A5 B5 A5 E5 B5 A5
back,
back,
I'm

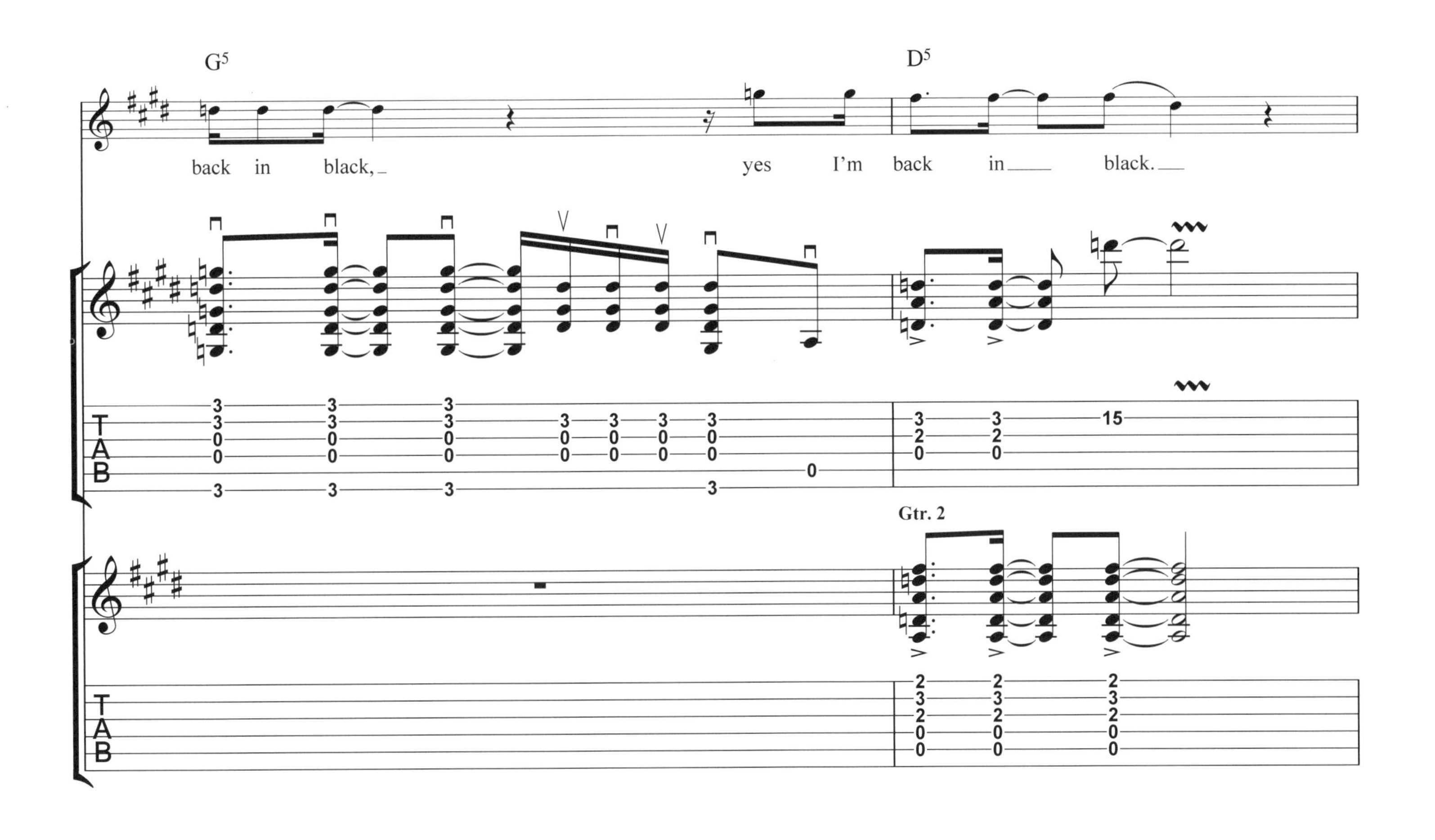
G5
D5
back in black,
yes I'm back in black.
T
A
B
Gtr. 2
T
A
B

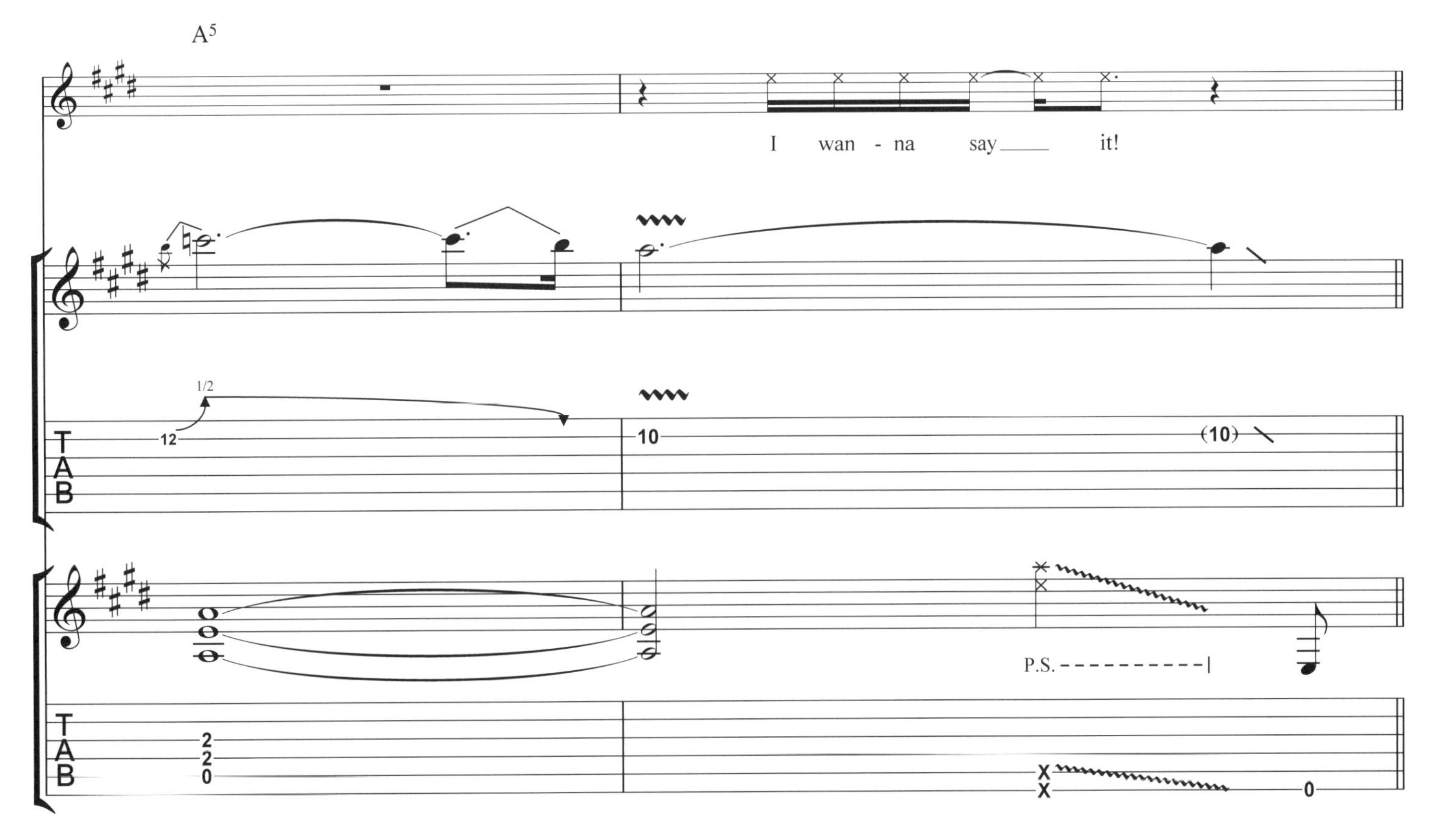
A5
I wan - na say it!
1/2
T
A
B
P.S.
T
A
B

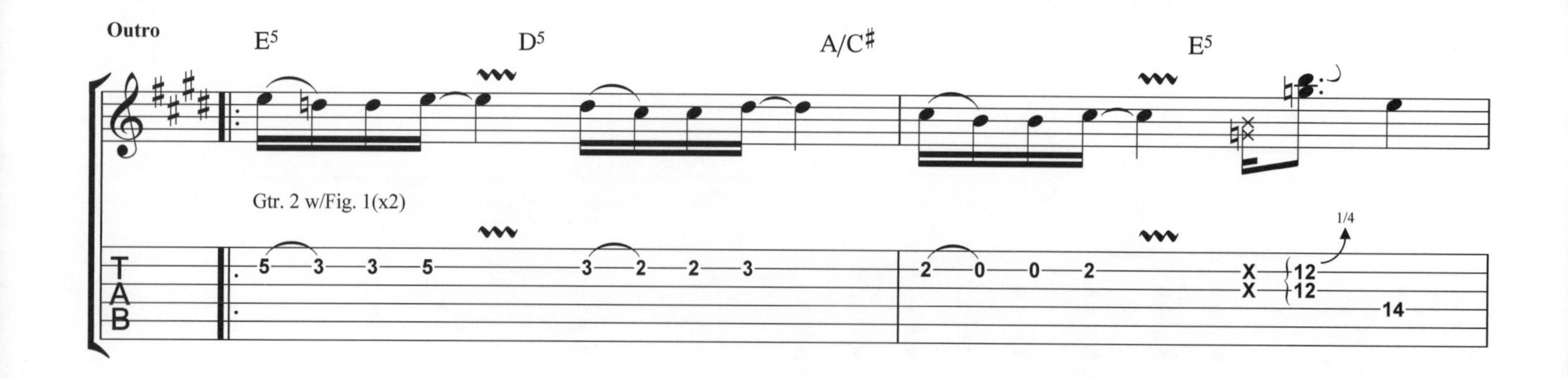
Outro
E5
D5
A/C♯
E5
Gtr. 2 w/Fig. 1(x2)
1/4

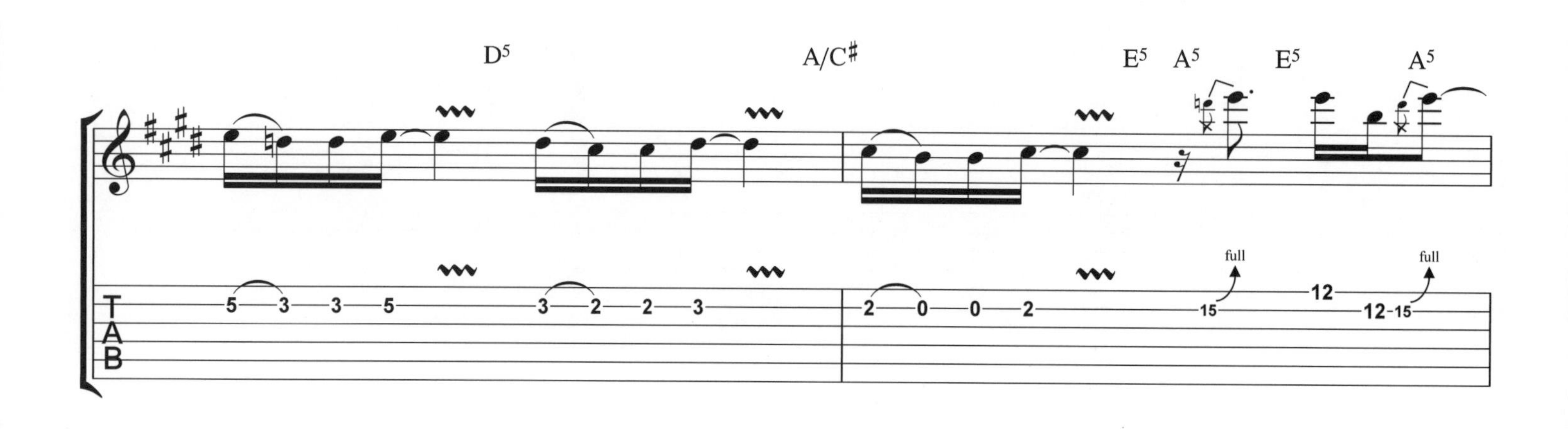
D5
A/C♯
E5
A5
E5
A5
full
full

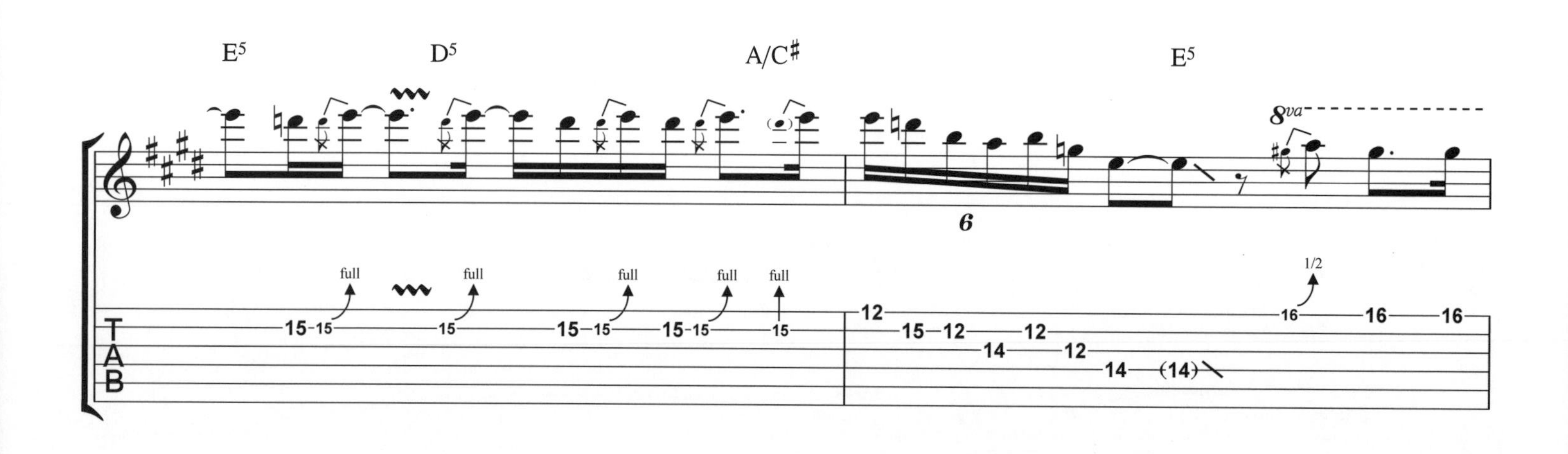
E5
D5
A/C♯
E5
8va
full
full
full
full
full
1/2

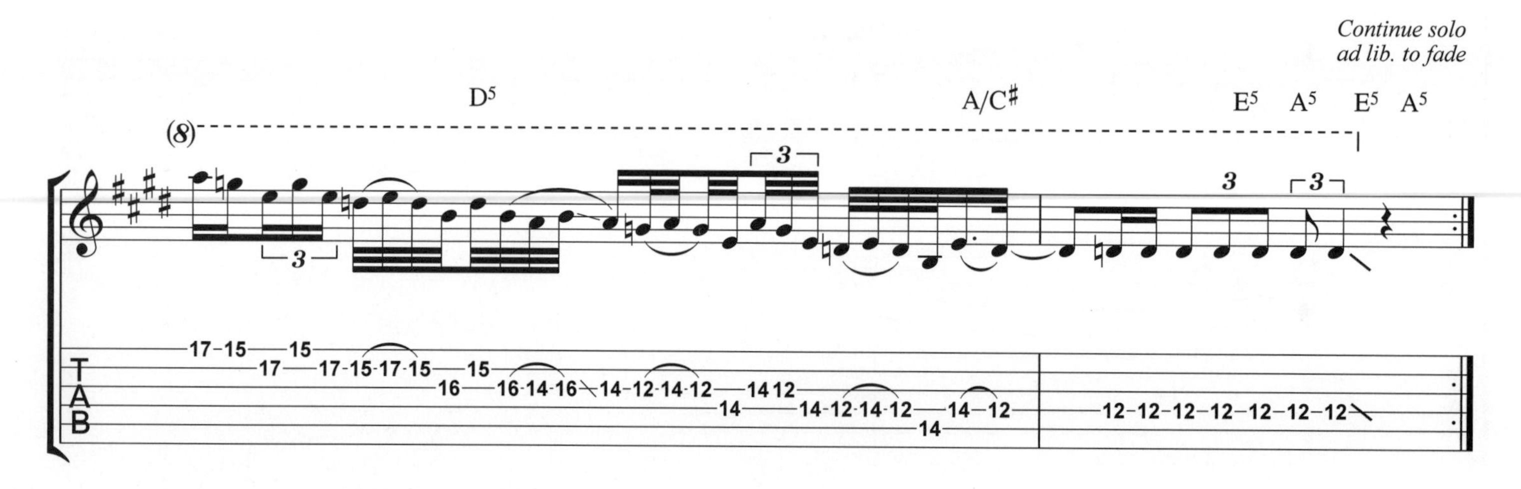
Continue solo
ad lib. to fade
D5
A/C♯
E5
A5
E5
A5

# dirty deeds done dirt cheap

Words & Music by
Angus Young, Malcolm Young & Bon Scott



**Full performance demo: CD 1 track 2**
**Backing only: CD 2 track 2**

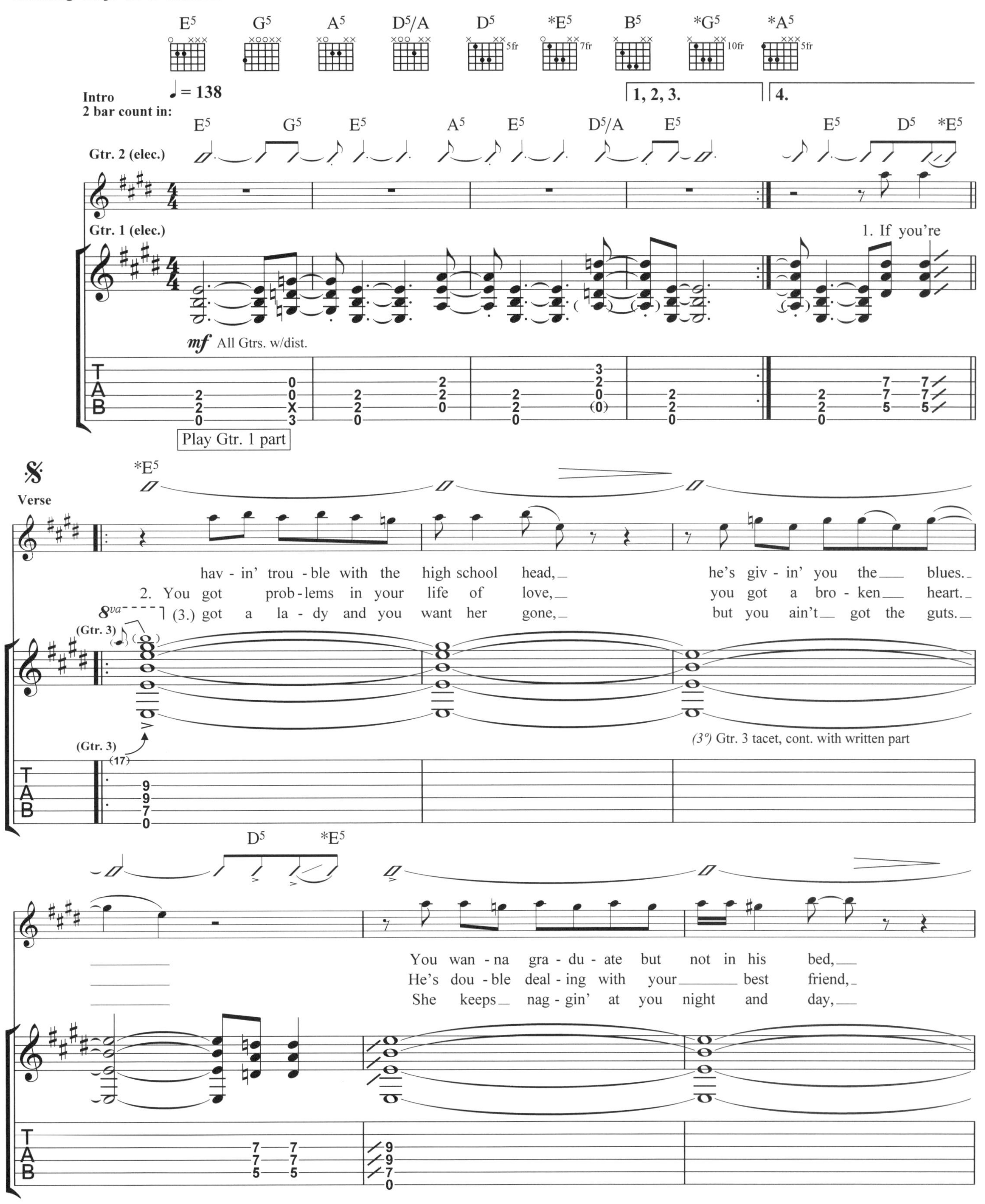

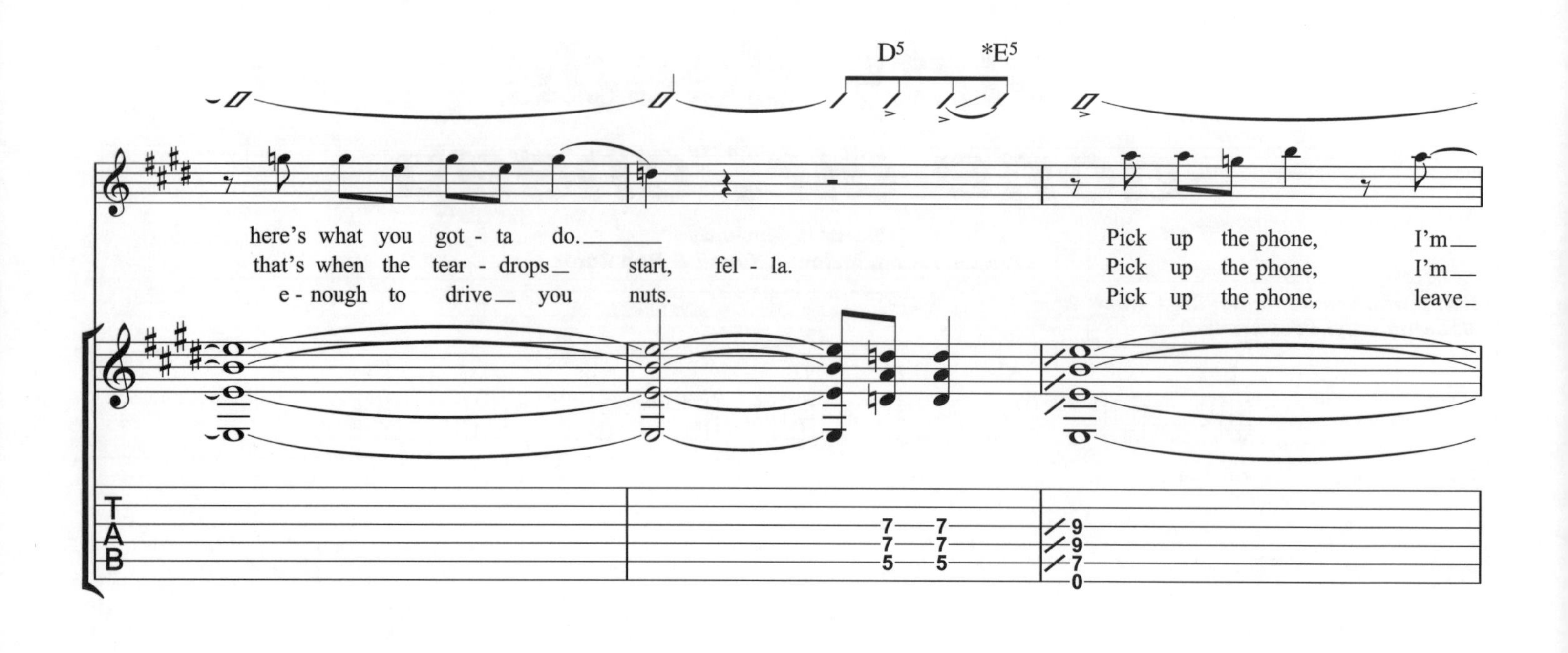
D5 *E5
here's what you got - ta do.
that's when the tear - drops start, fel - la.
e - nough to drive you nuts.
Pick up the phone, I'm
Pick up the phone, I'm
Pick up the phone, leave

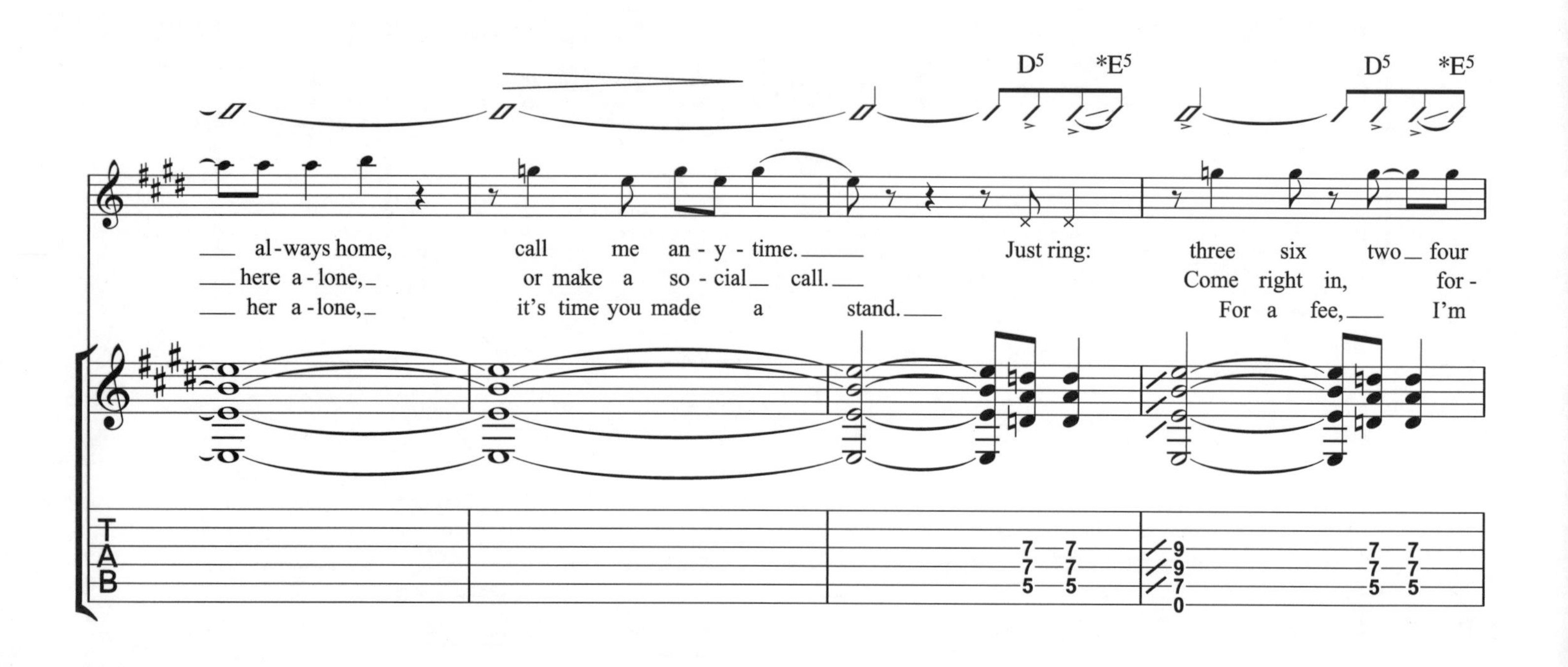
D5 *E5 D5 *E5
al - ways home, call me an - y - time. Just ring: three six two four
here a - lone, or make a so - cial call. Come right in, for -
her a - lone, it's time you made a stand. For a fee, I'm

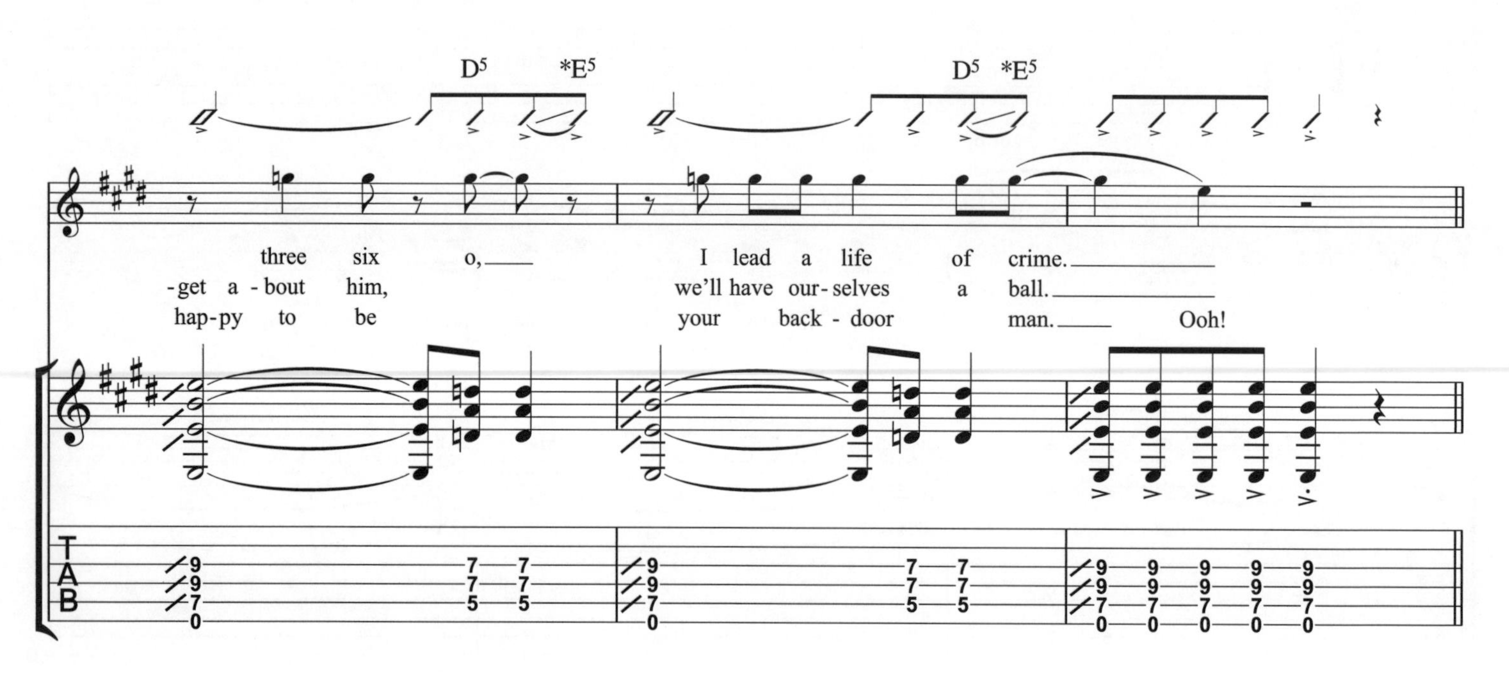
D5 *E5 D5 *E5
three six o, I lead a life of crime.
- get a - bout him, we'll have our - selves a ball.
hap - py to be your back - door man. Ooh!

Chorus
A5
A5
G ⑥ 3fr
A ⑤ 0fr
*E5
*E5
D5
*E5
A5
Dirt - y deeds_ done dirt cheap. Dirt - y deeds_ done dirt cheap. Dirt - y deeds_
A5
G ⑥ 3fr
A ⑤ 0fr
To Coda
*E5
done dirt cheap. Dirt - y deeds_ and they're done dirt cheap.
1.
D5
2.
Dirt - y deeds_ and they're done dirt cheap. done dirt cheap.
Gtr. 3 (elec)
ff w/dist.
Play Gtr. 3 part
Solo
B5
A5
B5
A5
full
full
full
hold bend...
full
1/2
full
1/2

B5
A5
Harm.
Harm.
B5
D5
A
⑤
0fr
full
E5
G5
E5
A5
E5
D5
E5

E5
G5
A5
D5
D.S. al Coda
3. If you
8va
Coda
Dirt - y deeds_ and they're done dirt cheap. Dirt - y deeds_ and they're done dirt cheap.
let ring...
(1º)
D5/A
mf
Con - crete shoes, cy - a-nide, T. N. T. done dirt cheap.

E5 G5 E5 A5 E5 E5 D5/A E5
Neck - ties, con - tracts, high volt - age, done dirt cheap.
1. 2.
E5 G5 E5 A5 E5 E5 D5/A E5 E5 D5/A E5 (*E5)
Dirt - y deeds done dirt cheap. done dirt cheap.
*E5 *G5 *E5 A5 *E5 E5 D5/A E5 (*E5)
Dirt - y deeds, they're read - y to send you on the cruise, done dirt cheap.
*E5 *G5 *E5 *A5 *E5 *E5 D5 *E5
E D E
7fr 5fr 7fr
Dirt - y deeds, dirt - y deeds, dirt - y deeds done dirt cheap. Aagh!

# for those about to rock (we salute you)

Words & Music by
Angus Young, Malcolm Young & Brian Johnson

**Full performance demo: CD 1 track 3**
**Backing only: CD 2 track 3**

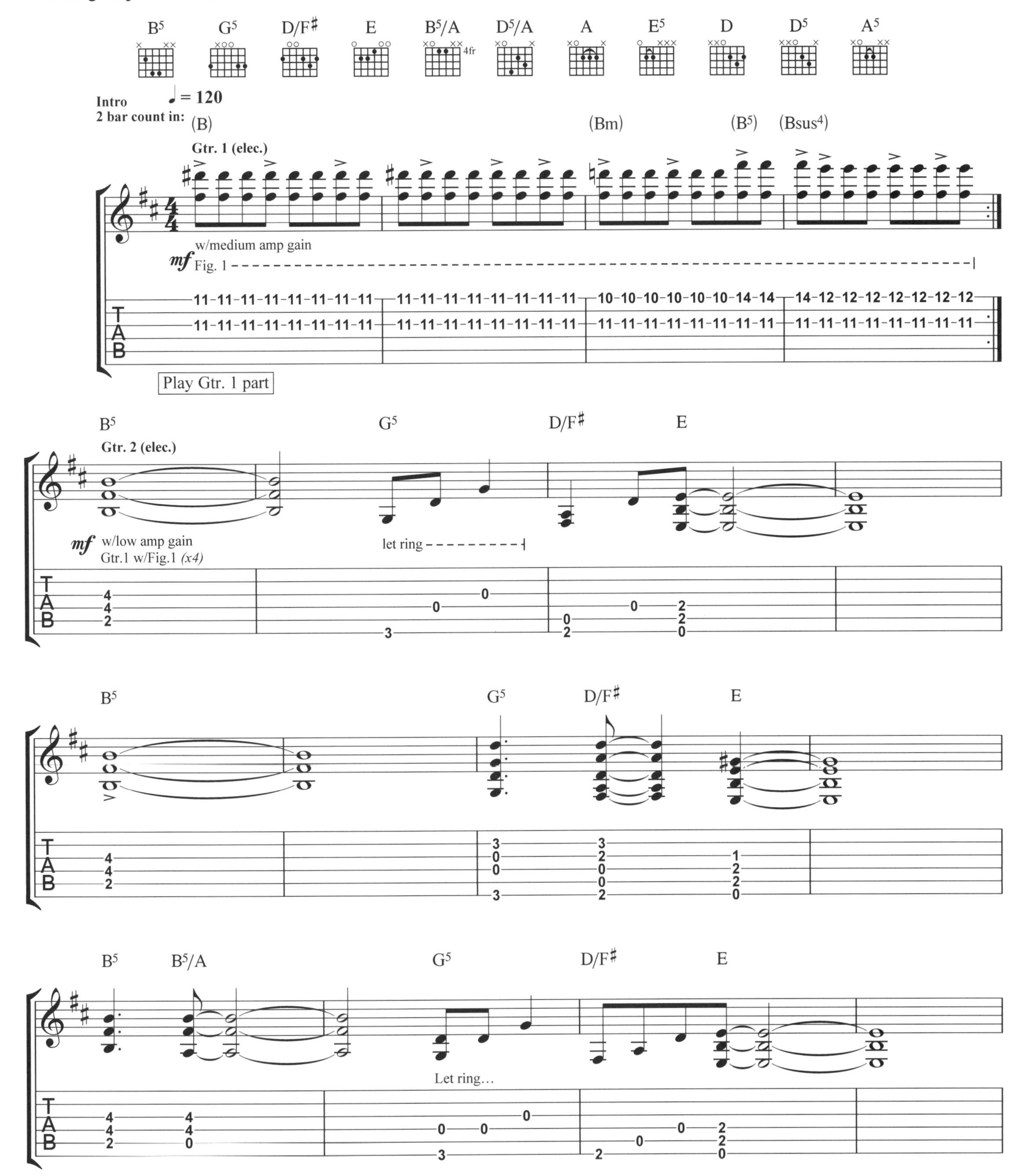

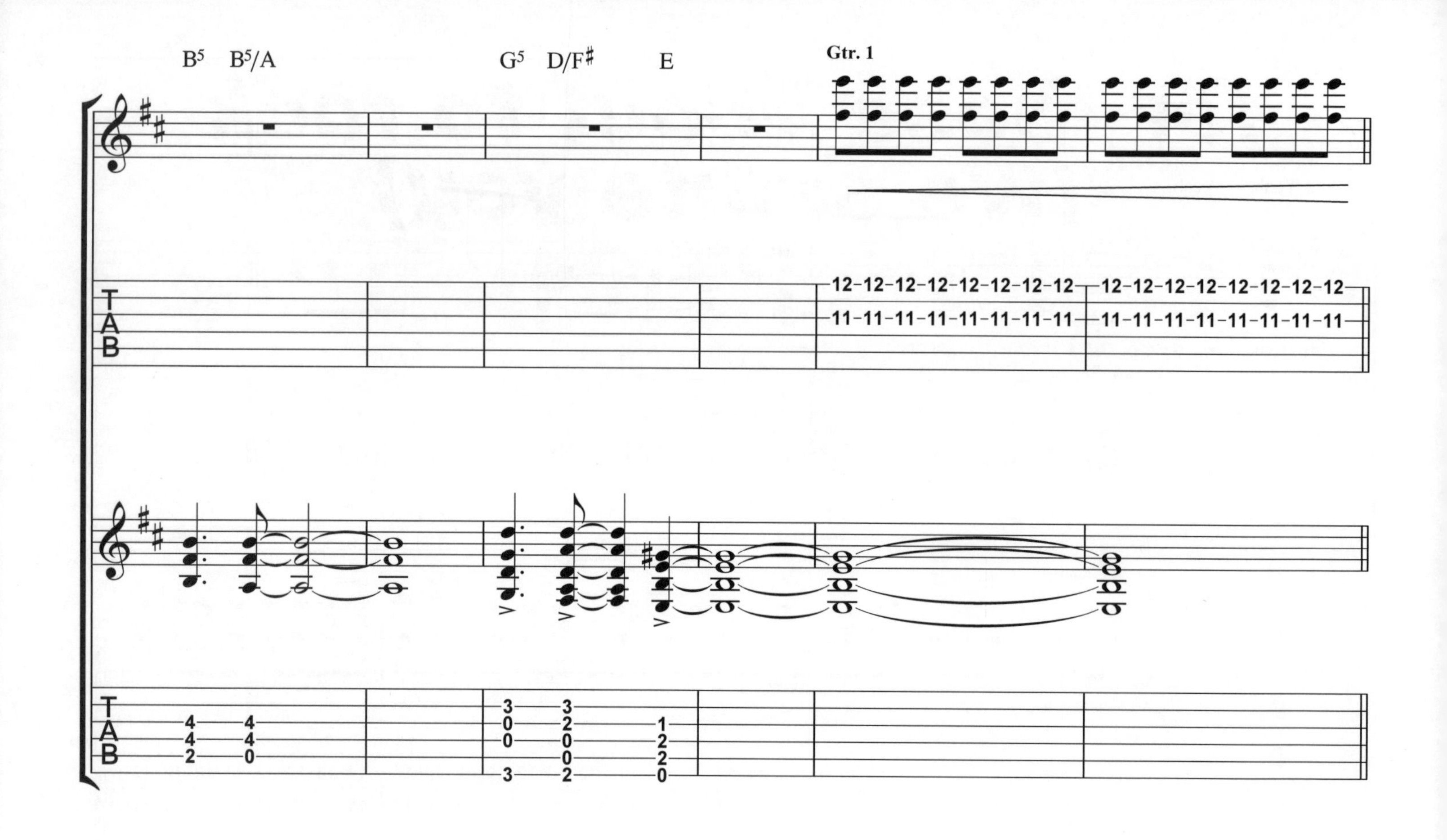
B5 B5/A
G5 D/F♯
E
Gtr. 1

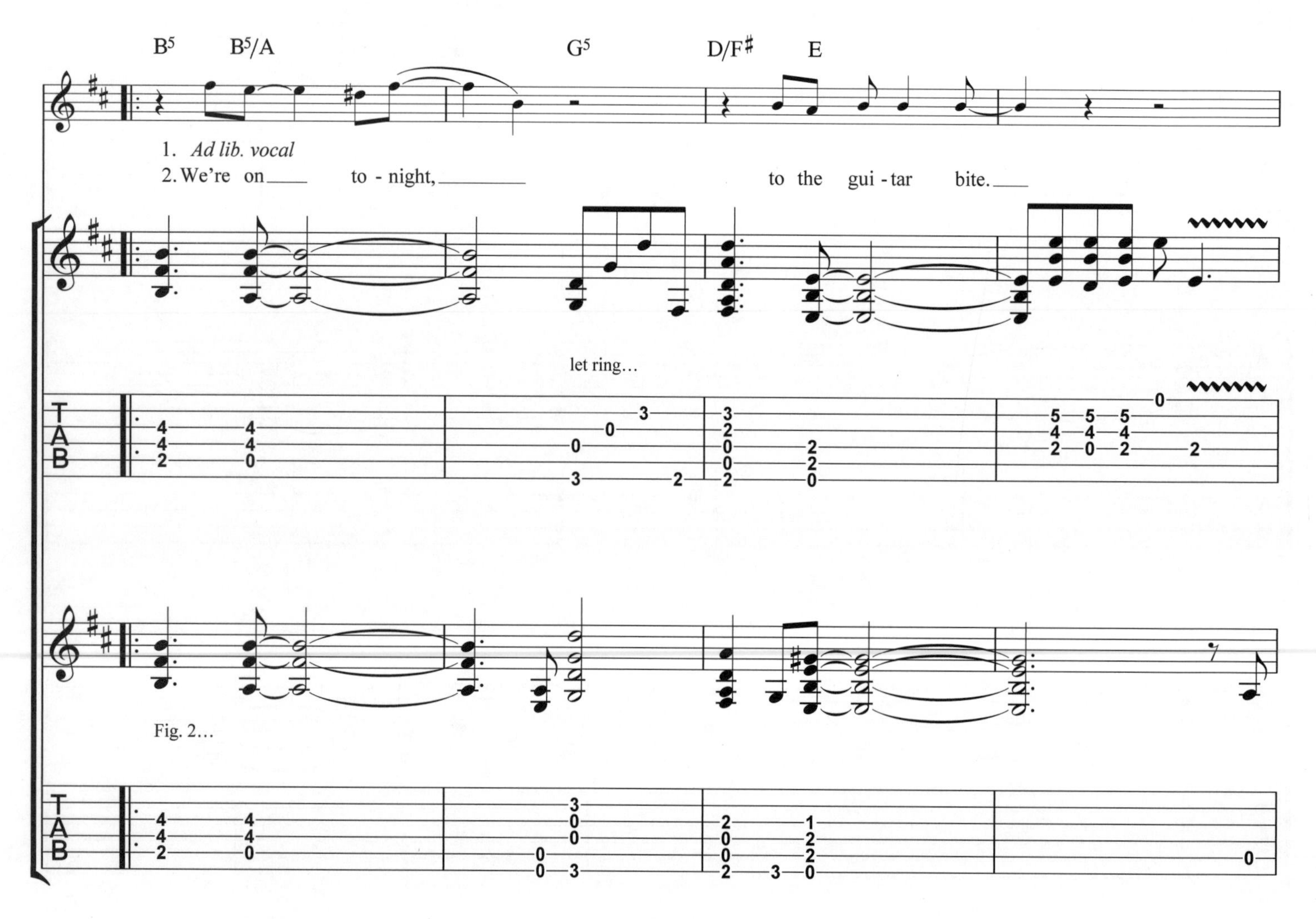
B5
B5/A
G5
D/F♯
E
1. Ad lib. vocal
2. We're on to - night, to the gui - tar bite.
let ring…
Fig. 2…

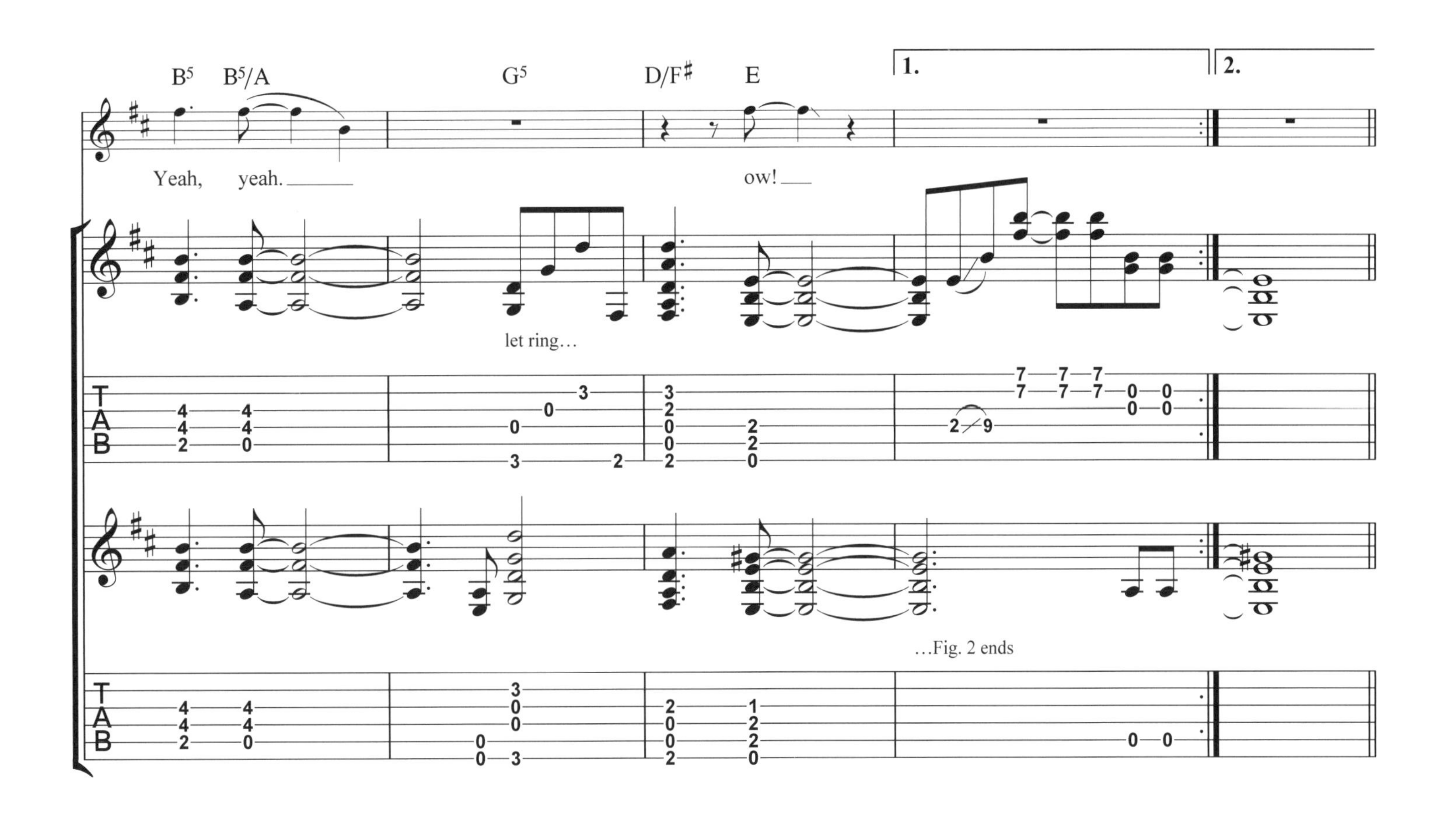
B5 B5/A G5 D/F♯ E
1.
2.
Yeah, yeah.
ow!
let ring…
…Fig. 2 ends

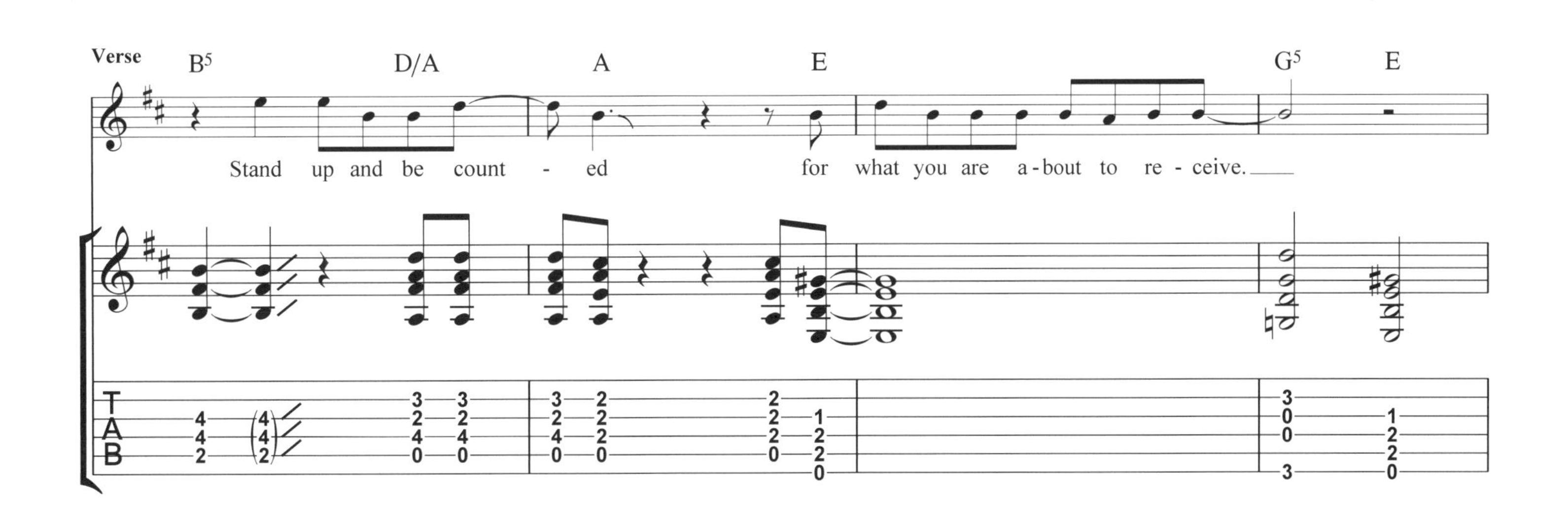
Verse
B5 D/A A E G5 E
Stand up and be count - ed for what you are a-bout to re - ceive.

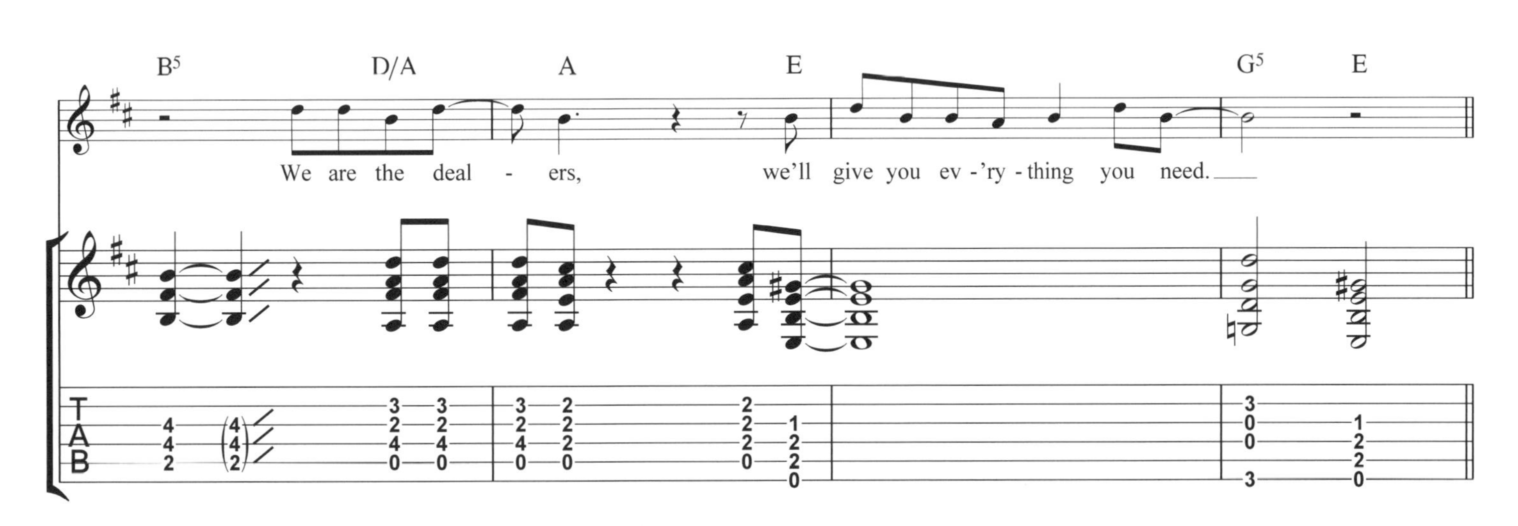
B5 D/A A E G5 E
We are the deal - ers, we'll give you ev-'ry-thing you need.

B5 D/A A E G5 E
Hail, hail to the good times, 'cause rock has got the right of way. We
rock at dawn on the front line, like a bolt right - a out of the blue. The
Gtrs. 1+2
B5 D/A A E G5 E
ain't no le - gend ain't no cause, we're just liv - in' for to - day.
sky's a - light with a gui - tar bite, heads will roll and rock to - night.
For
Chorus
B5 B5/A G5 D/F# E5
those a - bout to rock, we sa - lute you. For
Gtr. 1
Gtr. 2 w/Fig. 2
let ring
B5 B5/A G5 D/F# E5
1.
those a - bout to rock, we sa - lute you.
3. We

2.
B5
B5/A
G5
D/F♯
E5
For those a - bout to rock, we sa - lute you,
Gtr. 2 w/Fig. 2
yes we do. For those a - bout to rock, we sa - lute you.
Gtr. 3 (elec.)
let ring
full
Play Gtr. 3 part
Gtrs. 1+2
Ah!
Salute!

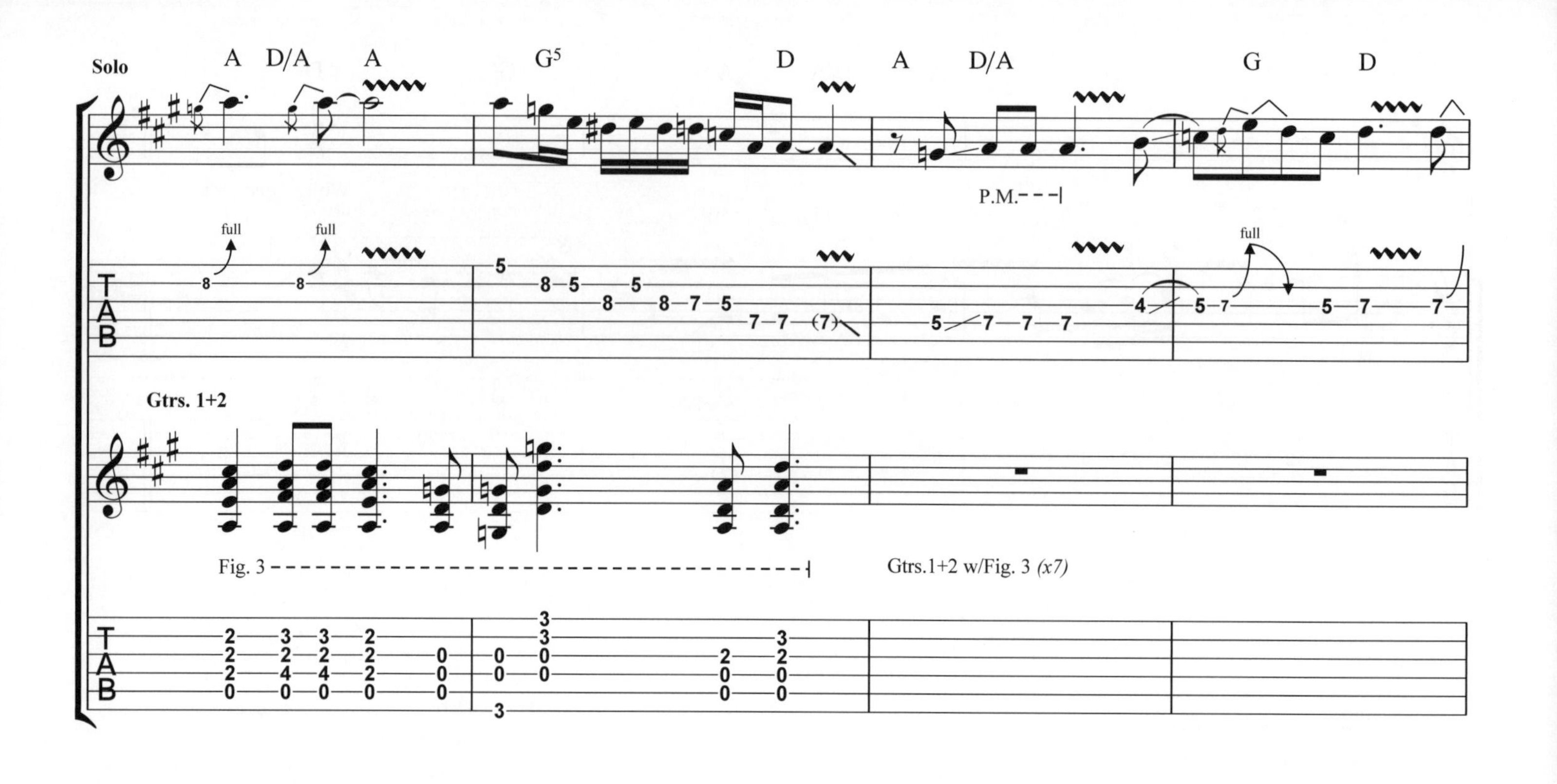
Solo
A D/A A G5 D A D/A G D
P.M.
full full full
Gtrs. 1+2
Fig. 3
Gtrs.1+2 w/Fig. 3 (x7)

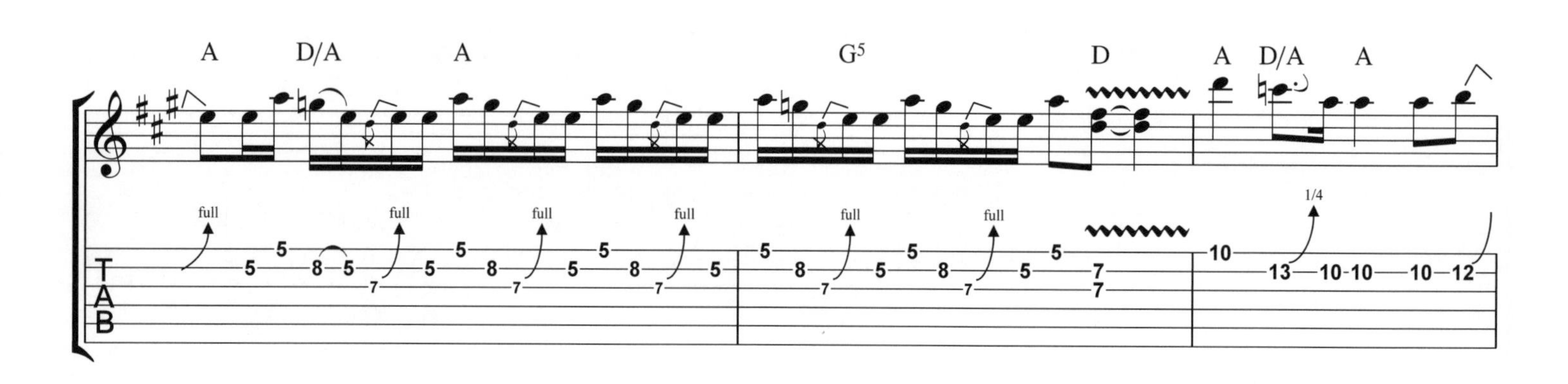
A D/A A G5 D A D/A A
full full full full full full 1/4

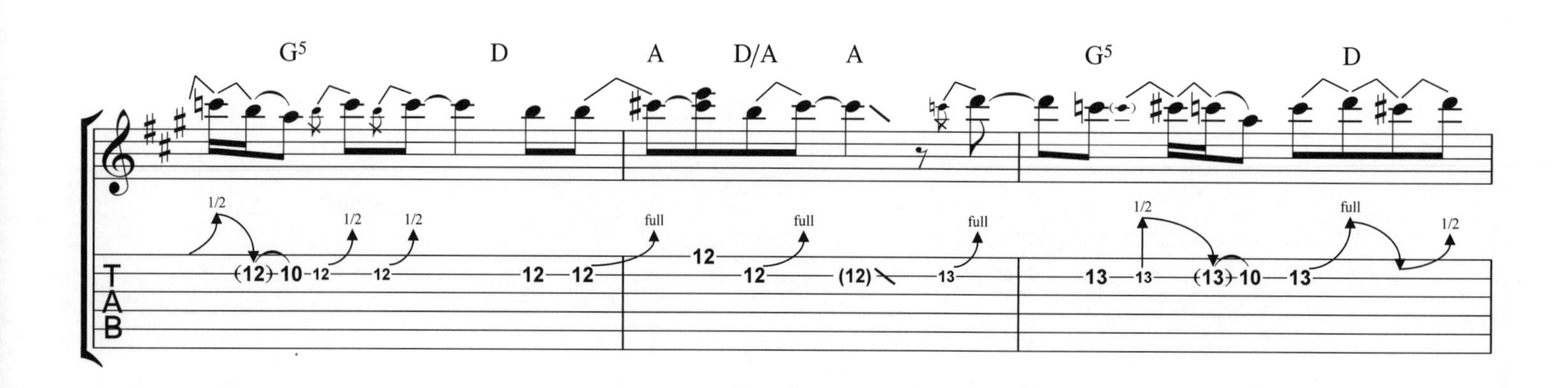
G5 D A D/A A G5 D
1/2 1/2 1/2 full full full 1/2 full 1/2

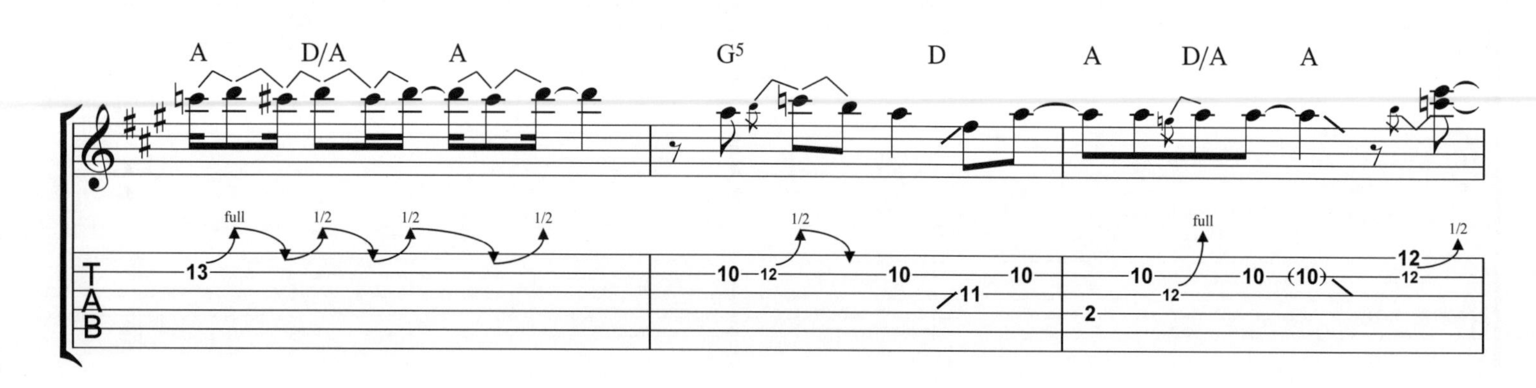
A D/A A G5 D A D/A A
full 1/2 1/2 1/2 1/2 full 1/2

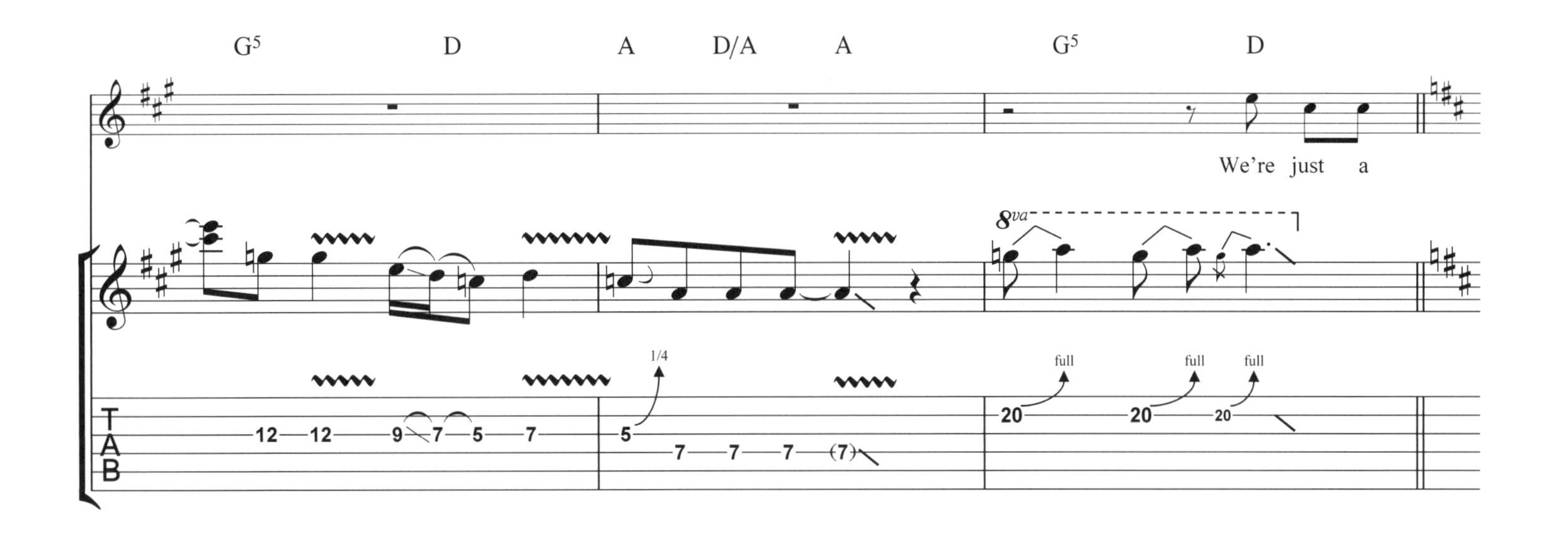
G5 D A D/A A G5 D
We're just a
8va
1/4
full full full

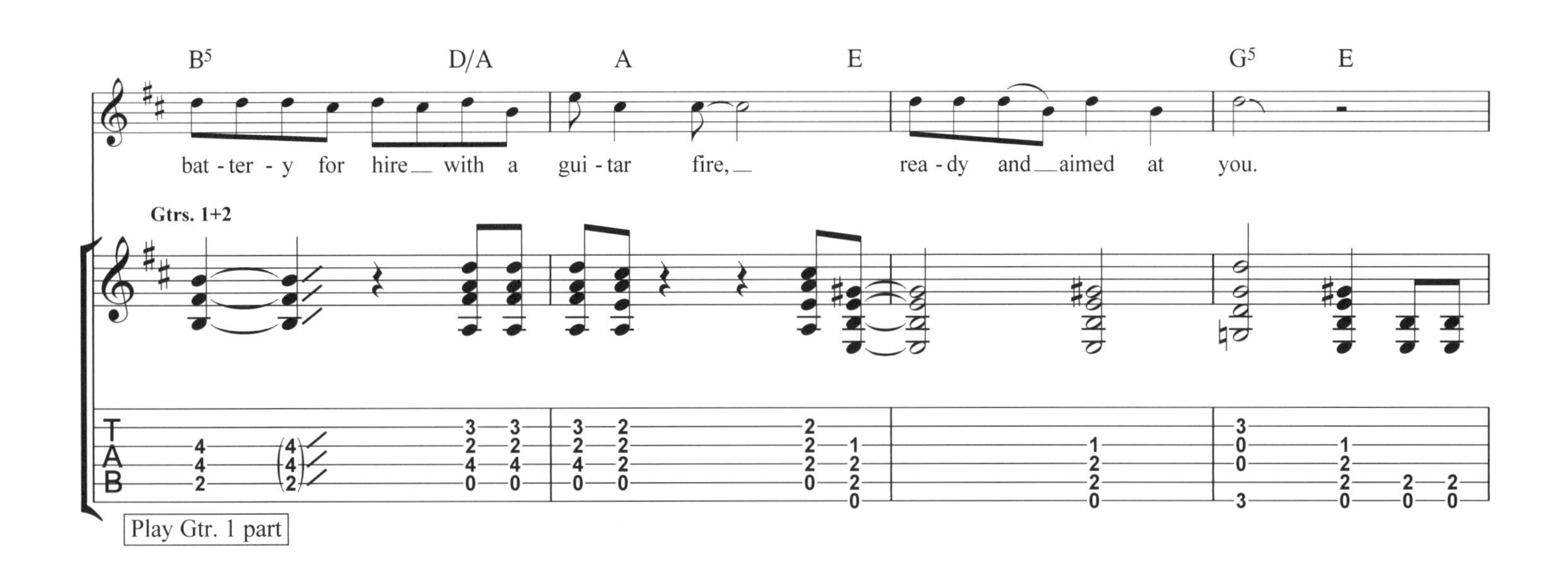
B5 D/A A E G5 E
bat - ter - y for hire with a gui - tar fire, rea - dy and aimed at you.
Gtrs. 1+2
Play Gtr. 1 part

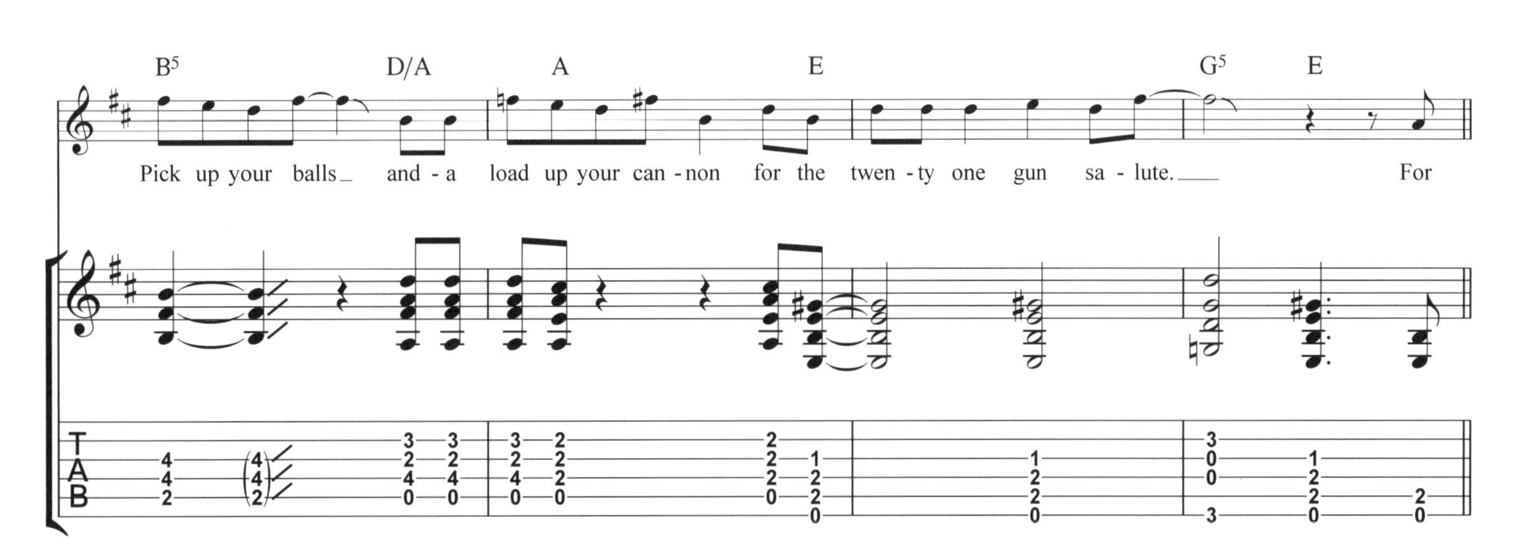
B5 D/A A E G5 E
Pick up your balls and - a load up your can - non for the twen - ty one gun sa - lute. For

1, 2.
3.
B5
G5
D
A
A
those a - bout to rock,
Fire!
2° tacet
We sa - lute you. Oh, for you.
full
Gtrs. 1+2

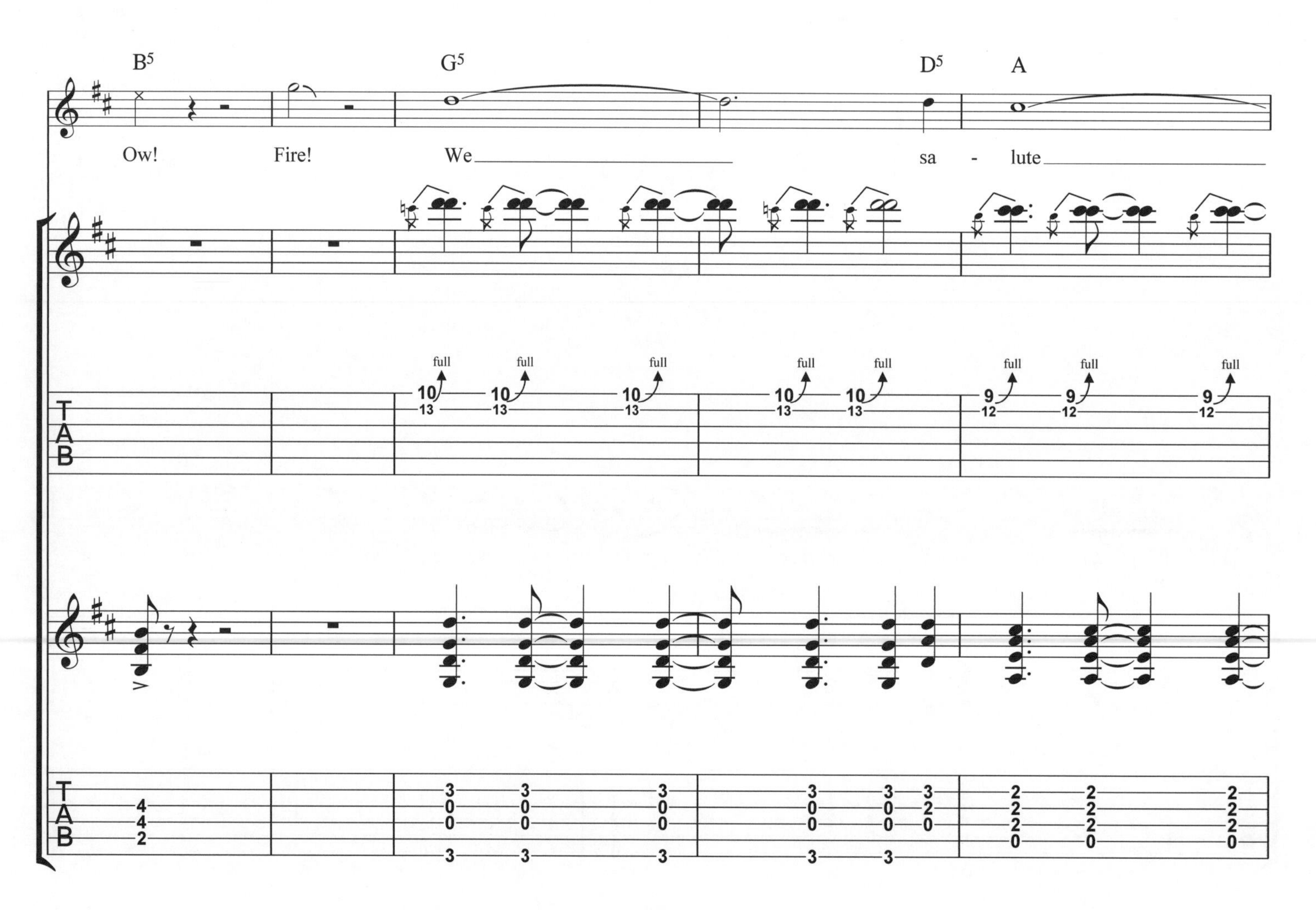
B5
G5
D5
A
Ow!
Fire!
We
sa - lute
full

B5
you.
full
T
A
B
G5
D5
A5
We sa - lute

G5
D5
A5
you.
Come on,
oh!
For
7
10
7
10
10
13
12
15
(12)
B5
G5
D5
those a - bout to rock,
we sa - lute
full
full
full
9
9
9
Fig. 4…

A5
B5
you.
For those a - bout to rock,
full
…Fig. 4 ends
1.
G5
D5
A5
we sa - lute you.
For

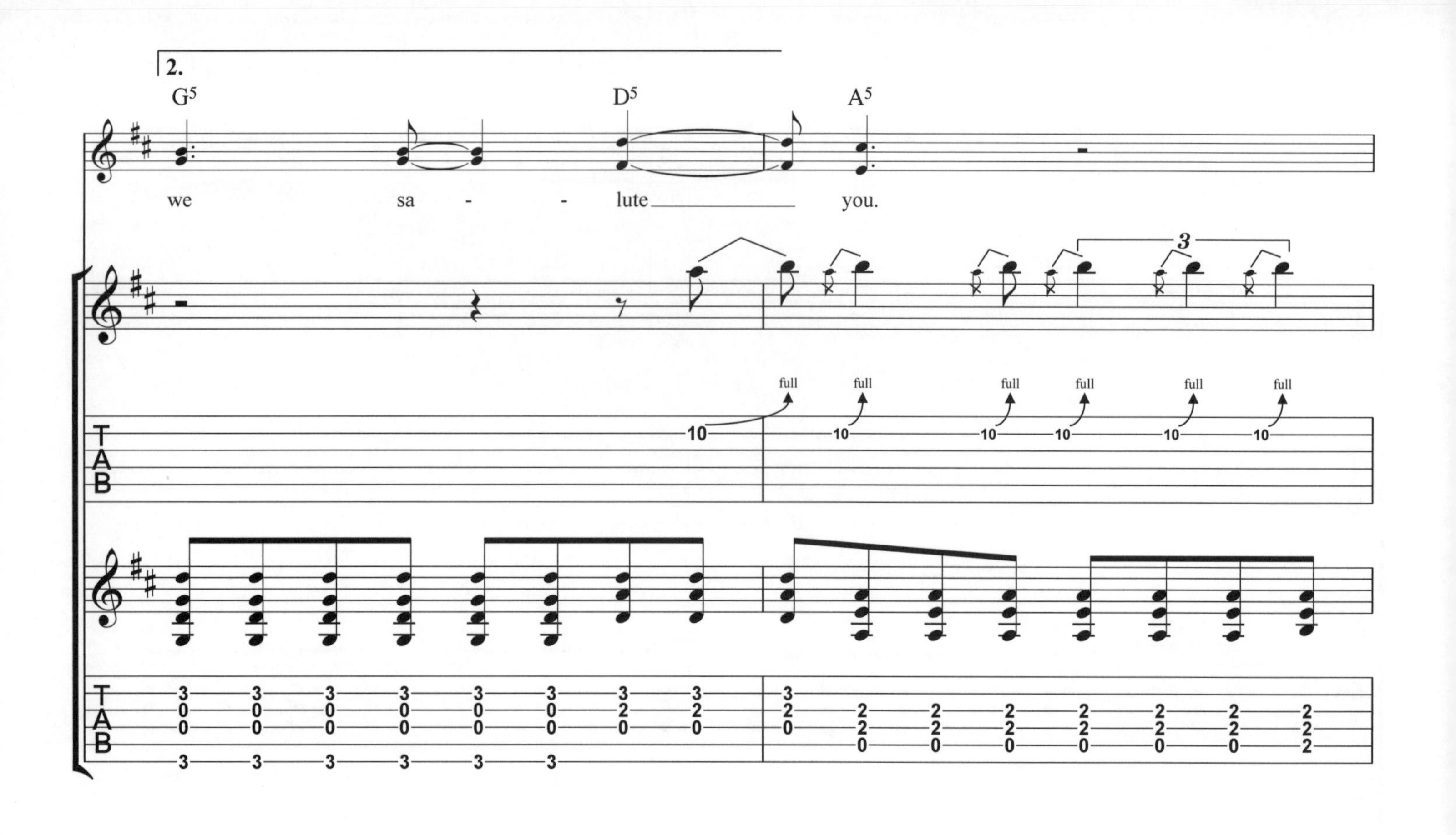
2.
G5
D5
A5
we sa - - lute you.
full
T
A
B


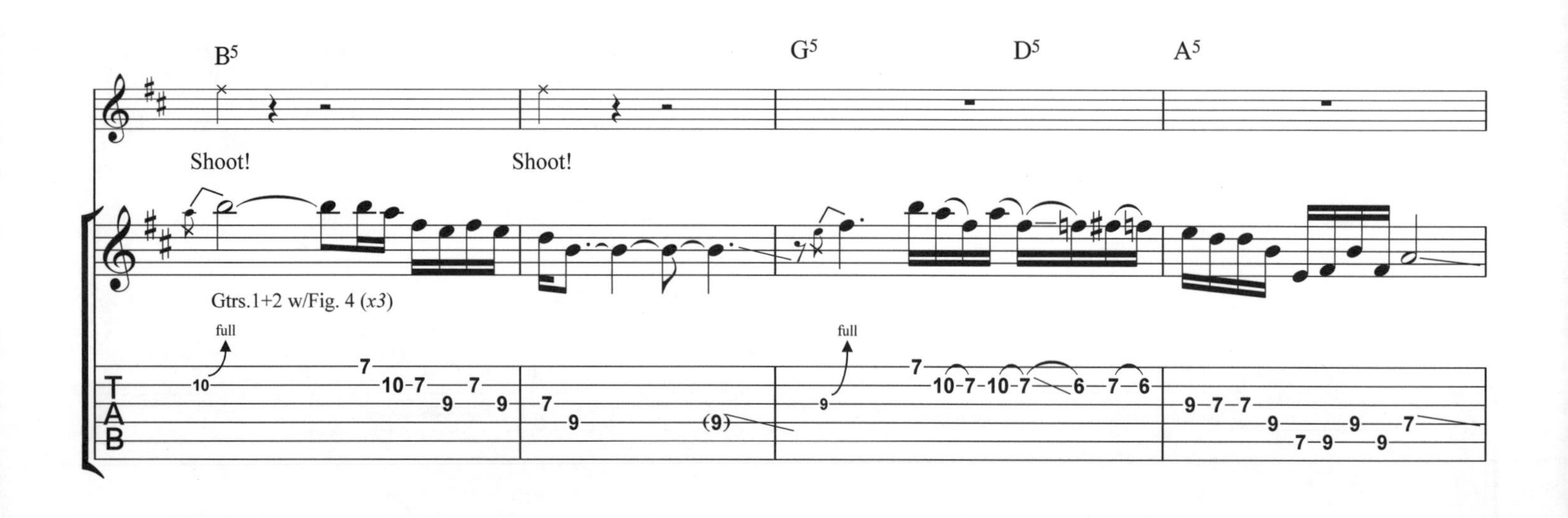
B5
G5
D5
A5
Shoot!
Shoot!
Gtrs.1+2 w/Fig. 4 (x3)
full


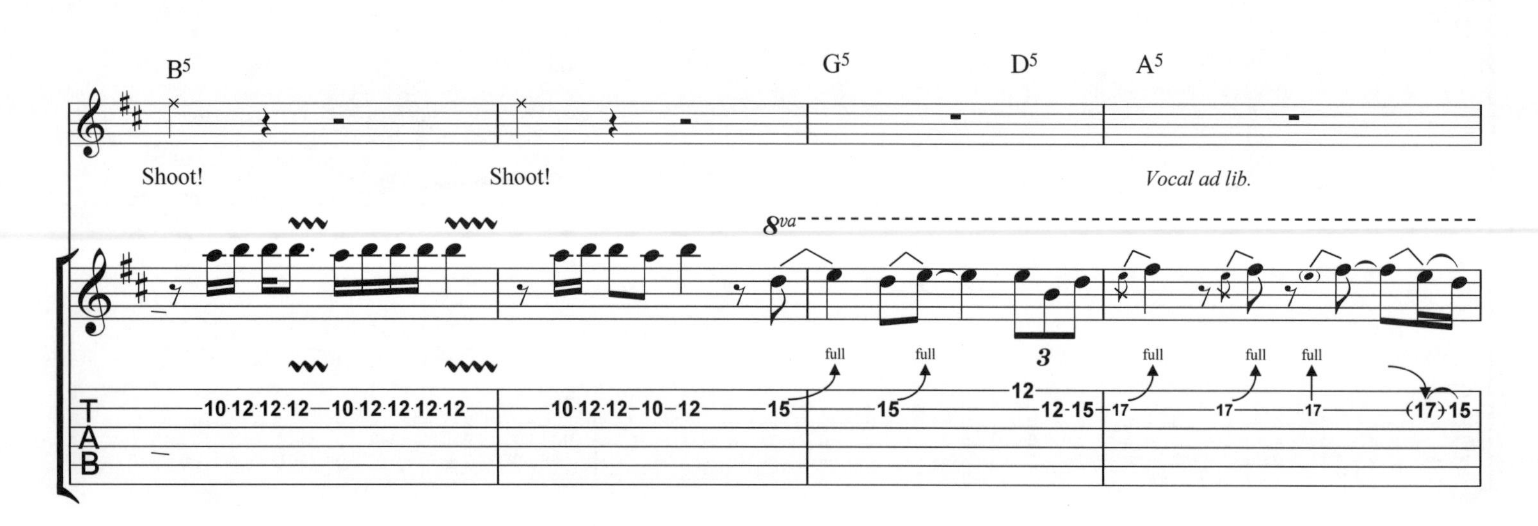
B5
G5
D5
A5
Shoot!
Shoot!
Vocal ad lib.
8va
full

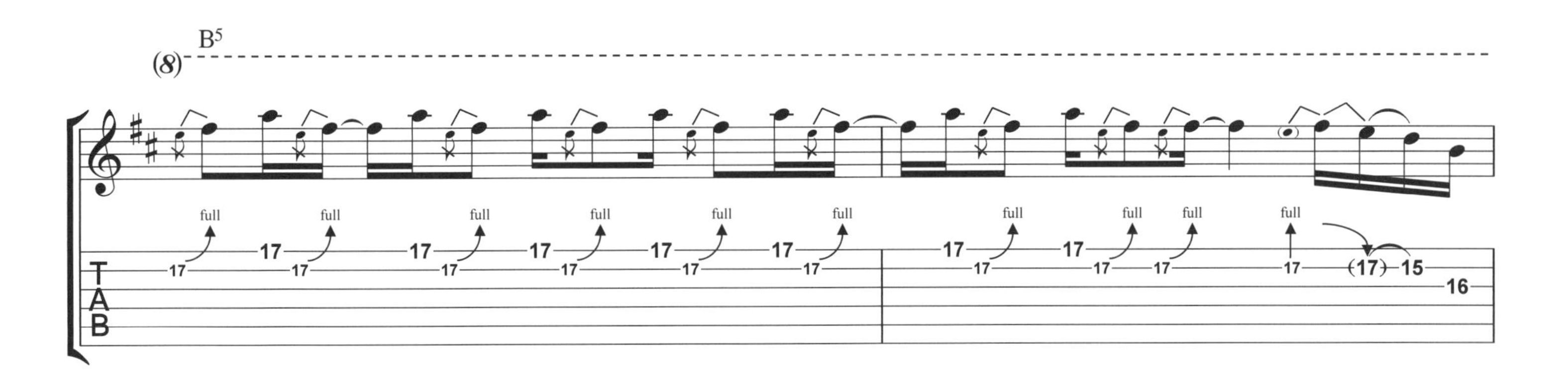
B5
(8)
full


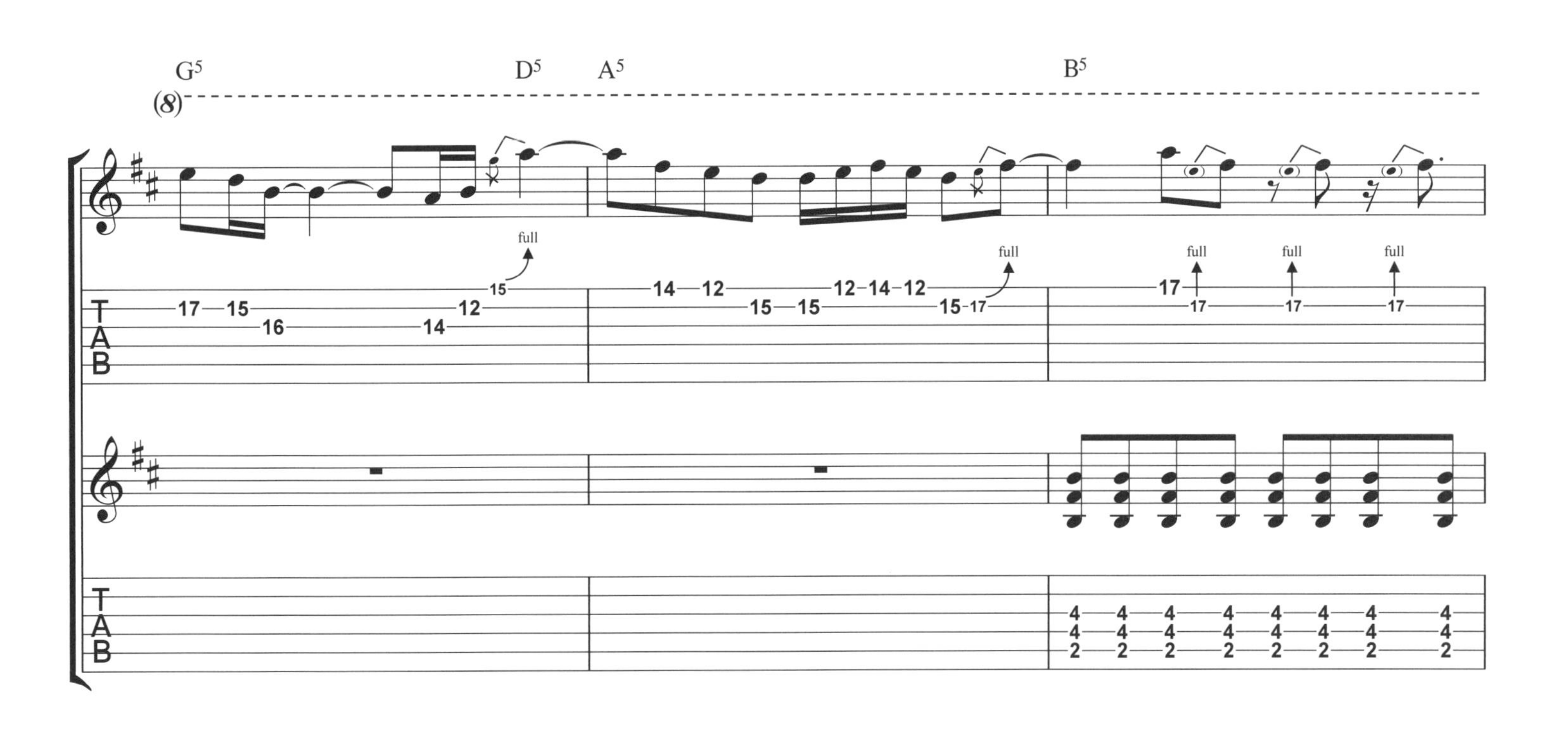
G5
D5
A5
B5
(8)
full


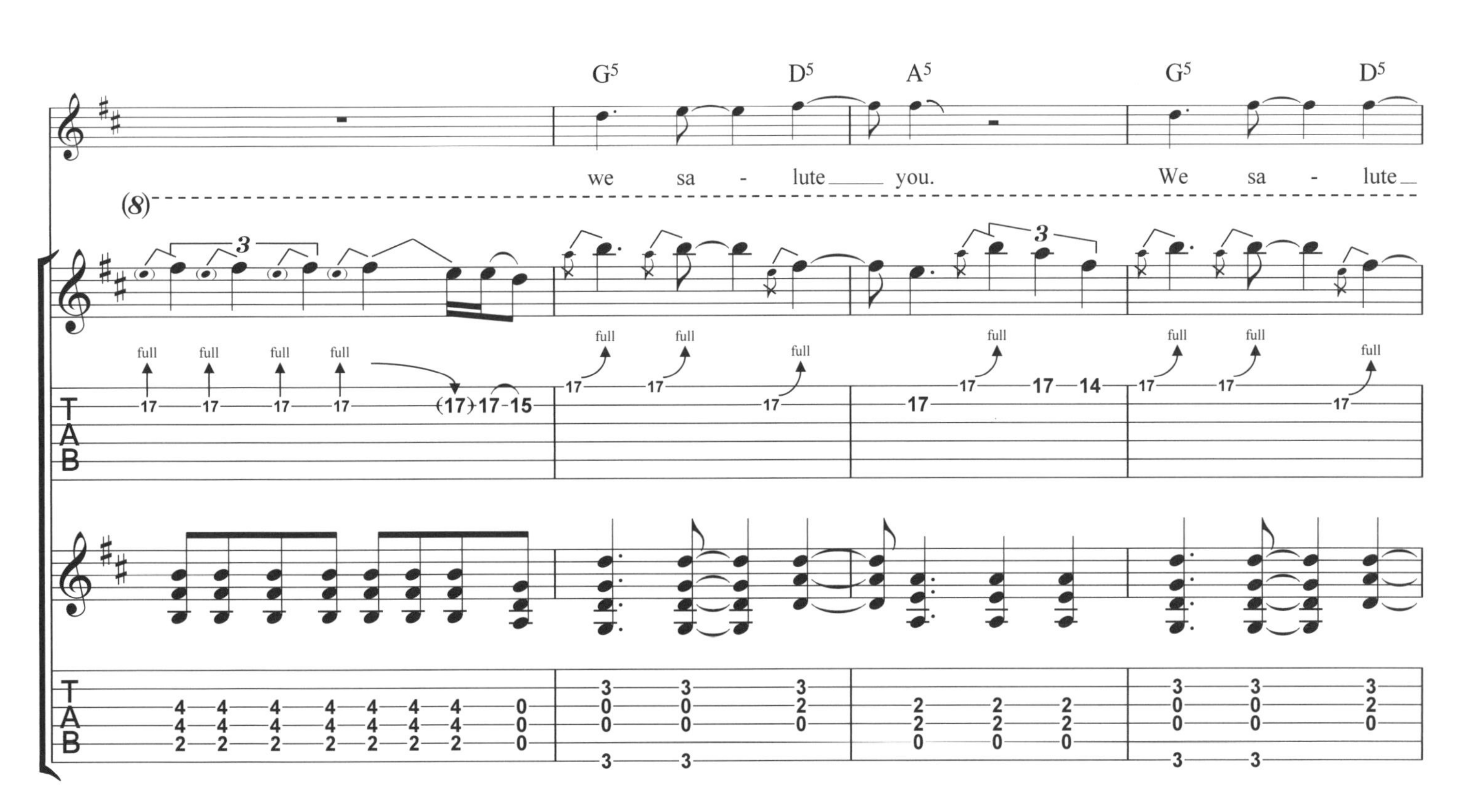
G5
D5
A5
G5
D5
we sa - lute you. We sa - lute
(8)
full

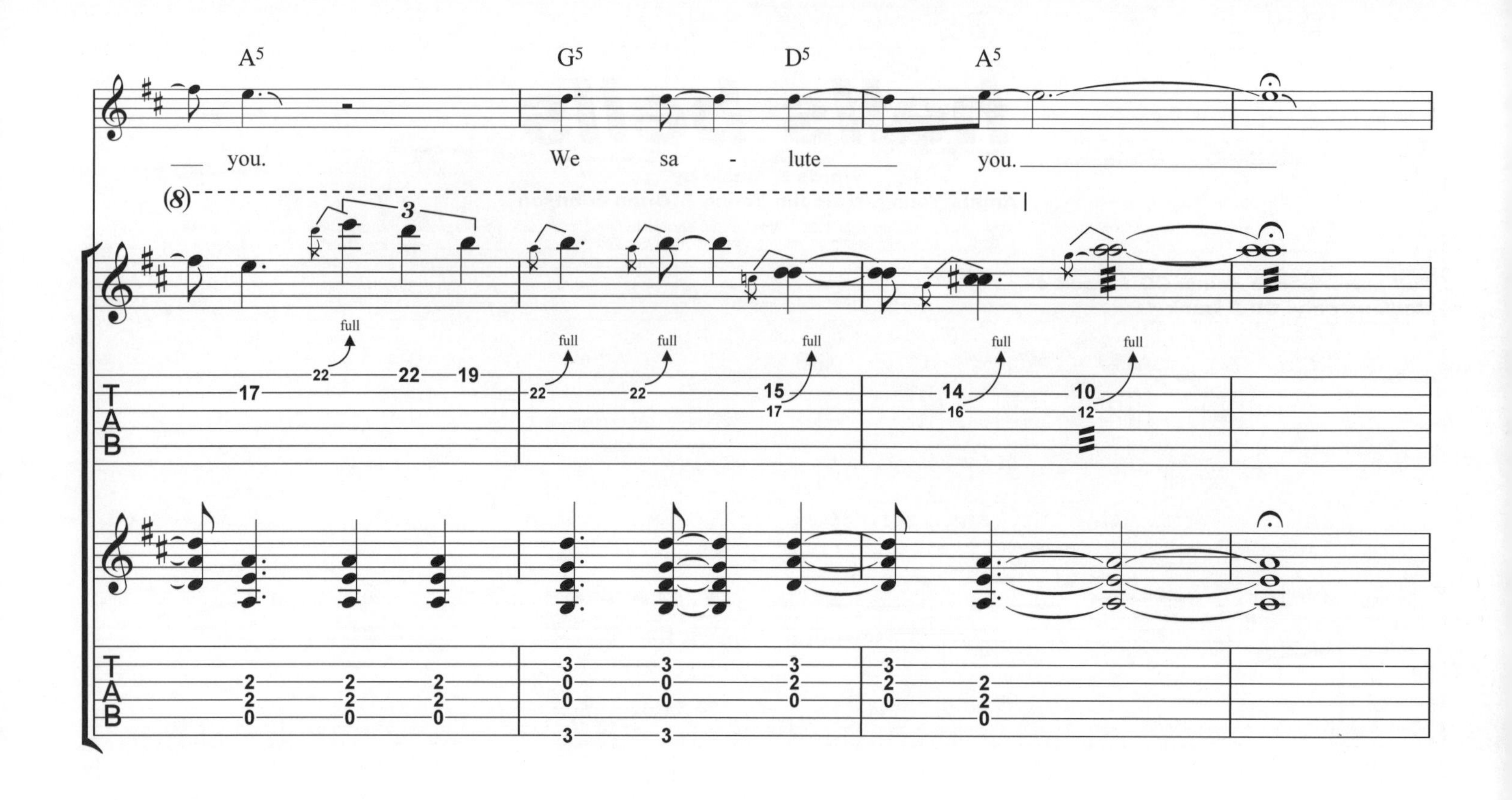
A5
G5
D5
A5
you.
We sa - lute
you.
(8)
3
full
full
full
full
full
full
17
22
22
19
22
22
15
17
14
16
10
12

**Free Time**

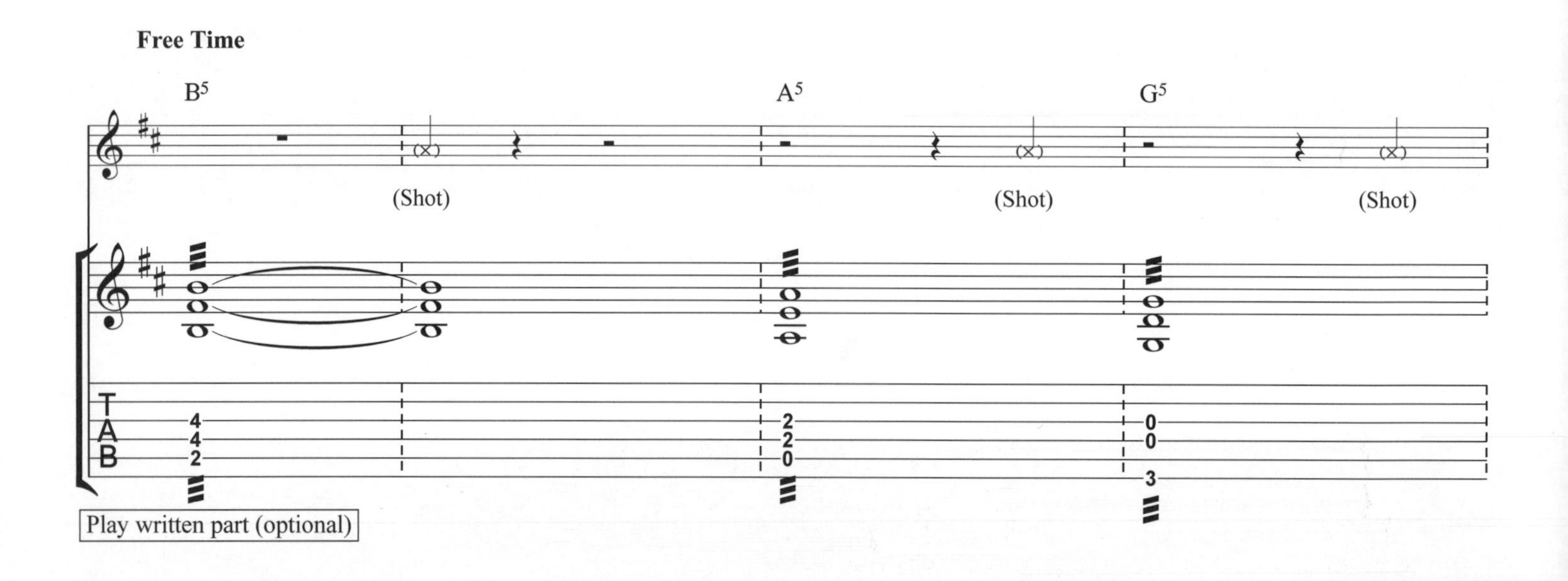
B5
A5
G5
(Shot)
(Shot)
(Shot)
Play written part (optional)

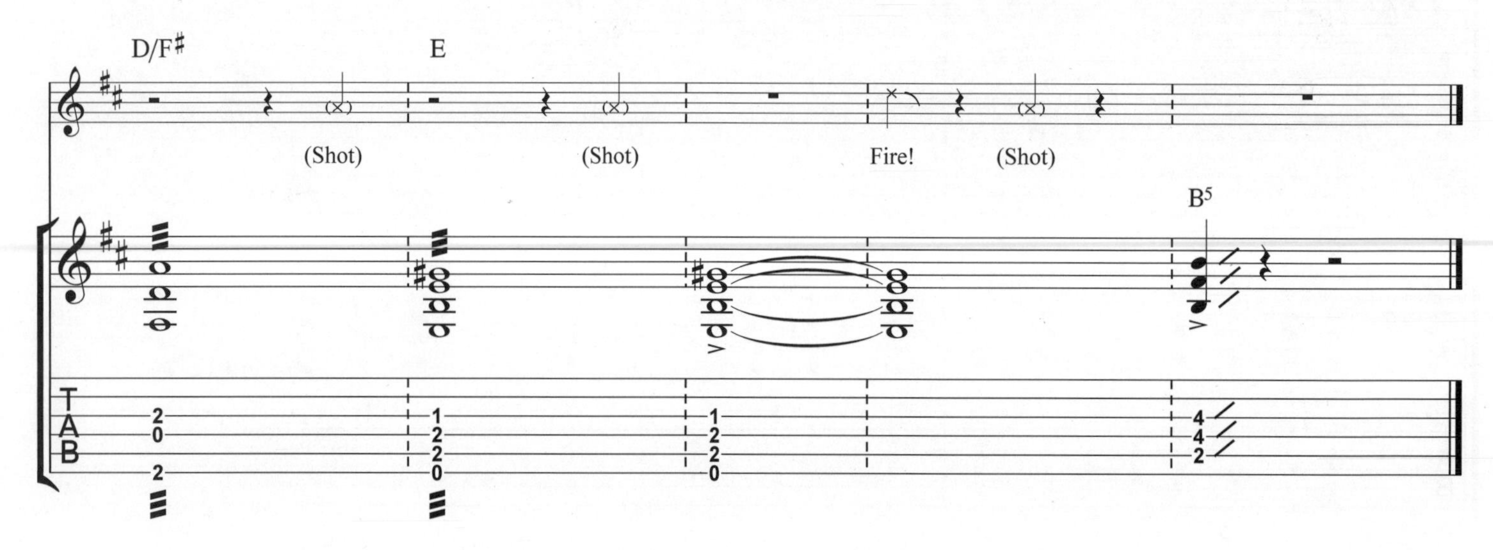
D/F♯
E
(Shot)
(Shot)
Fire!
(Shot)
B5

# hells bells

Words & Music by
Angus Young, Malcolm Young & Brian Johnson



**Full performance demo: CD 1 track 4**
**Backing only: CD 2 track 4**

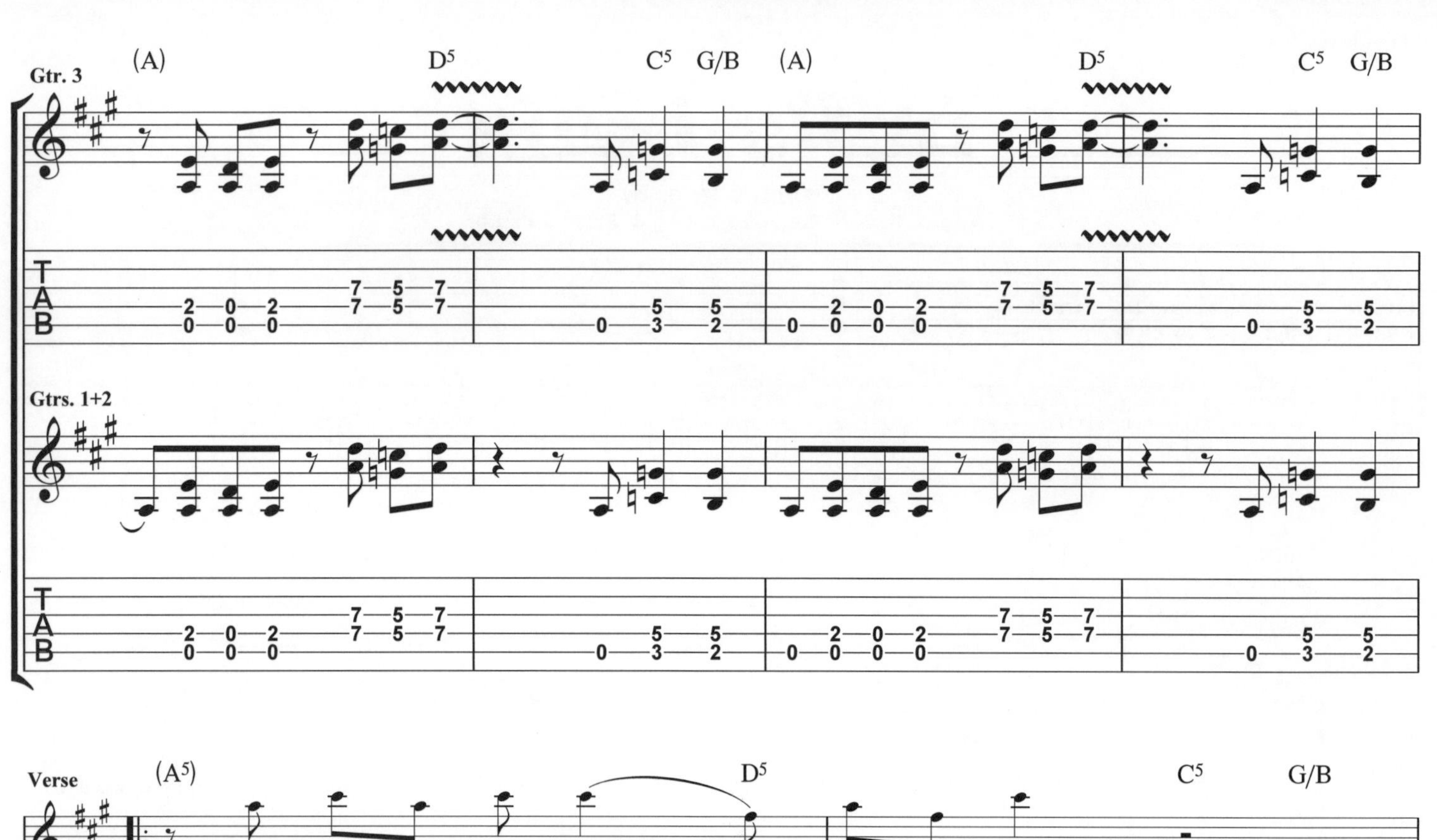
Gtr. 3
(A)
D5
C5 G/B
(A)
D5
C5 G/B
Gtrs. 1+2

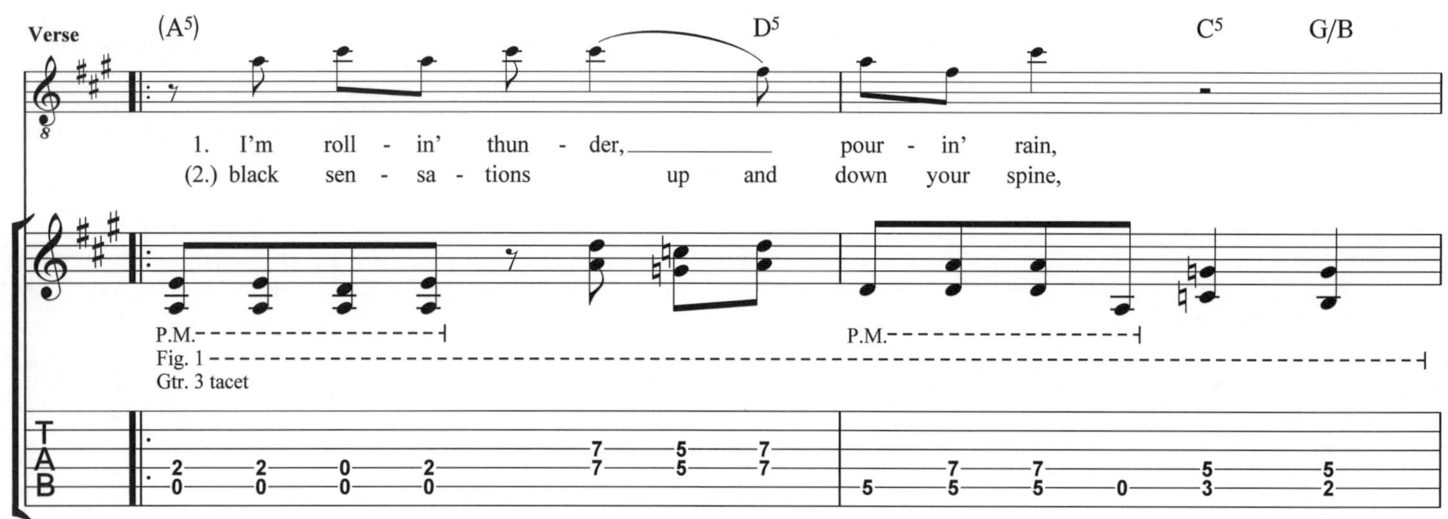
Verse
(A5)
D5
C5 G/B
1. I'm roll - in' thun - der, pour - in' rain,
(2.) black sen - sa - tions up and down your spine,
P.M.
P.M.
Fig. 1
Gtr. 3 tacet

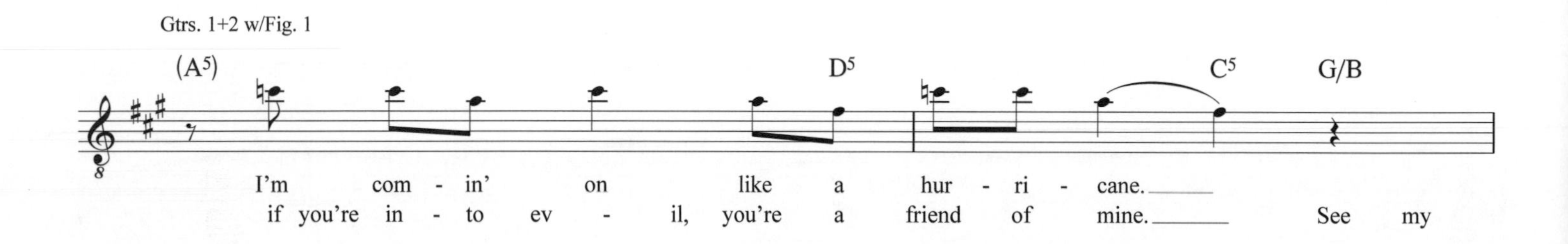
Gtrs. 1+2 w/Fig. 1
(A5)
D5
C5 G/B
I'm com - in' on like a hur - ri - cane.
if you're in - to ev - il, you're a friend of mine. See my

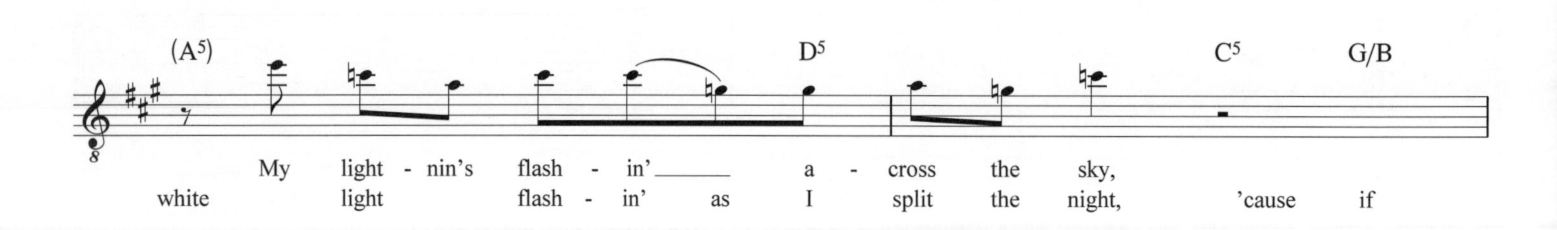
(A5)
D5
C5 G/B
My light - nin's flash - in' a - cross the sky,
white light flash - in' as I split the night, 'cause if

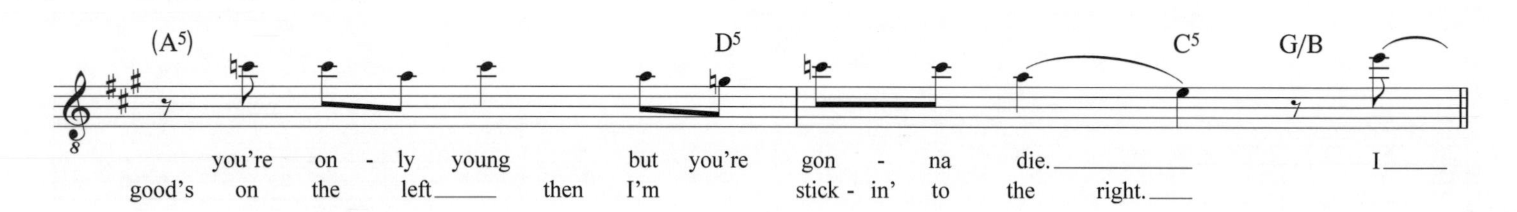
(A5)
D5
C5 G/B
you're on - ly young but you're gon - na die. I
good's on the left then I'm stick - in' to the right.

## Pre-Chorus

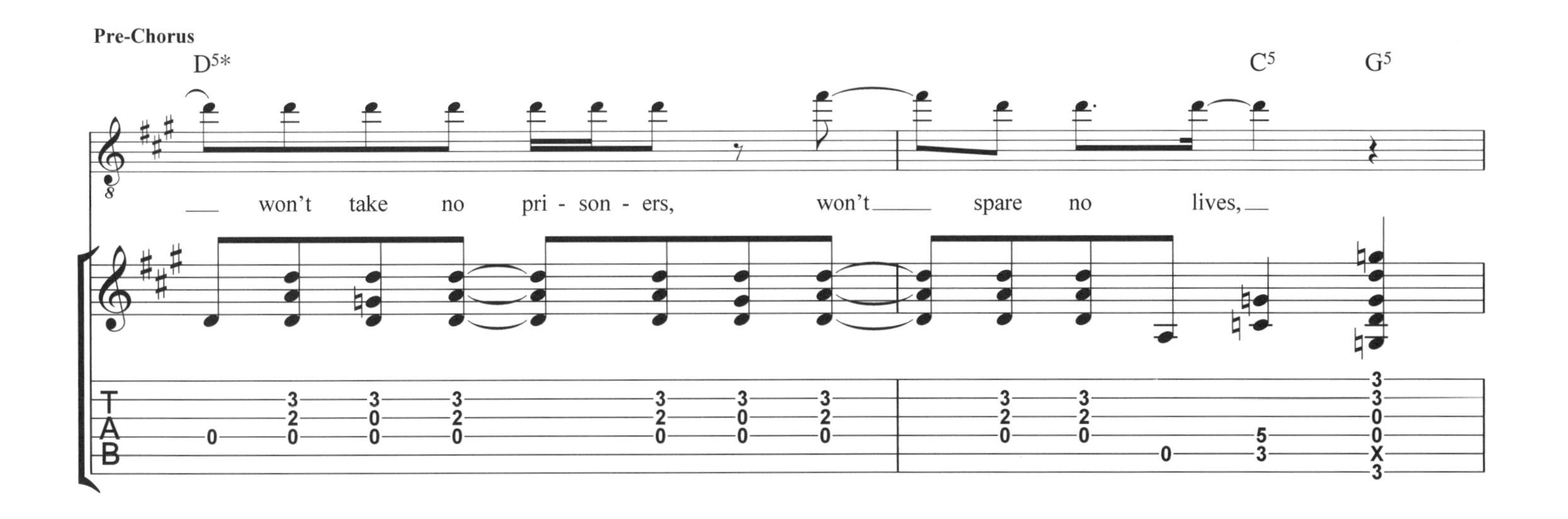
D5*
C5
G5
won't take no pri - son - ers, won't spare no lives,

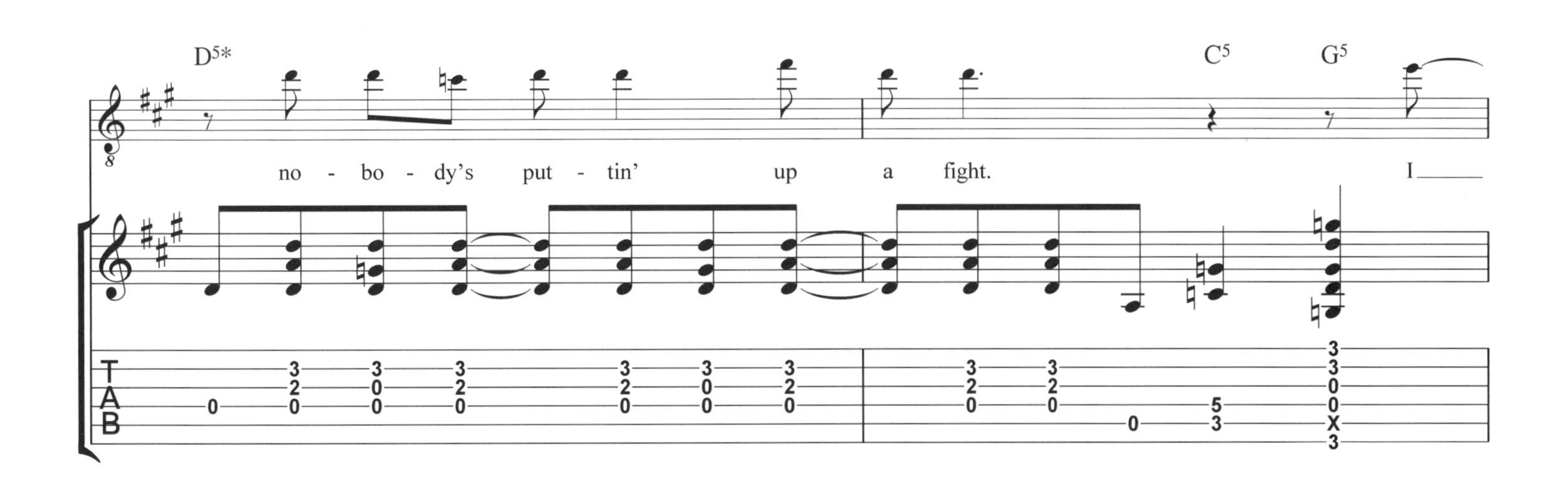
D5*
C5
G5
no - bo - dy's put - tin' up a fight. I

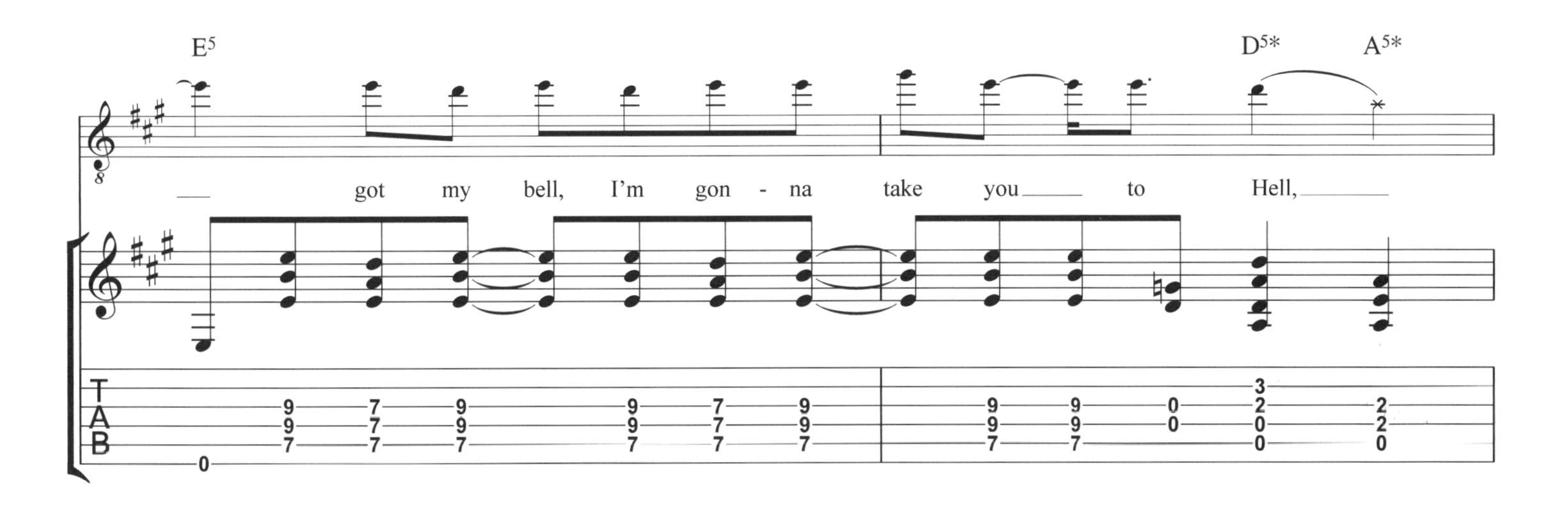
E5
D5*
A5*
got my bell, I'm gon - na take you to Hell,

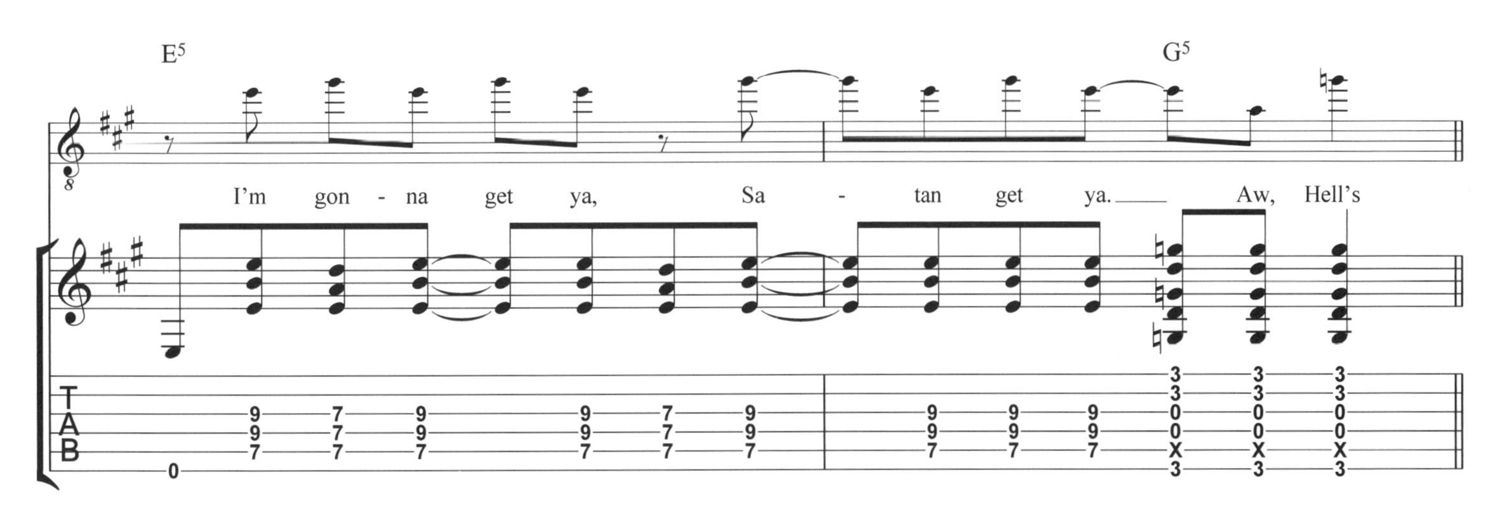
E5
G5
I'm gon - na get ya, Sa - tan get ya. Aw, Hell's

Chorus
A5 Asus4 Am7 Asus4 A5 Asus4 Am7
bells, yeah, Hell's bells.
(at 𝄋) Sa - tan's call - ing to you, Hell's bells, he's
Gtrs. 1+2+3
Gtr. 4 tacet at 𝄋
TAB

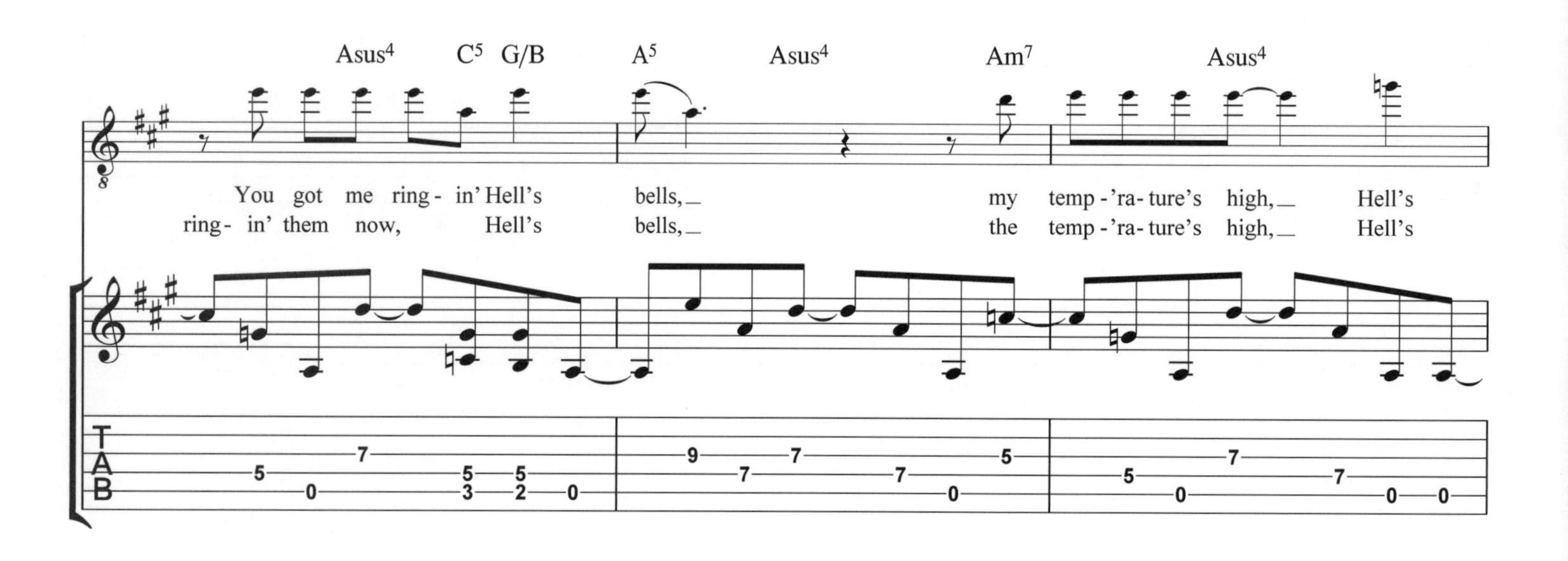
Asus4 C5 G/B A5 Asus4 Am7 Asus4
You got me ring - in' Hell's bells, my temp - 'ra - ture's high, Hell's
ring - in' them now, Hell's bells, the temp - 'ra - ture's high, Hell's
TAB

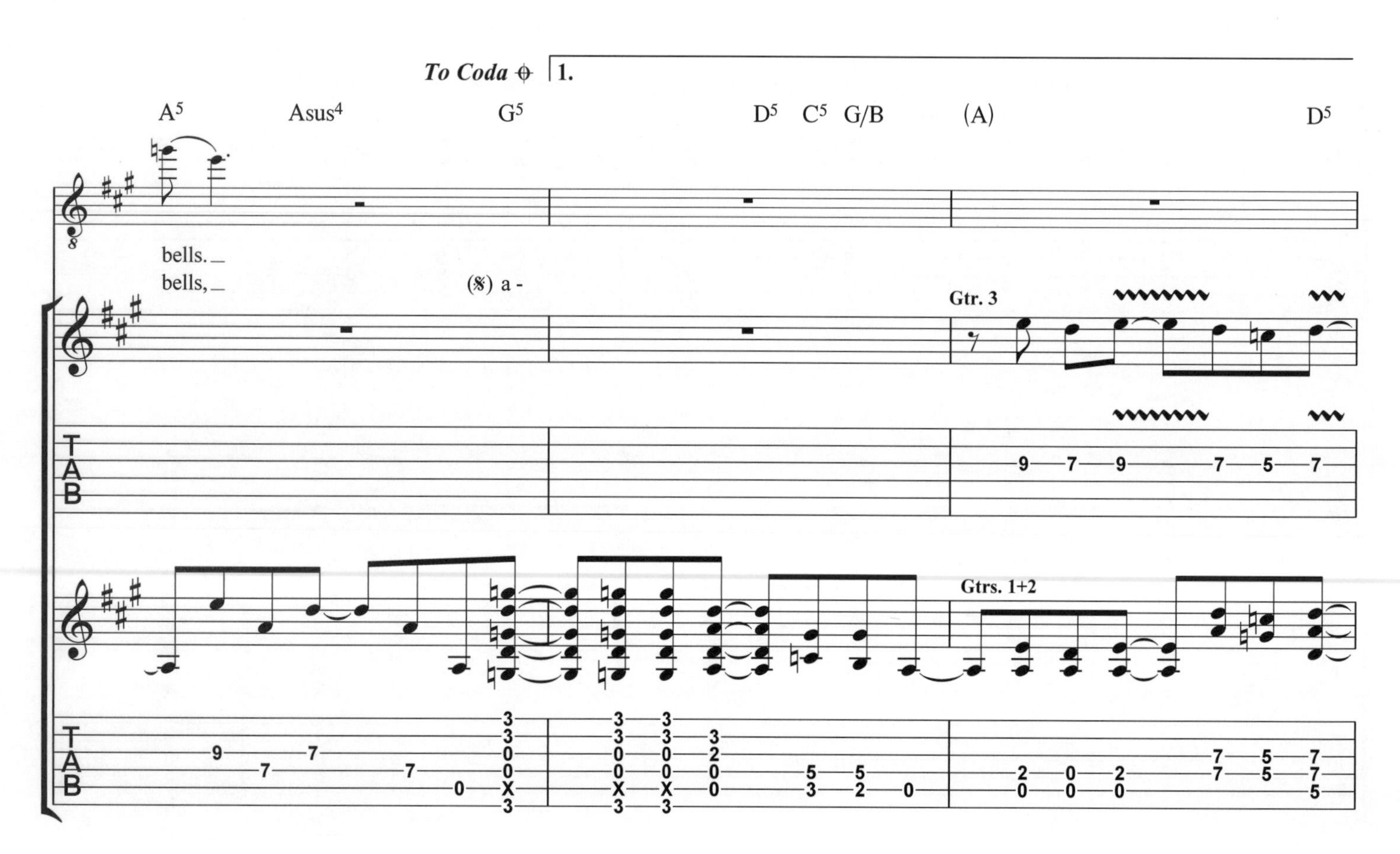
To Coda 1.
A5 Asus4 G5 D5 C5 G/B (A) D5
bells.
bells, (𝄋) a -
Gtr. 3
TAB
Gtrs. 1+2
TAB

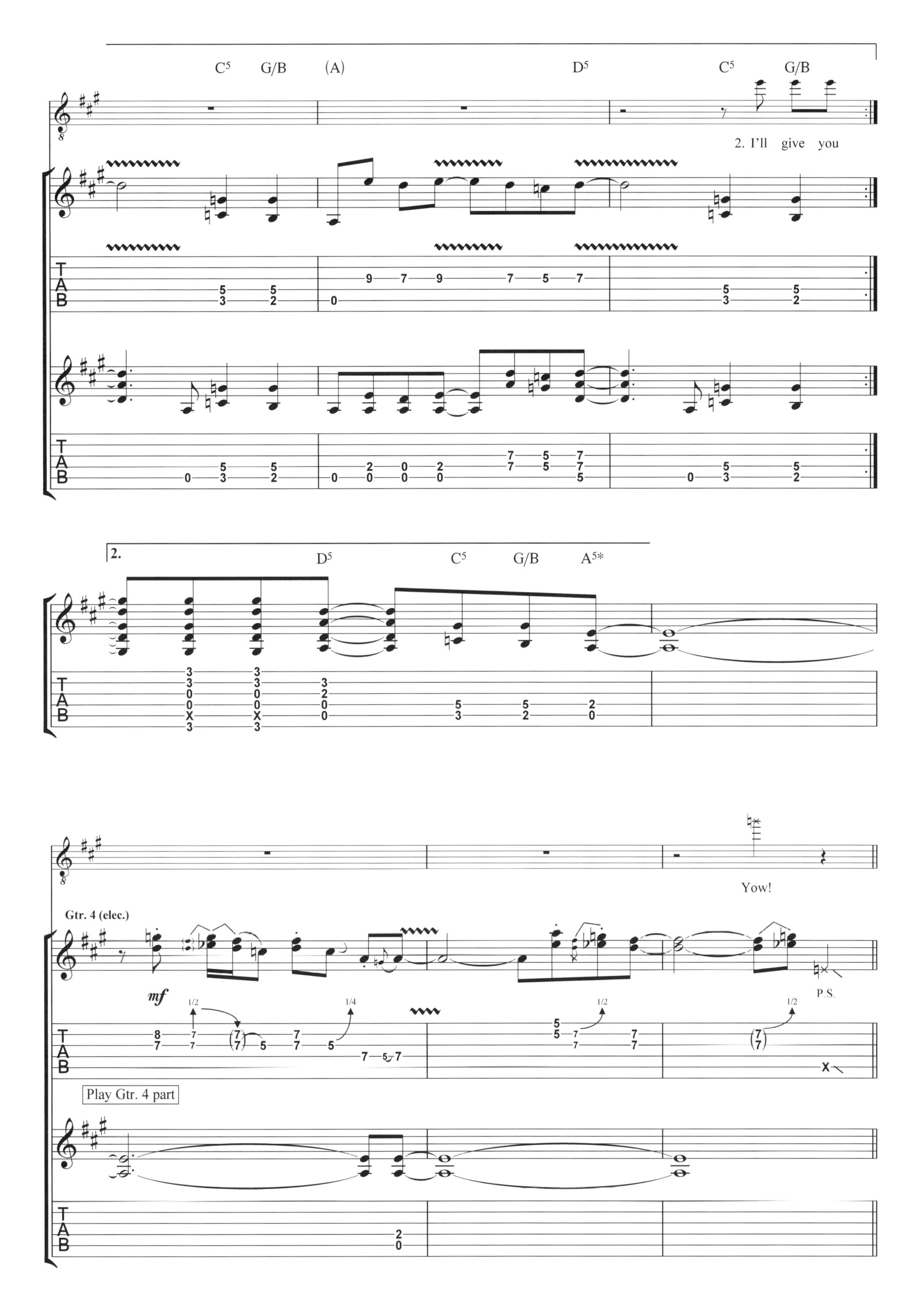

C5
G/B
(A)
D5
C5
G/B
2. I'll give you
2.
D5
C5
G/B
A5*
Yow!
Gtr. 4 (elec.)
mf
P.S.
Play Gtr. 4 part

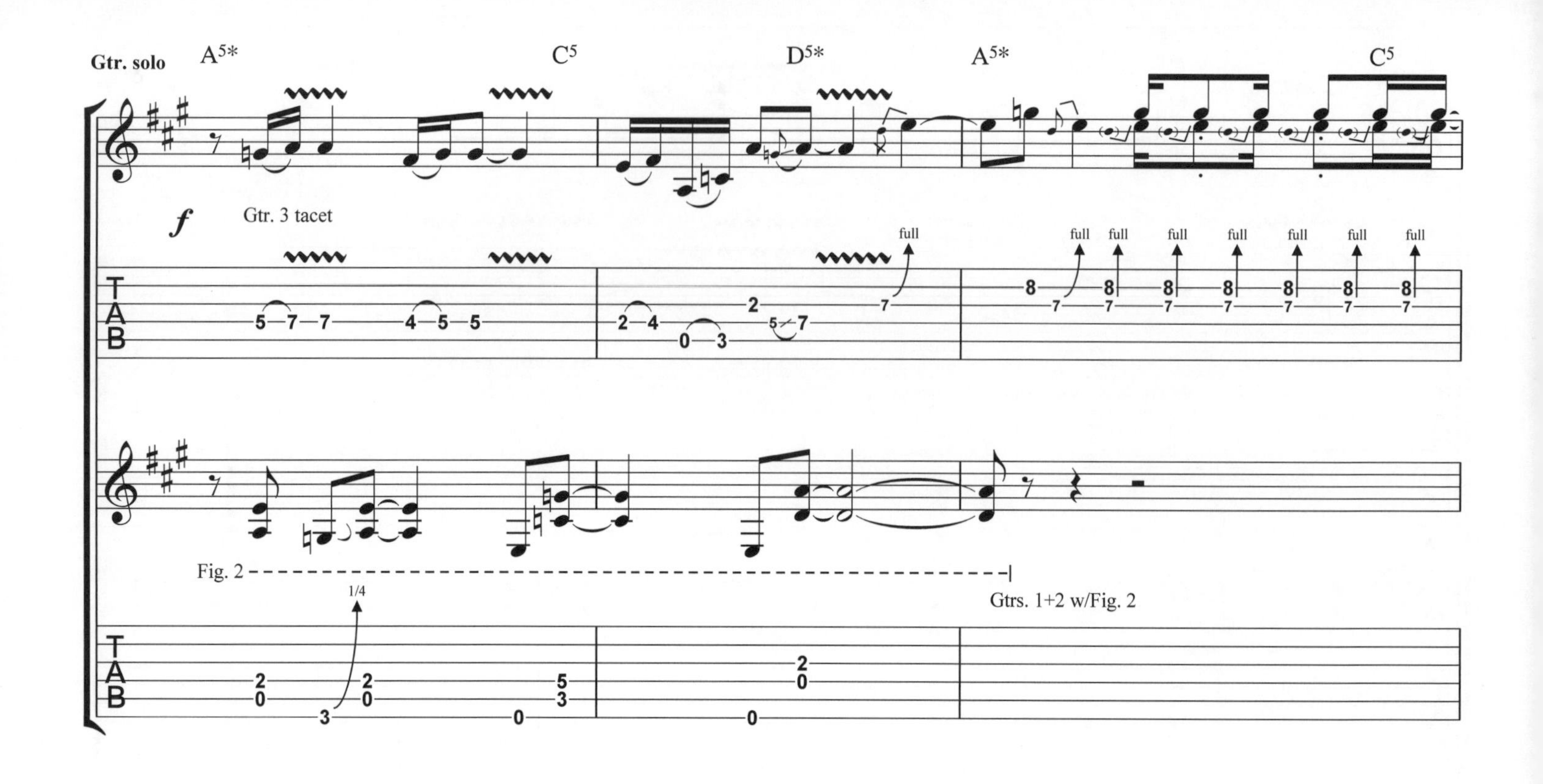
Gtr. solo
A5*
C5
D5*
A5*
C5
f
Gtr. 3 tacet
full
Fig. 2
1/4
Gtrs. 1+2 w/Fig. 2

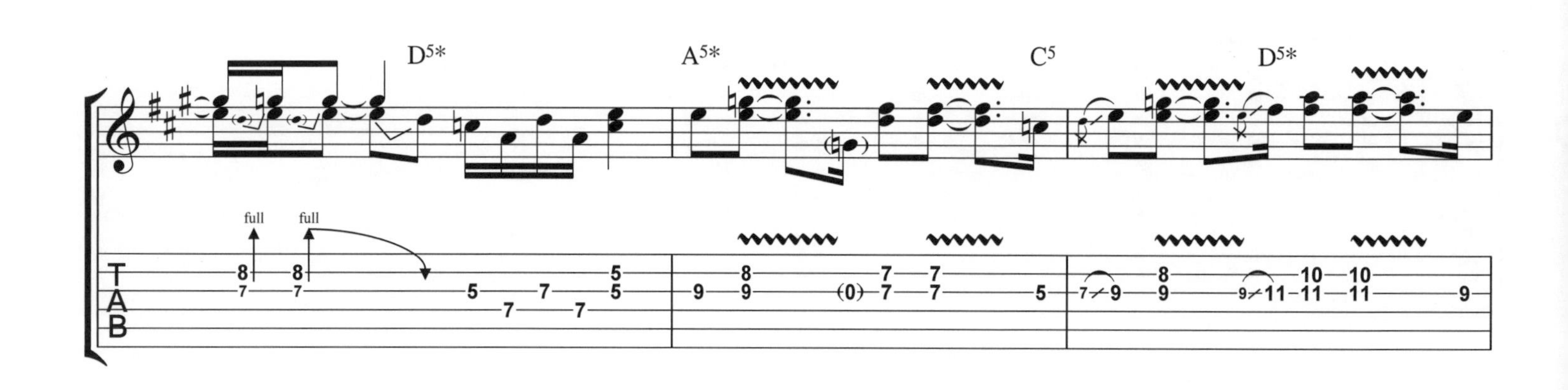
D5*
A5*
C5
D5*
full

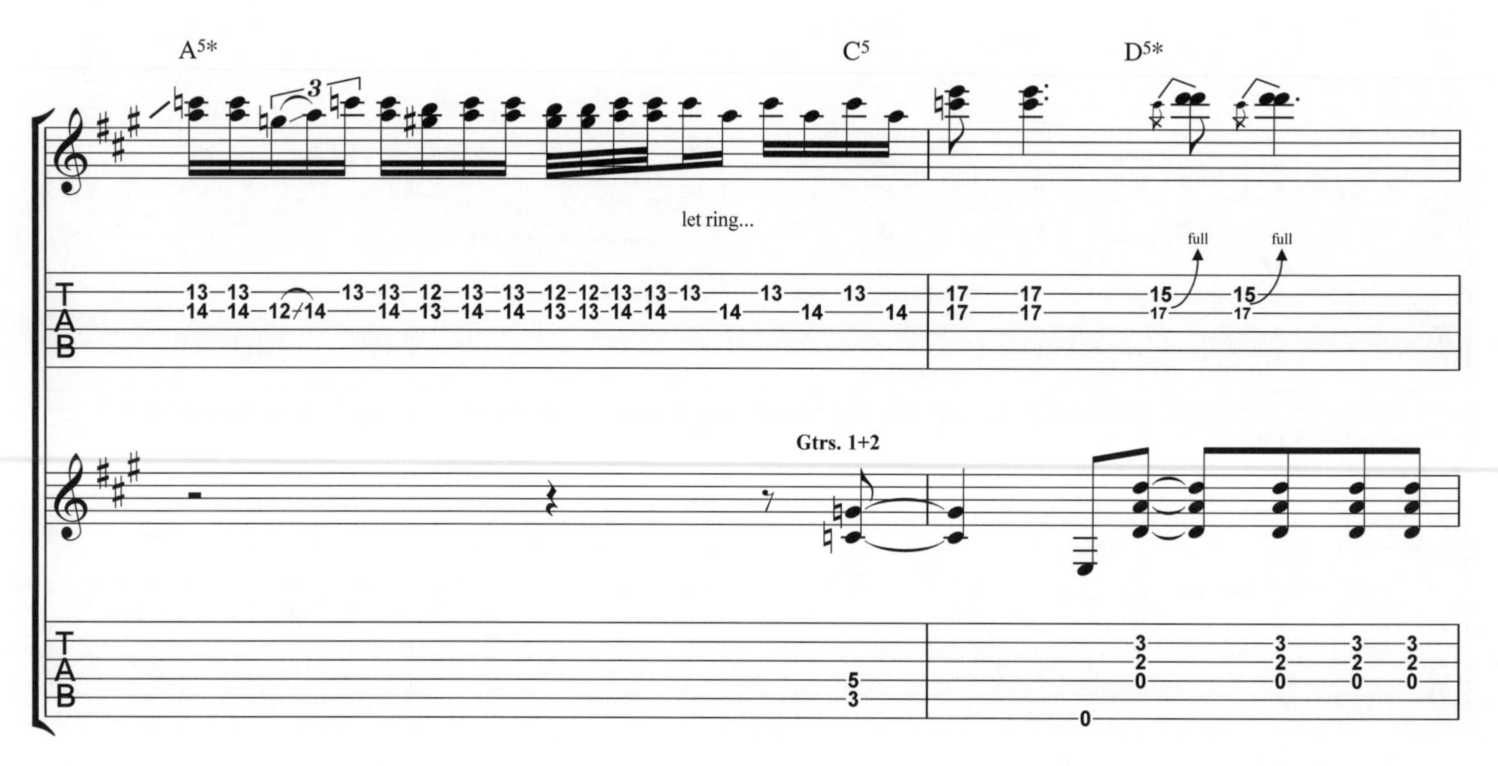
A5*
C5
D5*
let ring...
full
Gtrs. 1+2

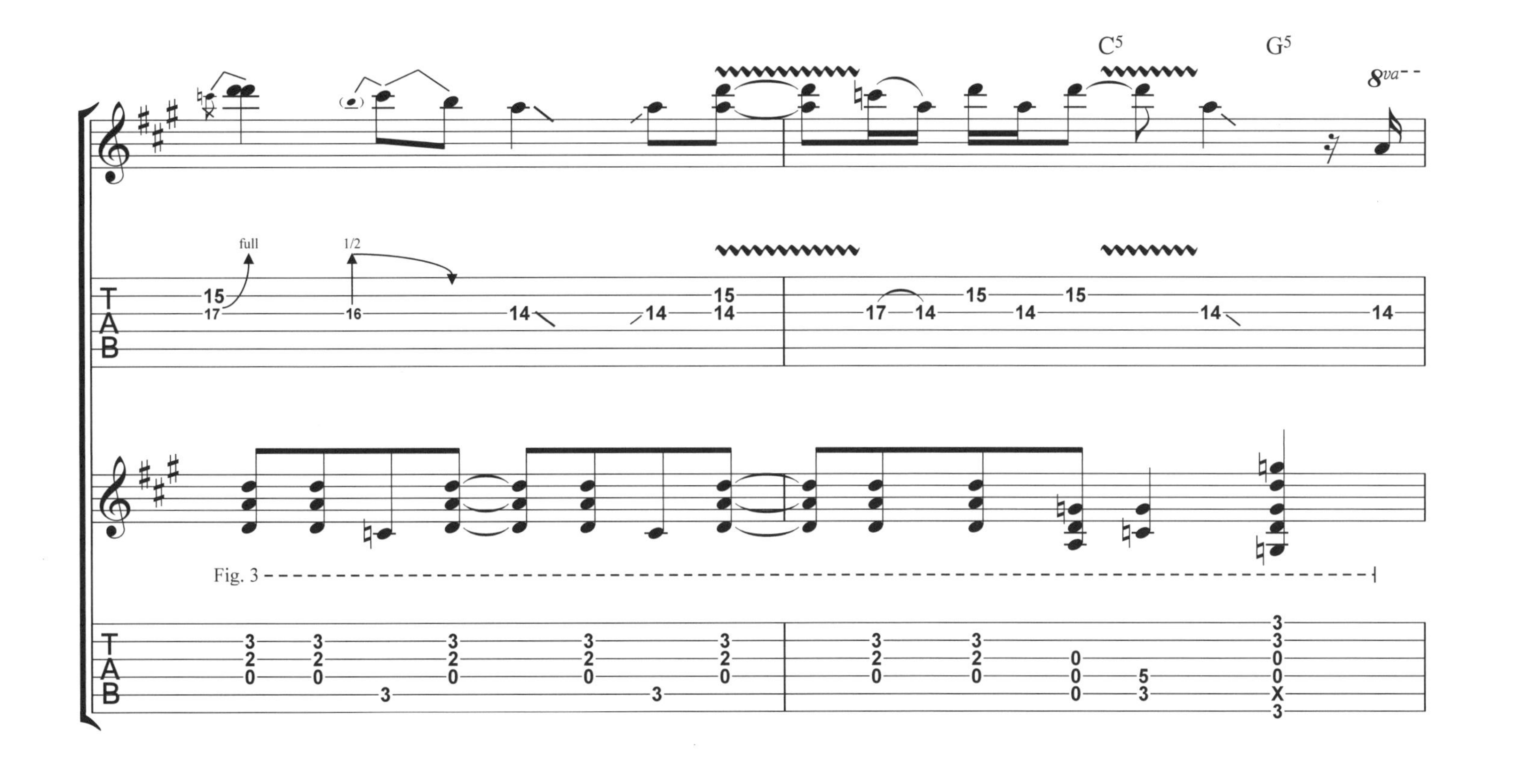
C5
G5
8va
full
1/2
Fig. 3

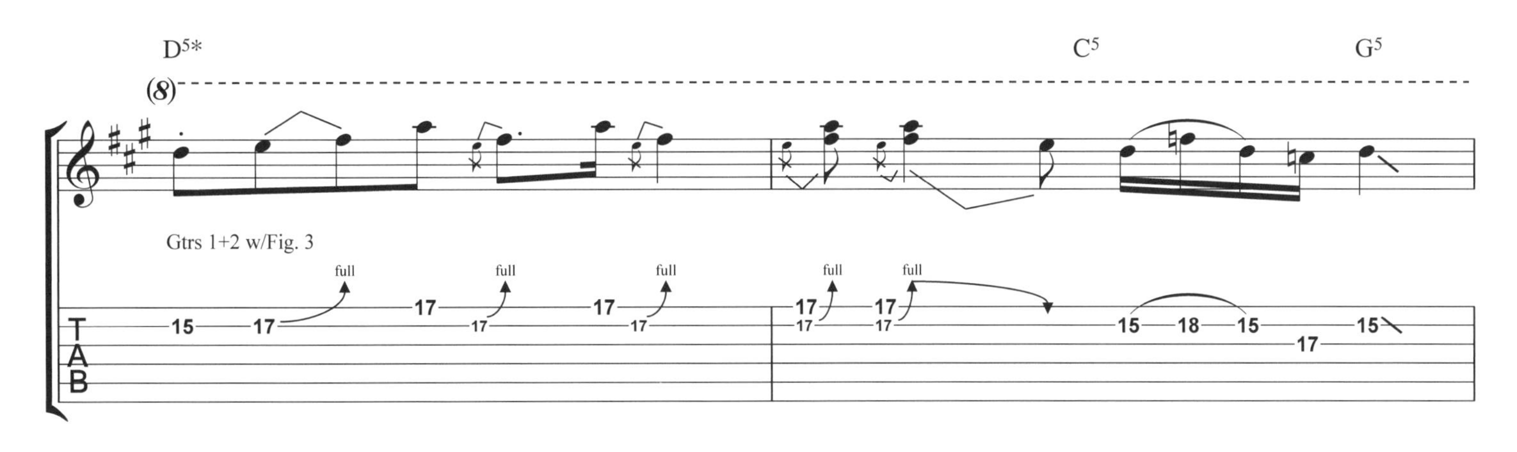
D5*
C5
G5
(8)
Gtrs 1+2 w/Fig. 3
full

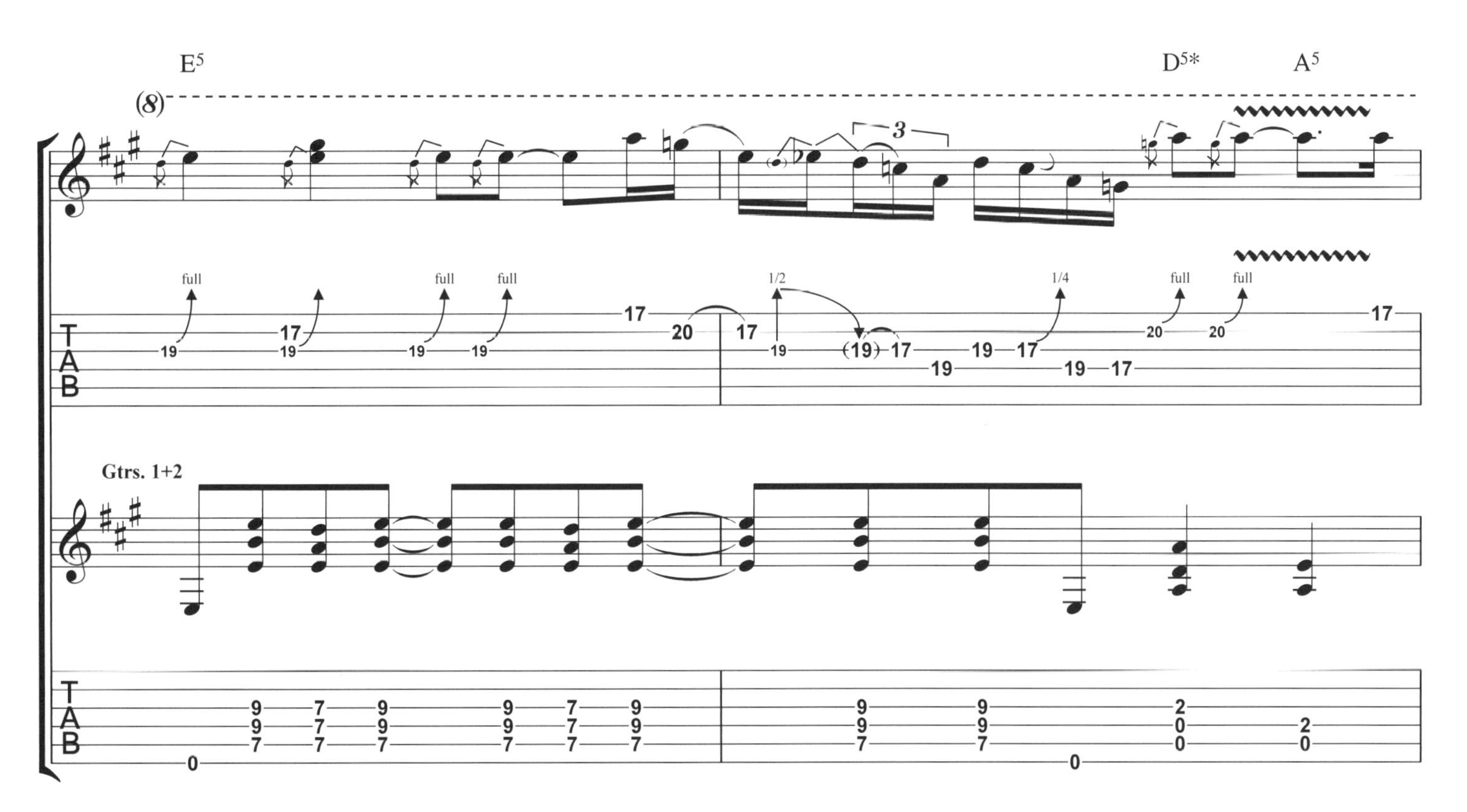
E5
D5*
A5
(8)
full
1/2
1/4
Gtrs. 1+2

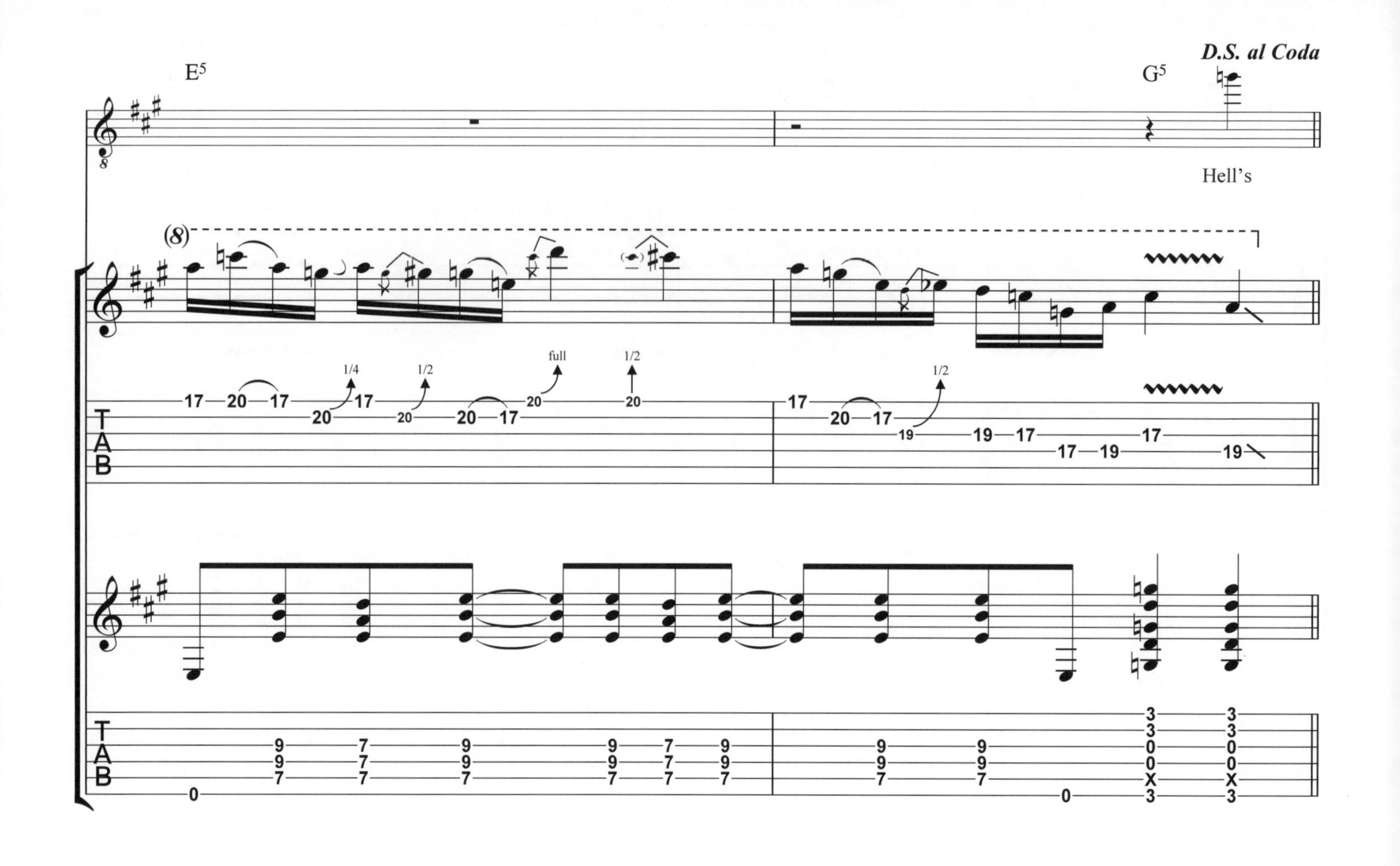
D.S. al Coda
E5
G5
Hell's
(8)
full
1/4
1/2
1/2


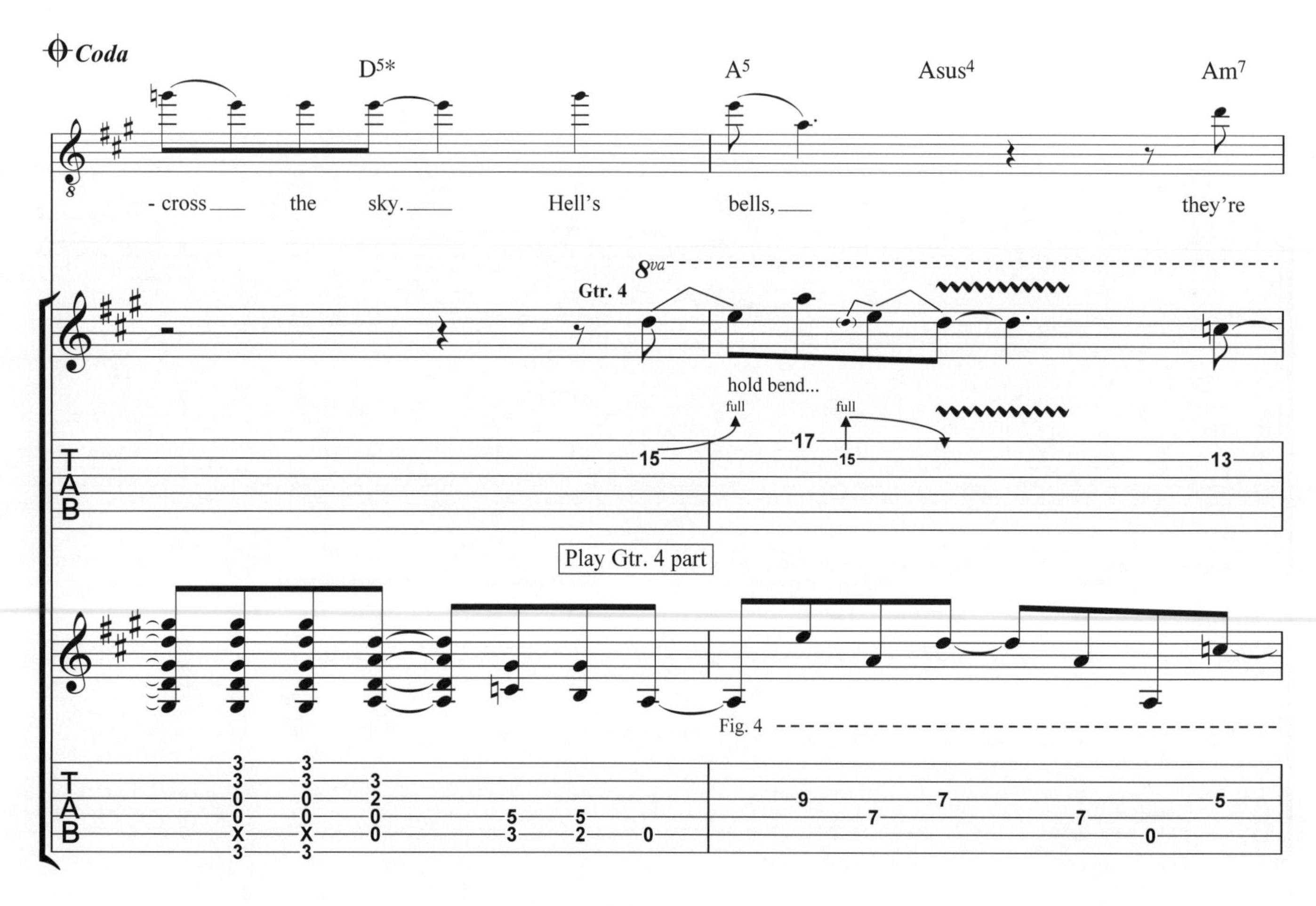
Coda
D5*
A5
Asus4
Am7
-cross the sky. Hell's bells, they're
8va
Gtr. 4
hold bend...
full
Play Gtr. 4 part
Fig. 4

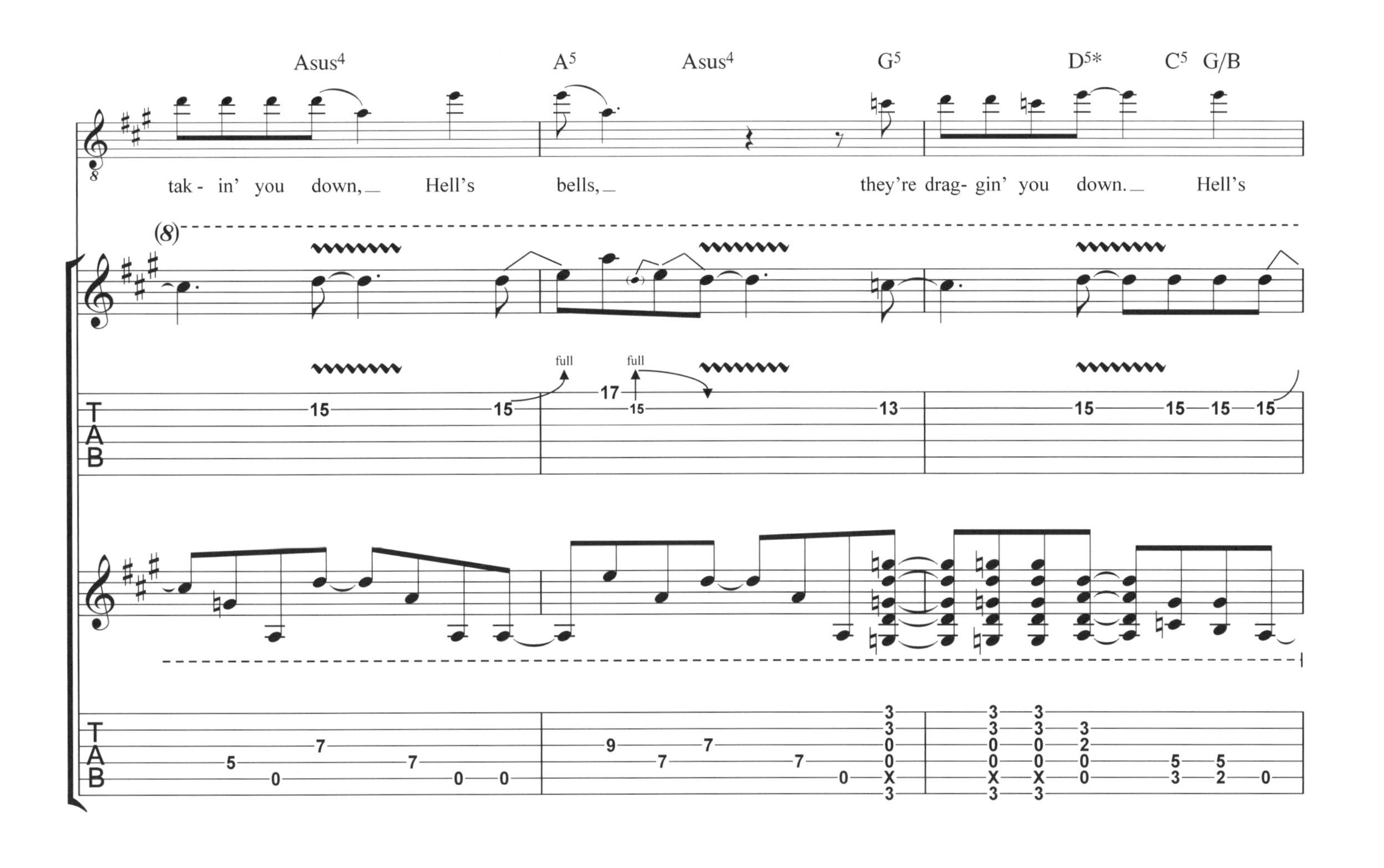
Asus4
A5
Asus4
G5
D5*
C5 G/B
tak - in' you down,_ Hell's bells,_ they're drag- gin' you down._ Hell's
(8)
full
full
17
15
13
15
3
0
X
5
7
9
2

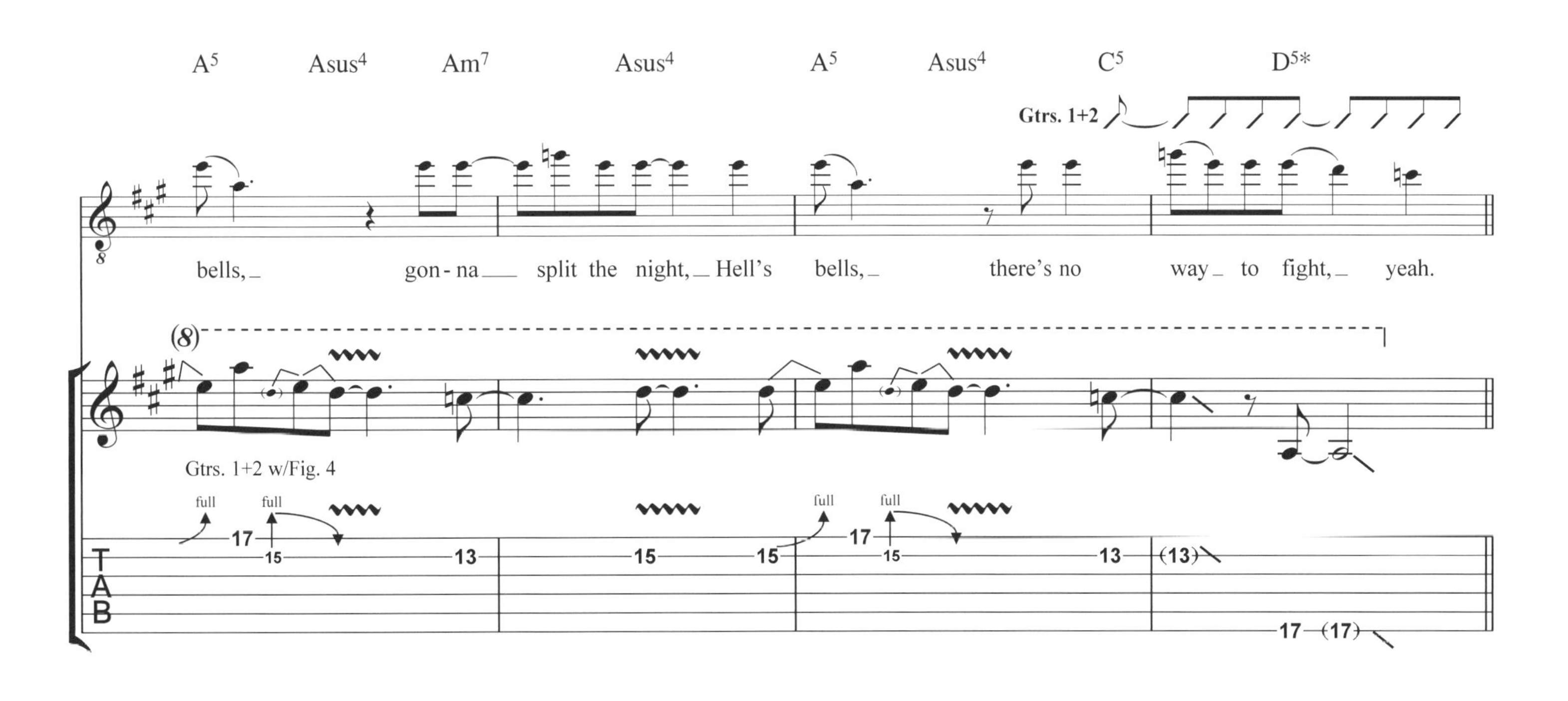
A5
Asus4
Am7
Asus4
A5
Asus4
C5
D5*
Gtrs. 1+2
bells,_ gon-na_ split the night,_ Hell's bells,_ there's no way_ to fight,_ yeah.
(8)
Gtrs. 1+2 w/Fig. 4
full
full
17
15
13
(13)
(17)

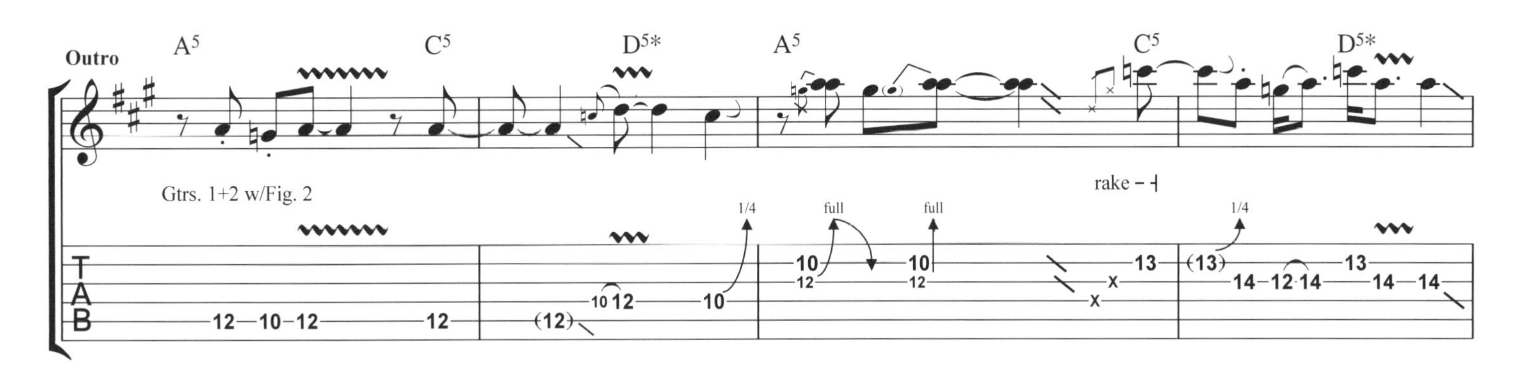
Outro
A5
C5
D5*
A5
C5
D5*
Gtrs. 1+2 w/Fig. 2
rake
1/4
full
full
12
10
(12)
13
(13)
14

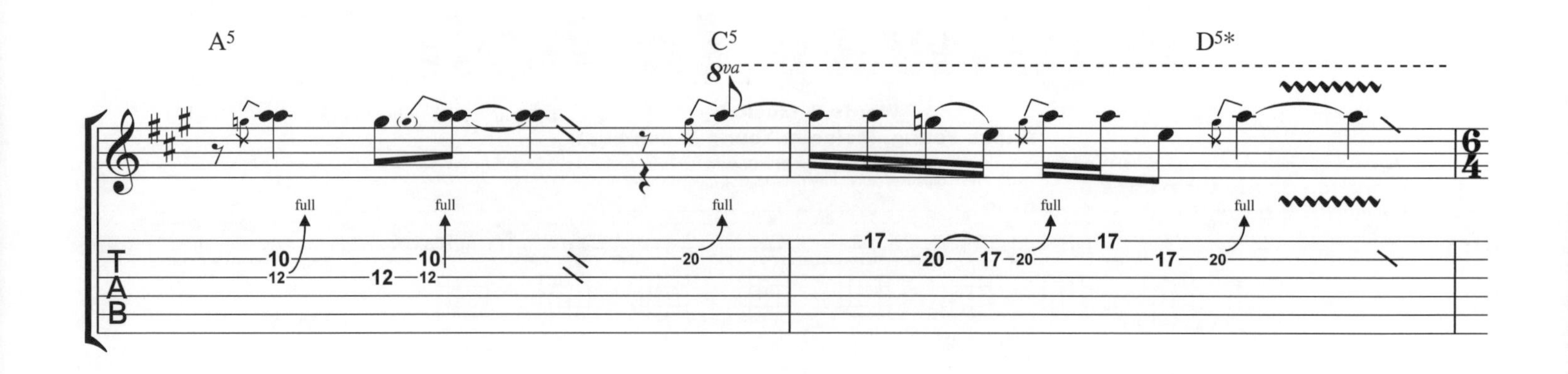
A5
C5
D5*
8va
full
full
full
full
full

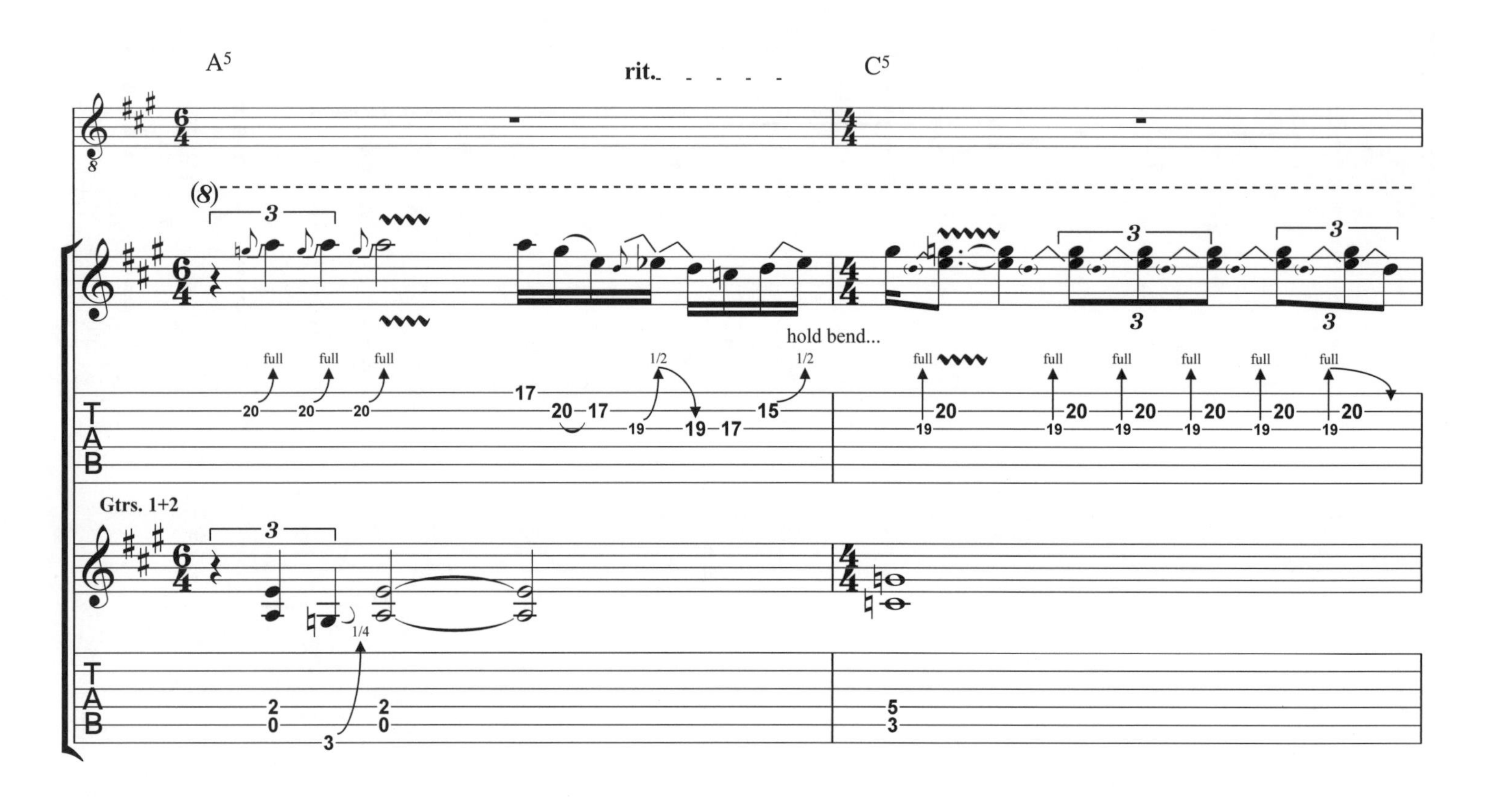
A5
rit.
C5
(8)
hold bend...
full
1/2
Gtrs. 1+2
1/4

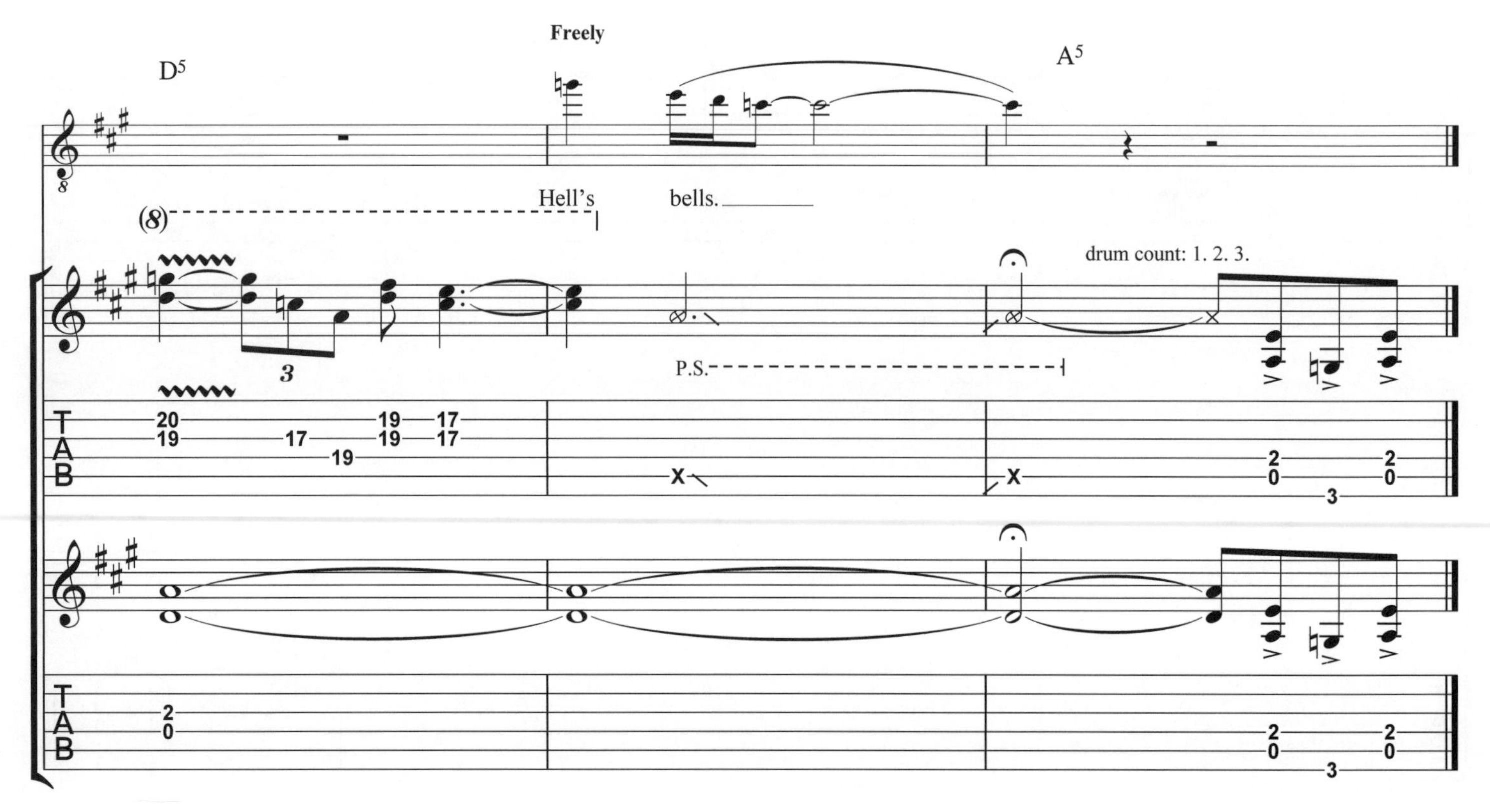
D5
Freely
A5
Hell's
bells.
(8)
drum count: 1. 2. 3.
P.S.

# highway to hell

Words & Music by
Angus Young, Malcolm Young & Bon Scott



**Full performance demo: CD 1 track 5**
**Backing only: CD 2 track 5**

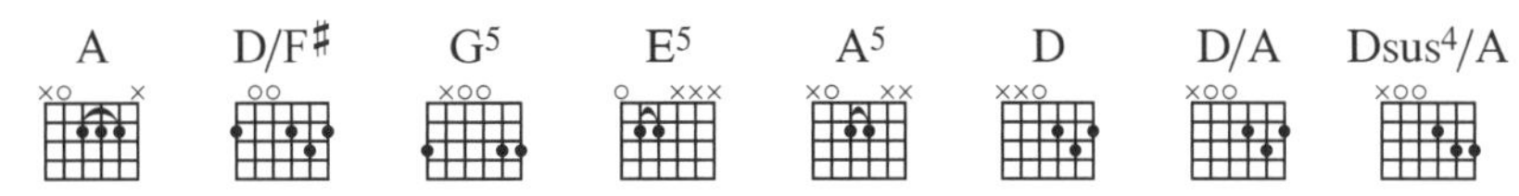


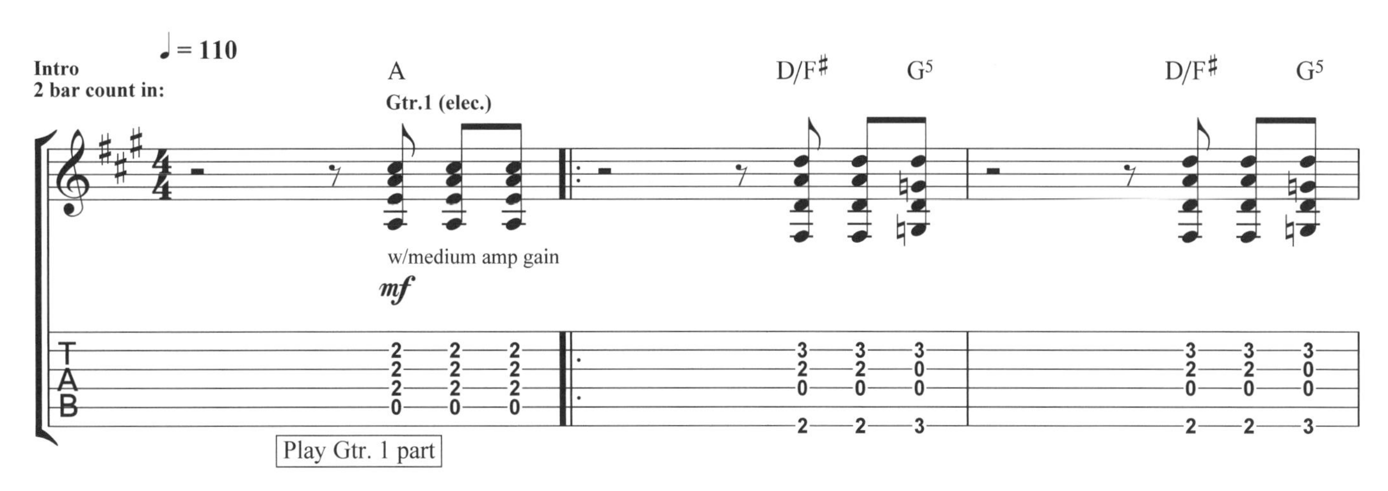


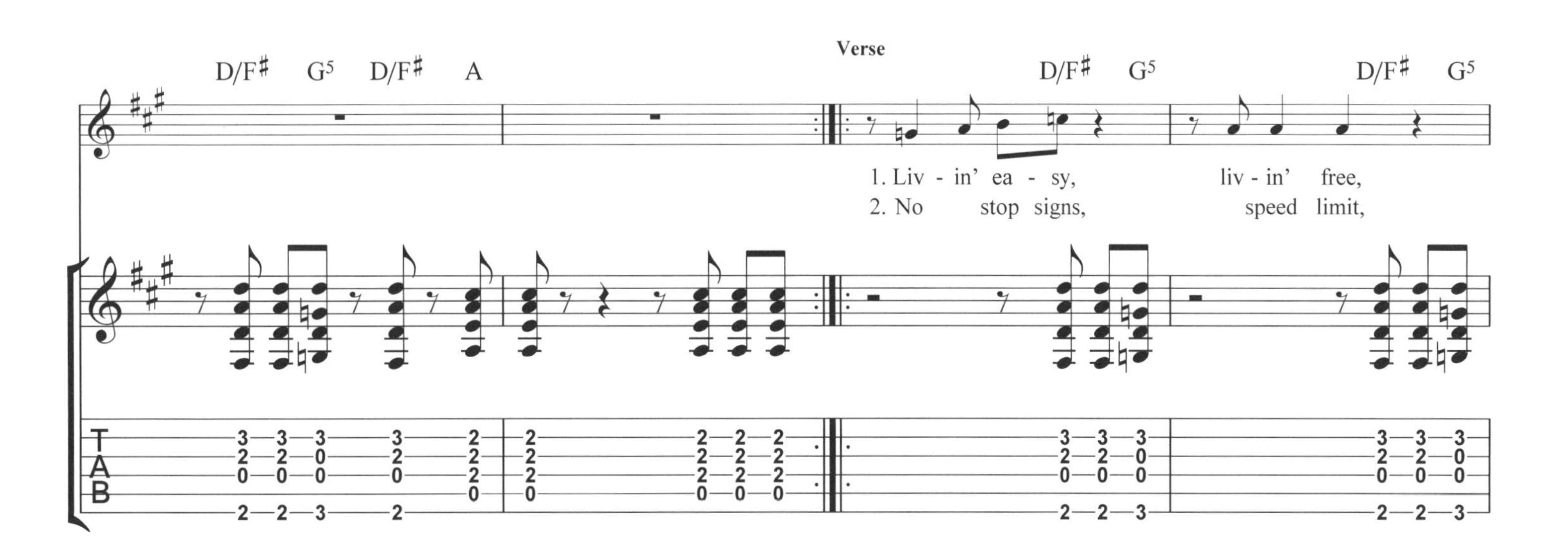


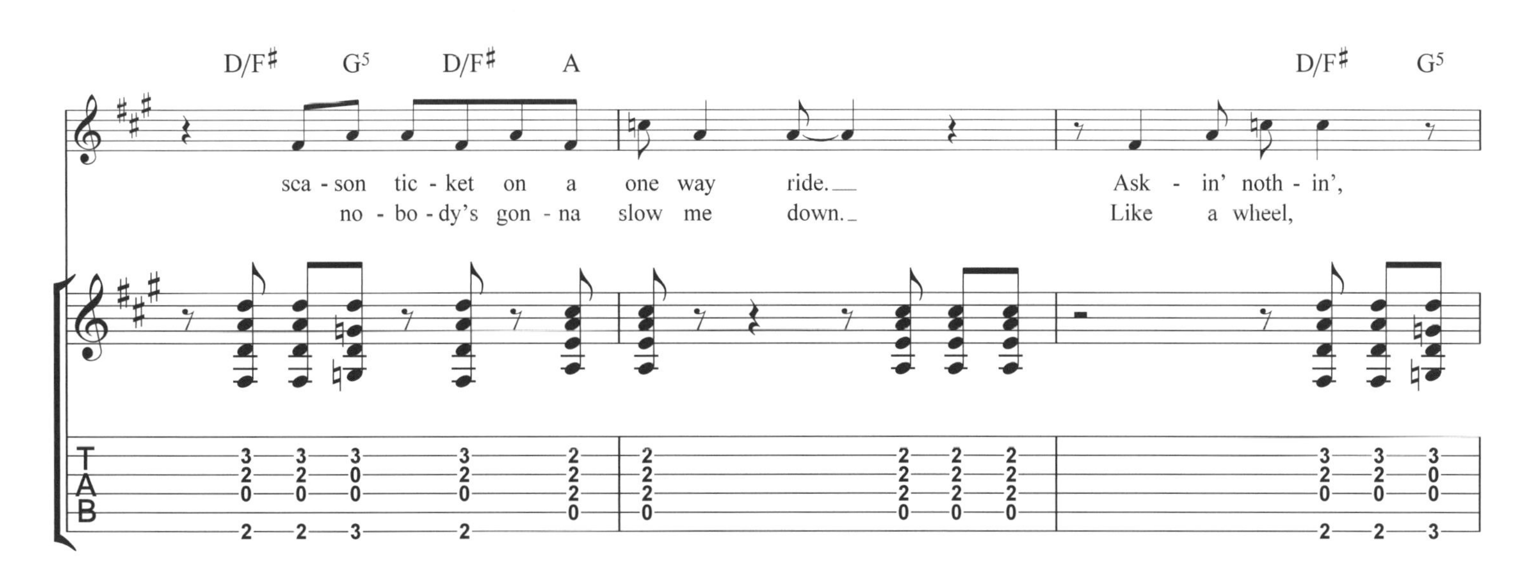

D/F♯ G5 D/F♯ G5 D/F♯ A
leave me be, tak - in' ev - 'ry - thin' in my stride.
gon - na spin it, no - bo - dy's gon - na mess me around.
D/F♯ G5 D/F♯ G5 D/F♯ G5 D/F♯ A
Don't need rea - son, don't need rhyme, ain't noth - in' I'd
Hey, Satan, pay'n' my dues, play - in' in a
D/F♯ G5 D/F♯ G5
rath - er do. Go - in' down, par - ty time,
rock - in' band. Hey mam - ma, look at me,
D/F♯ G5 D/F♯ E5
my friends are gon - na be there too.
I'm on the way to the prom - ised land.
I'm on the
w/Gtr. 2 (elec.)
sim.
Gtr. 2 w/low amp gain

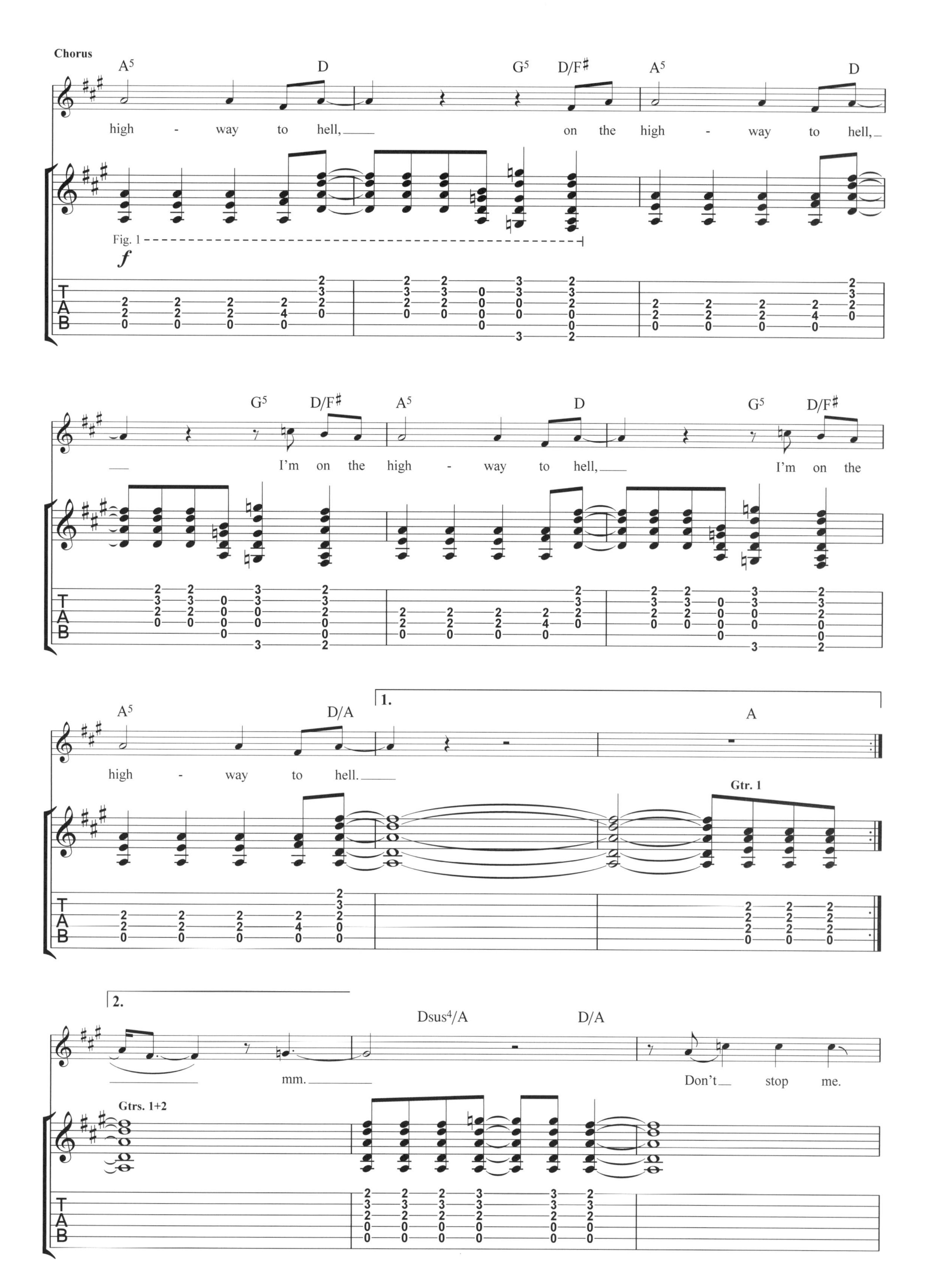
Chorus
A5
D
G5
D/F♯
high - way to hell,
on the high - way to hell,
I'm on the high - way to hell,
I'm on the
Fig. 1
f
D/A
1.
A
high - way to hell.
Gtr. 1
2.
Dsus4/A
mm.
Don't stop me.
Gtrs. 1+2
T
A
B

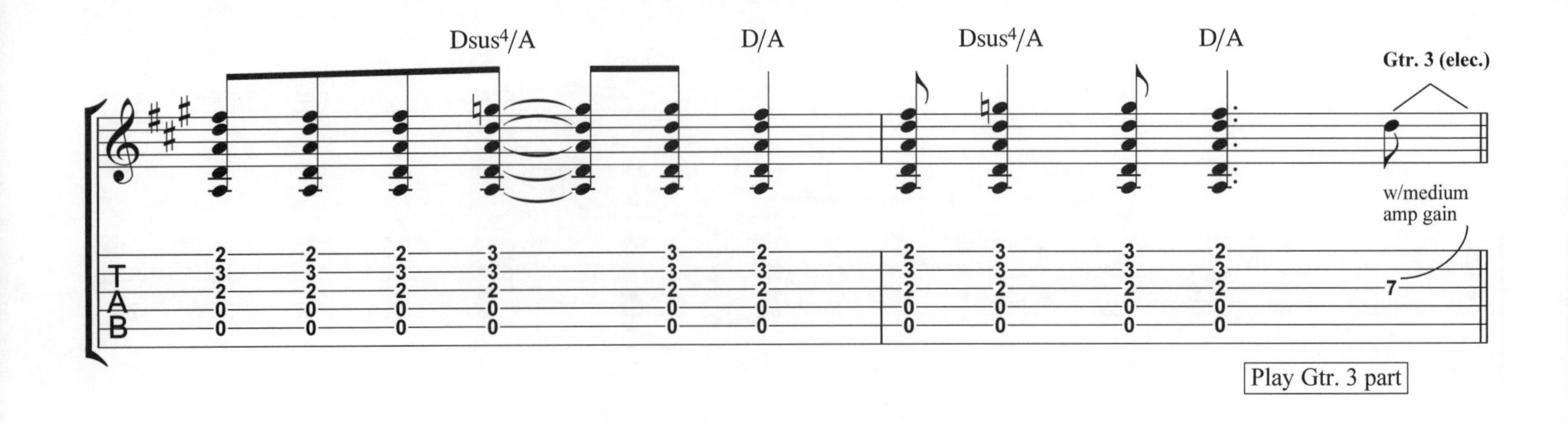
Dsus4/A
D/A
Dsus4/A
D/A
Gtr. 3 (elec.)
w/medium
amp gain
Play Gtr. 3 part

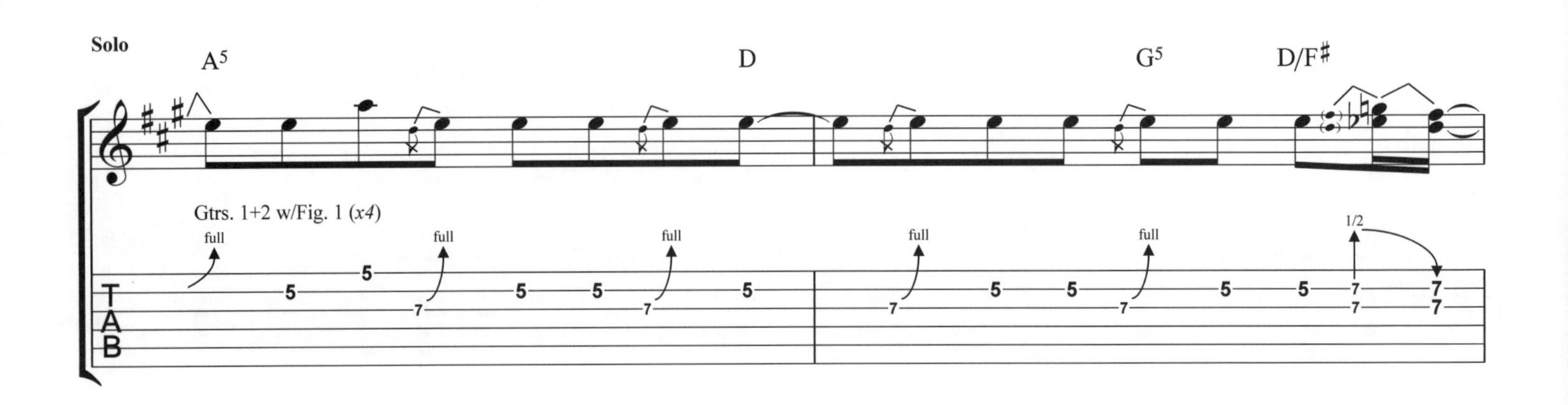
Solo
A5
D
G5
D/F♯
Gtrs. 1+2 w/Fig. 1 (x4)
full
1/2

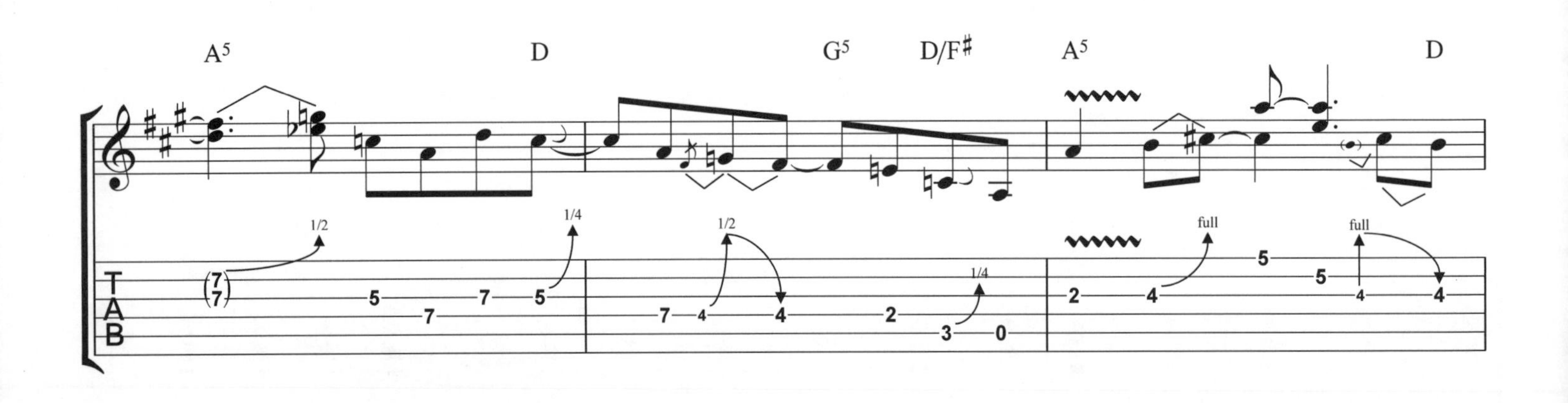
A5
D
G5
D/F♯
A5
D
1/2
1/4
full

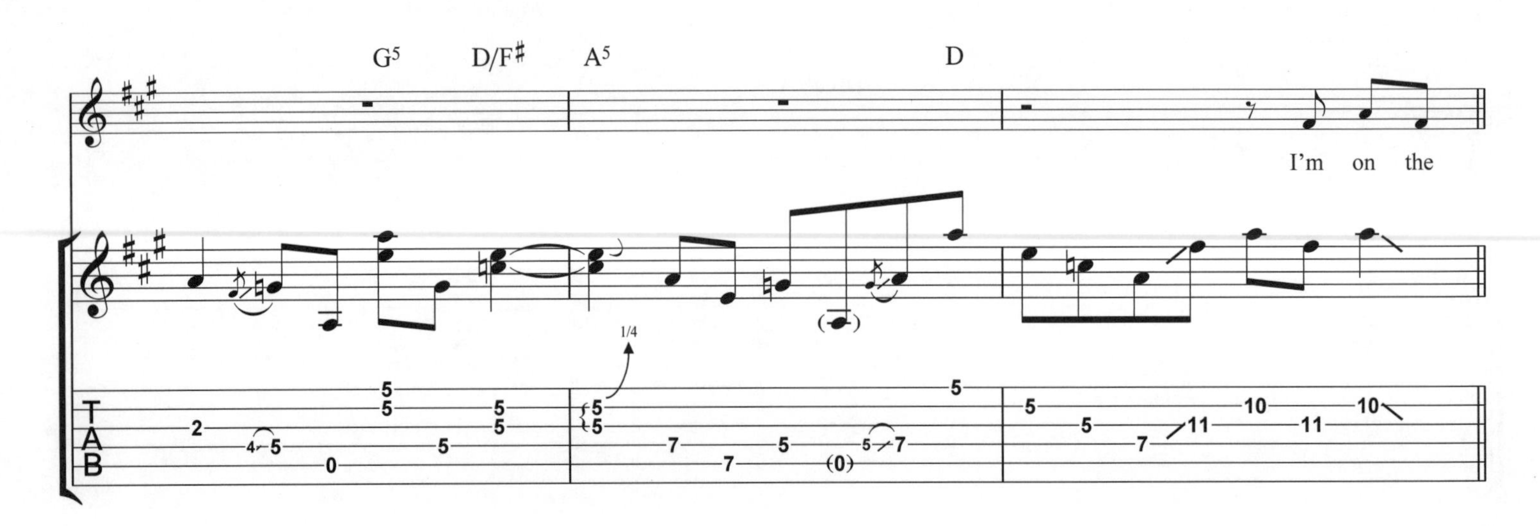
G5
D/F♯
A5
D
I'm on the
1/4

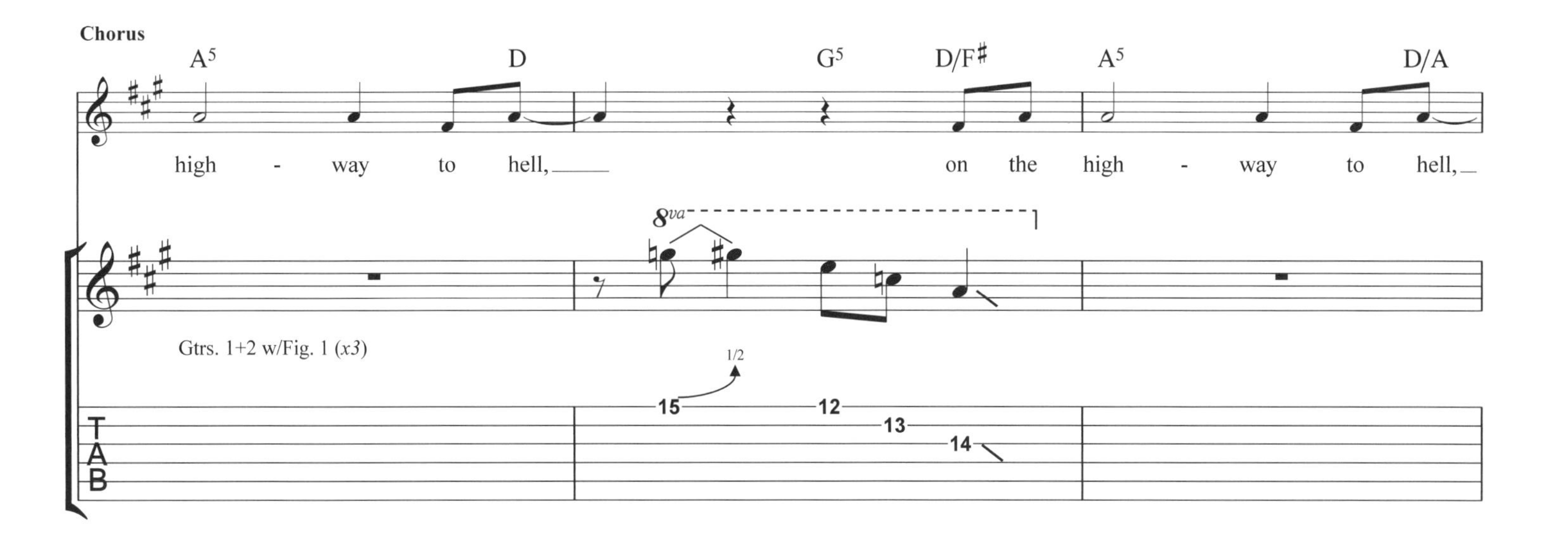
Chorus
A5 D G5 D/F♯ A5 D/A
high - way to hell, on the high - way to hell,
8va
Gtrs. 1+2 w/Fig. 1 (x3)
1/2
T
A
B
15 12 13 14

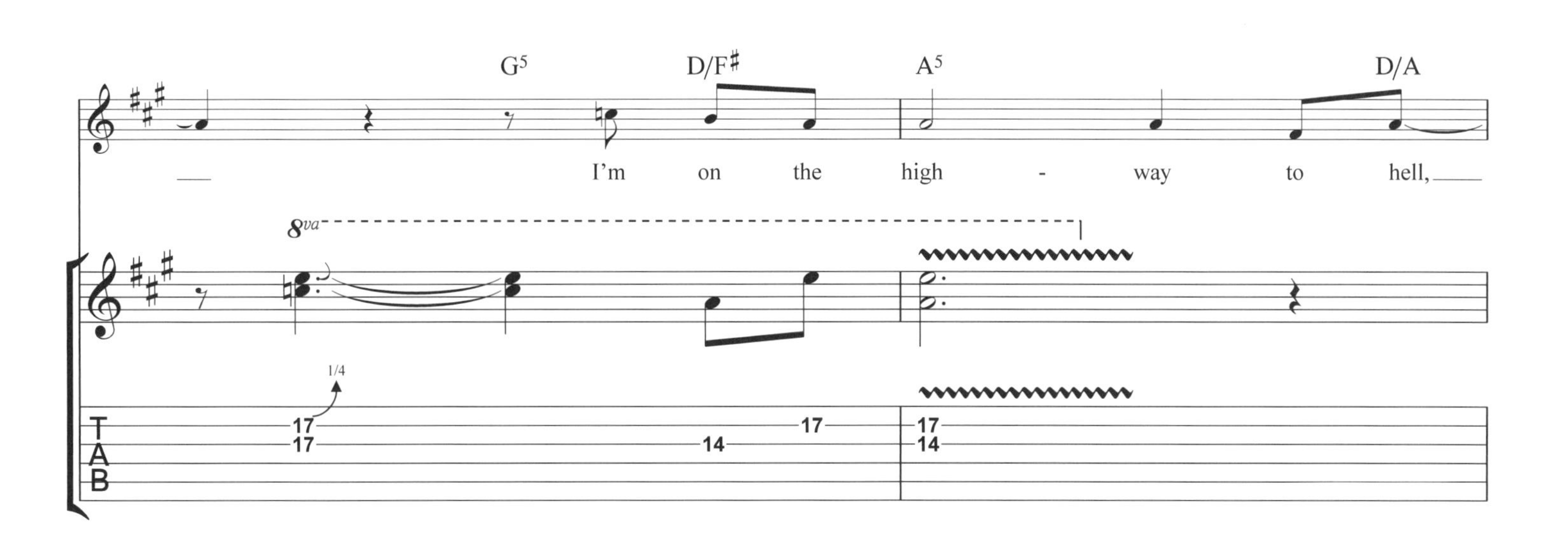
G5 D/F♯ A5 D/A
I'm on the high - way to hell,
8va
1/4
T
A
B
17 17 14 17 17 14

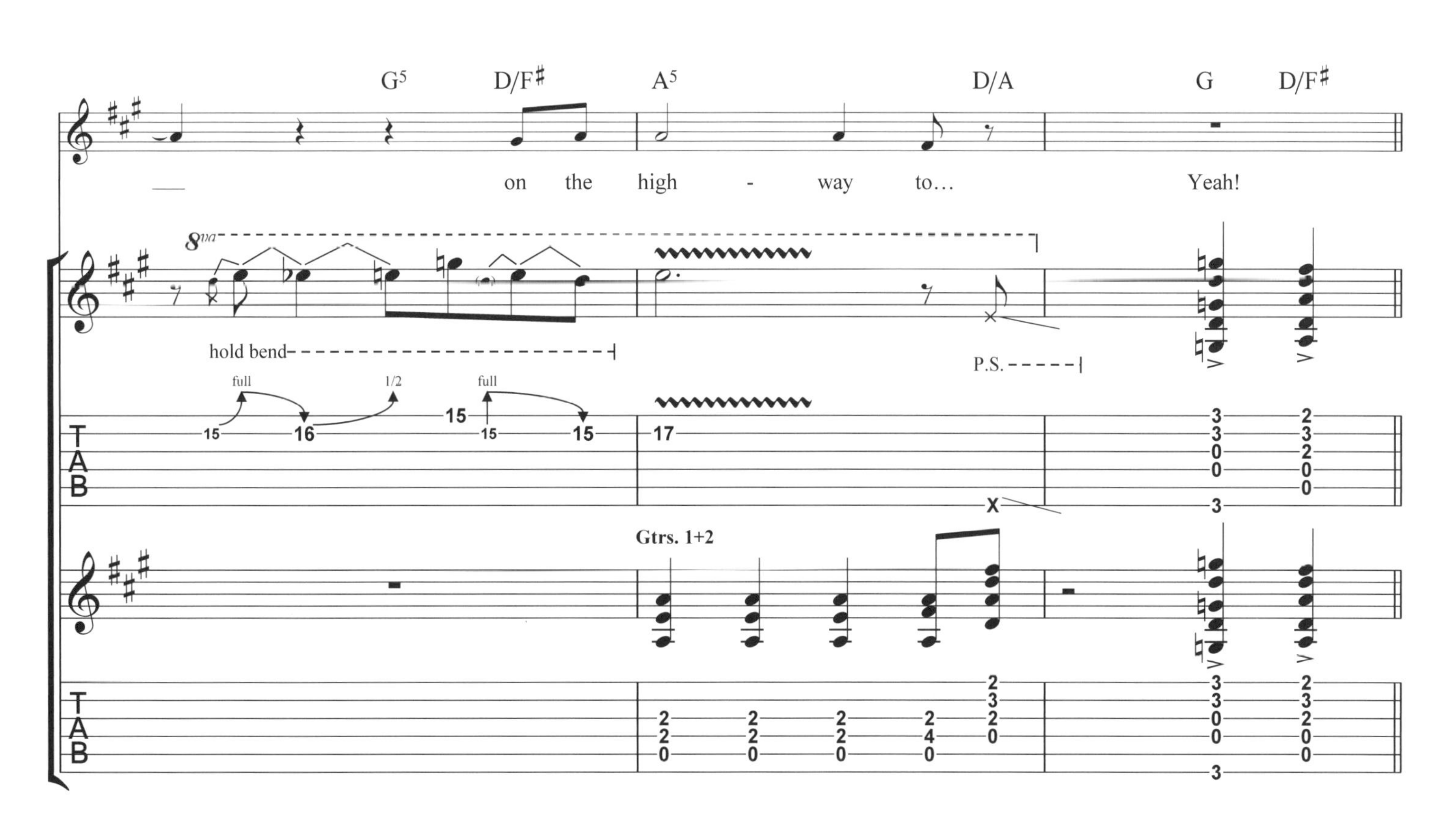
G5 D/F♯ A5 D/A G D/F♯
on the high - way to... Yeah!
8va
hold bend
P.S.
full 1/2 full
T
A
B
Gtrs. 1+2

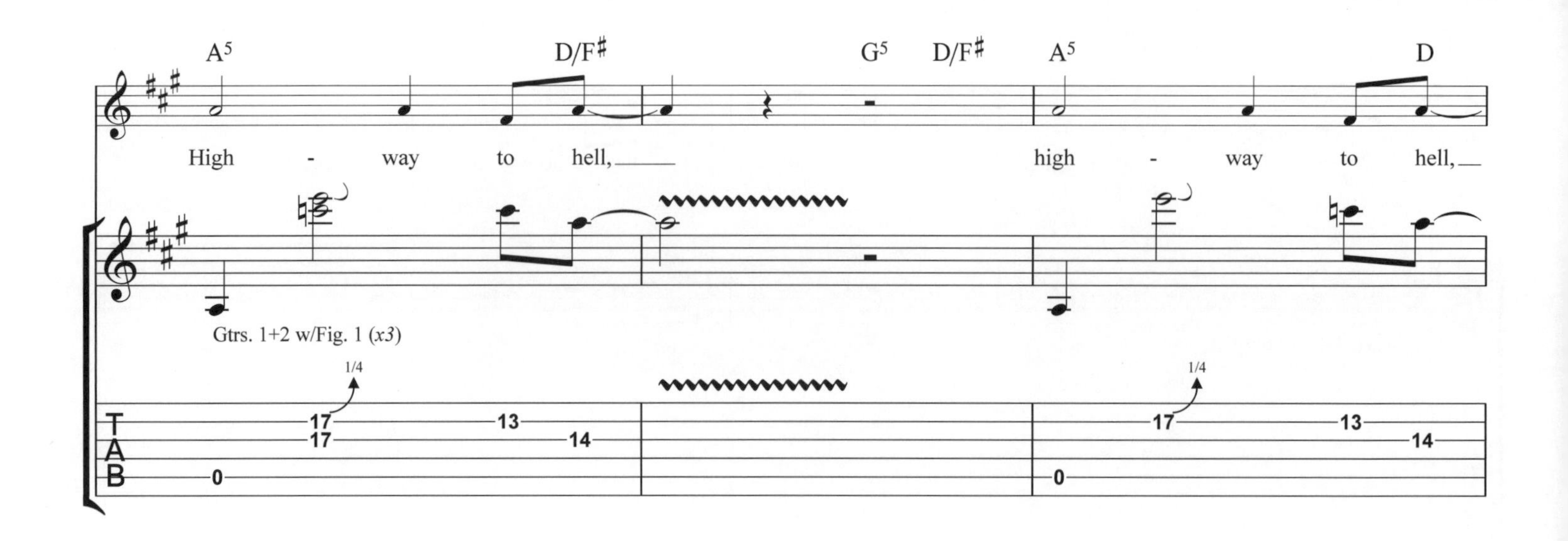
A5
D/F#
G5
D/F#
A5
D
High - way to hell,
high - way to hell,
Gtrs. 1+2 w/Fig. 1 (x3)
1/4
full

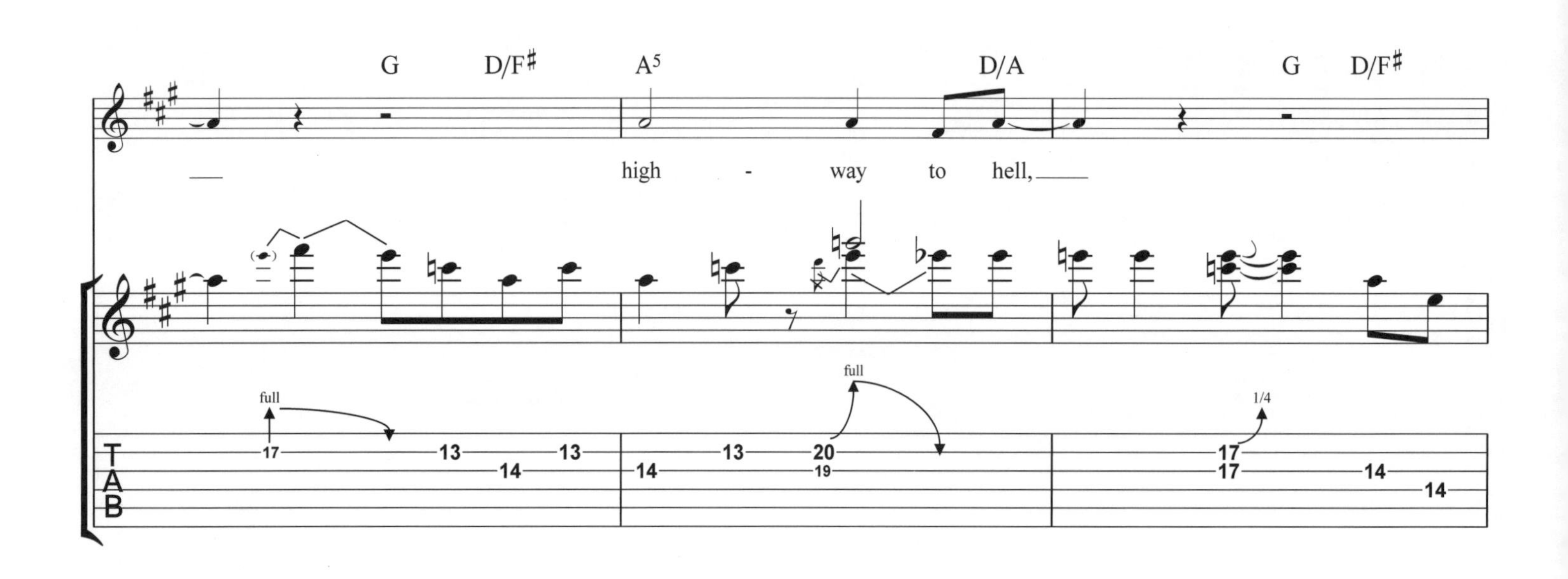
G
D/F#
A5
D/A
G
D/F#
high - way to hell,
full
1/4

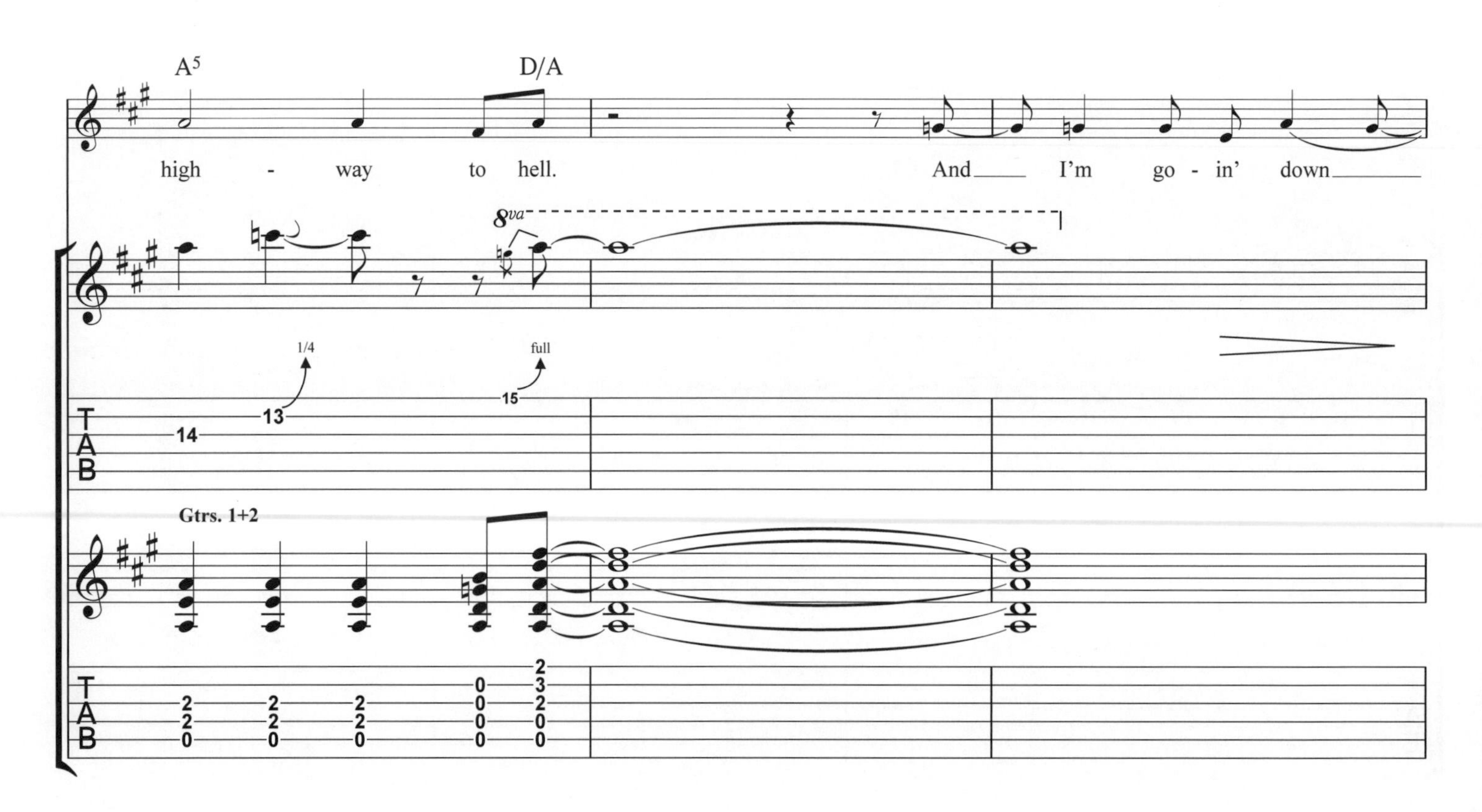
A5
D/A
high - way to hell.
And I'm go - in' down
8va
1/4
full
Gtrs. 1+2

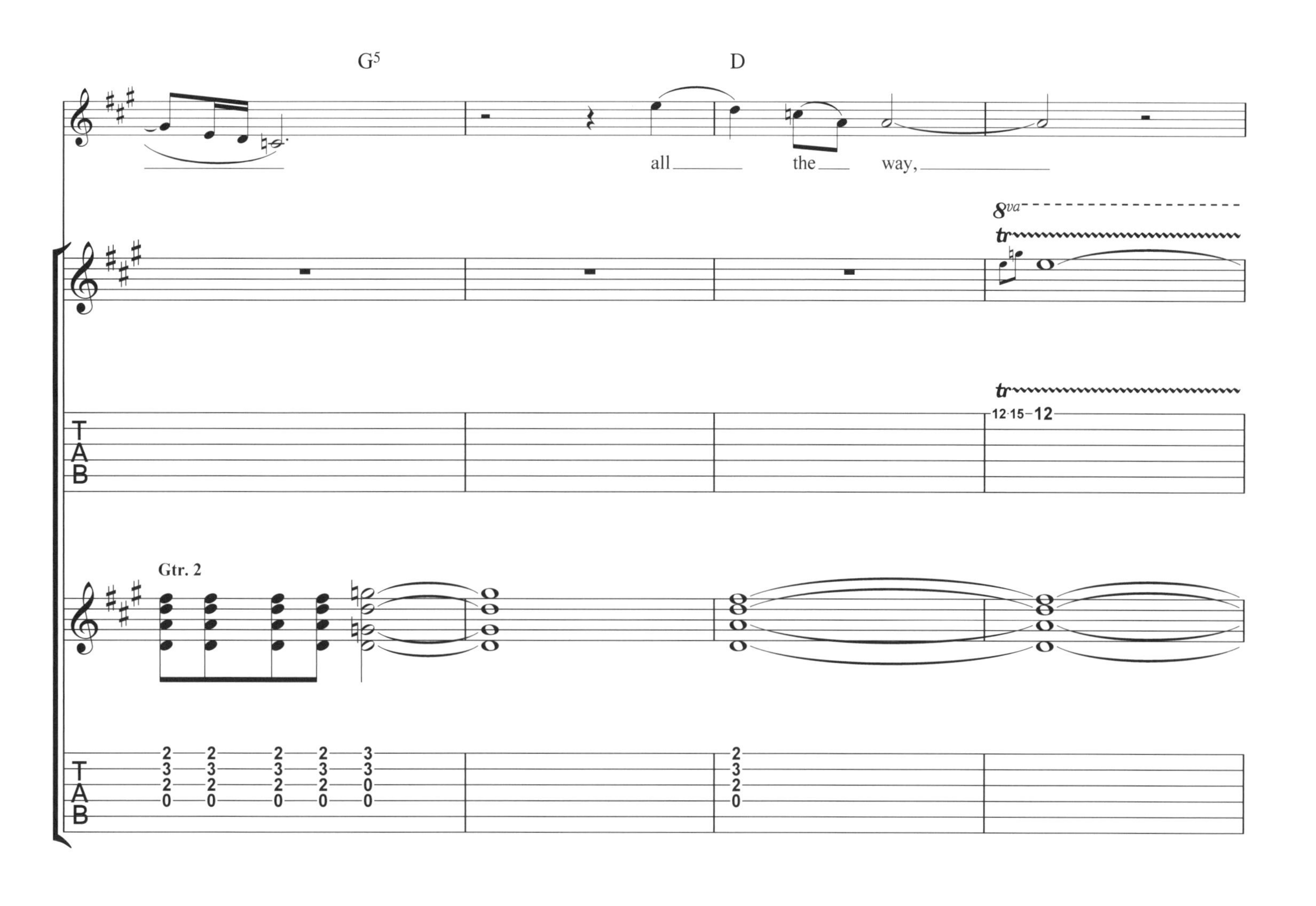
G5
D
all the way,
8va
tr
Gtr. 2
T
A
B
12 15 12
2 3 2 0
3 3 0 0


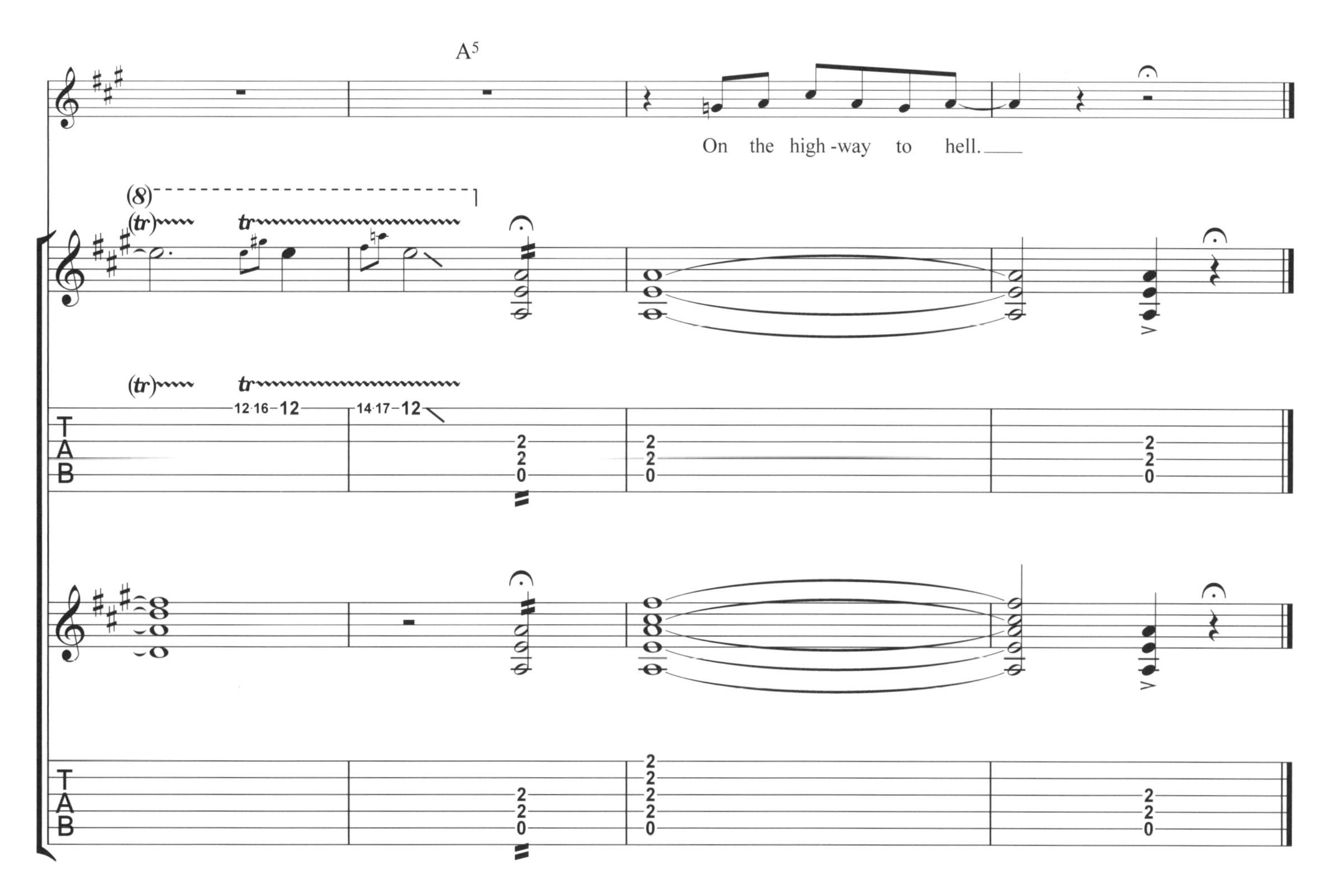
A5
On the high-way to hell.
(8)
(tr)
tr
12 16 12
14 17 12
T
A
B

# it's a long way to the top (if you wanna rock 'n' roll)

Full performance demo: CD 1 track 6
Backing only: CD 2 track 6

Words & Music by
Angus Young, Malcolm Young & Bon Scott

- in' on the by - ways, play - in' rock 'n' roll. Get - tin' robbed,
- dies do the hard sell, know the rea - son why. Get - tin' old,

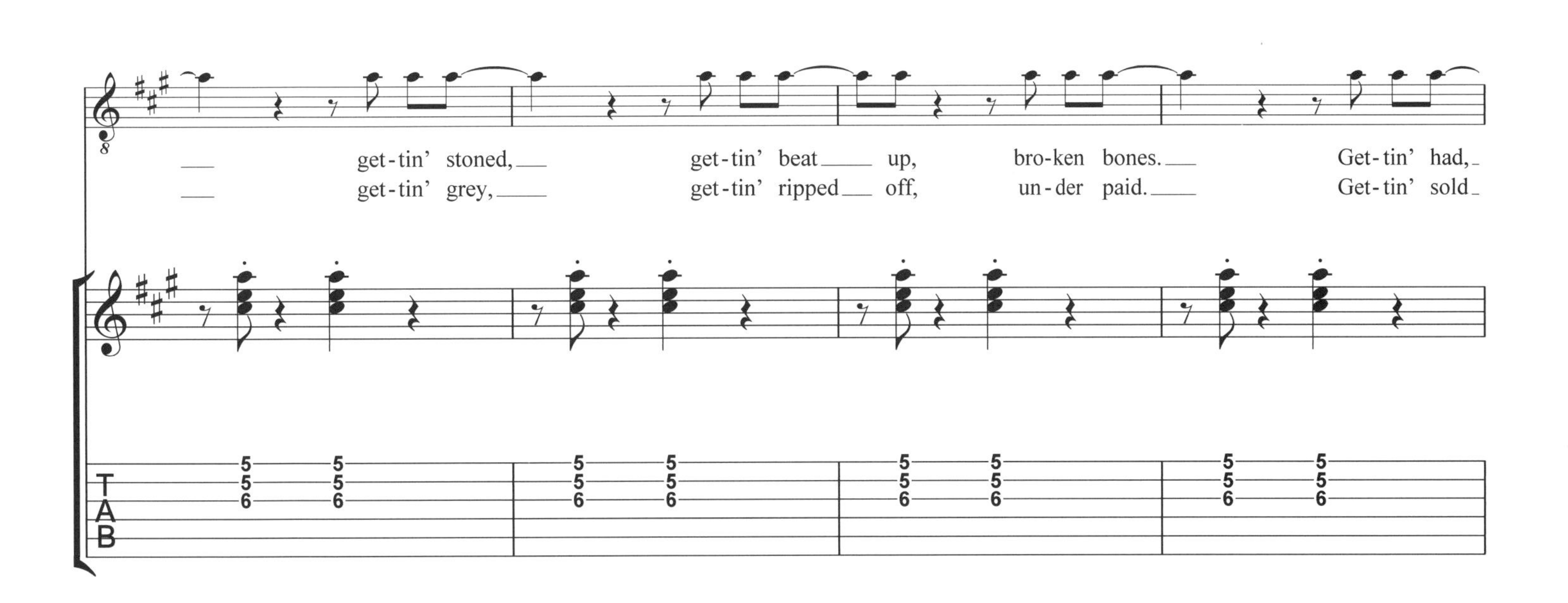
get - tin' stoned, get - tin' beat up, bro - ken bones. Get - tin' had,
get - tin' grey, get - tin' ripped off, un - der paid. Get - tin' sold

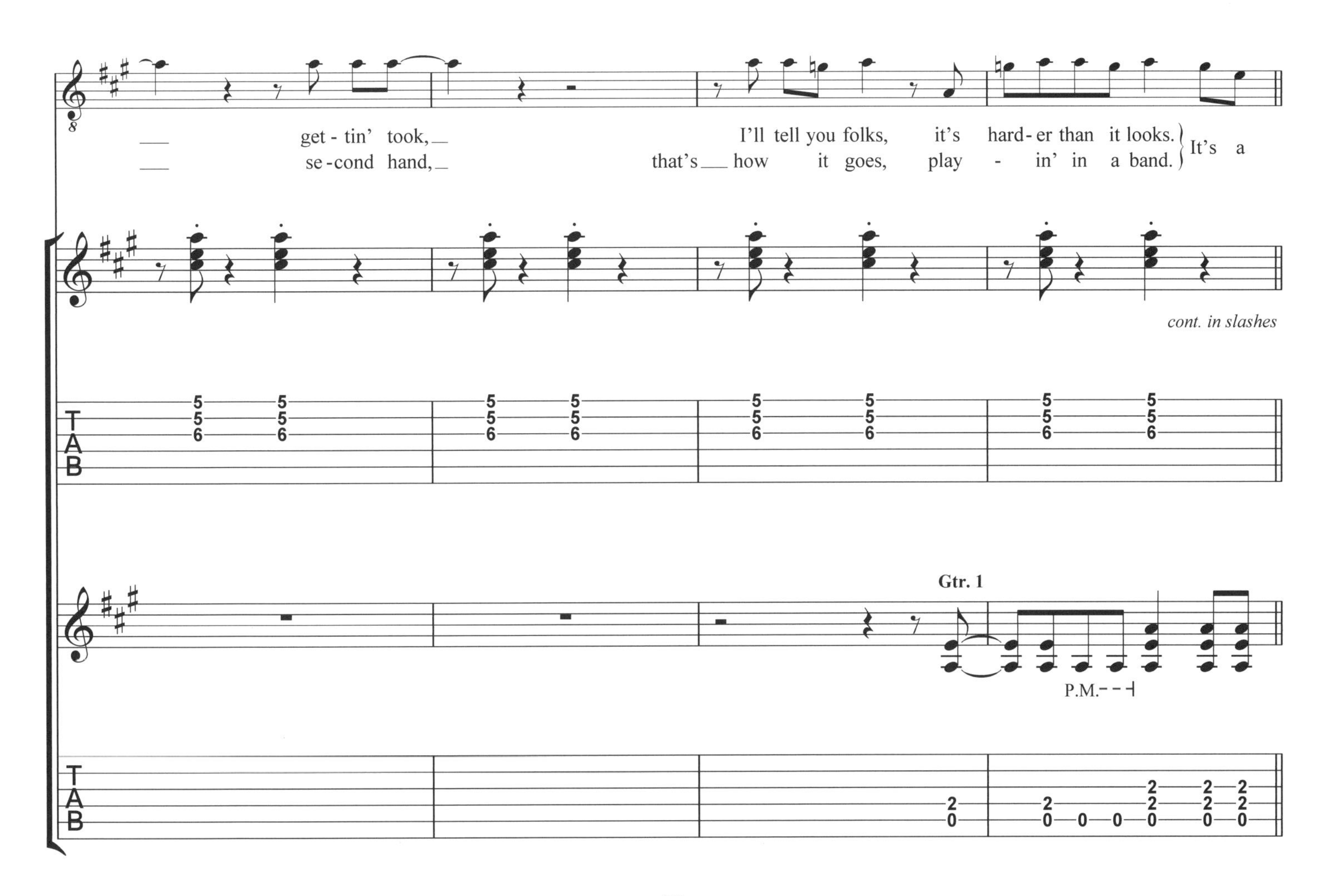
get - tin' took, I'll tell you folks, it's hard - er than it looks.
se - cond hand, that's how it goes, play - in' in a band.
It's a
cont. in slashes
Gtr. 1
P.M.

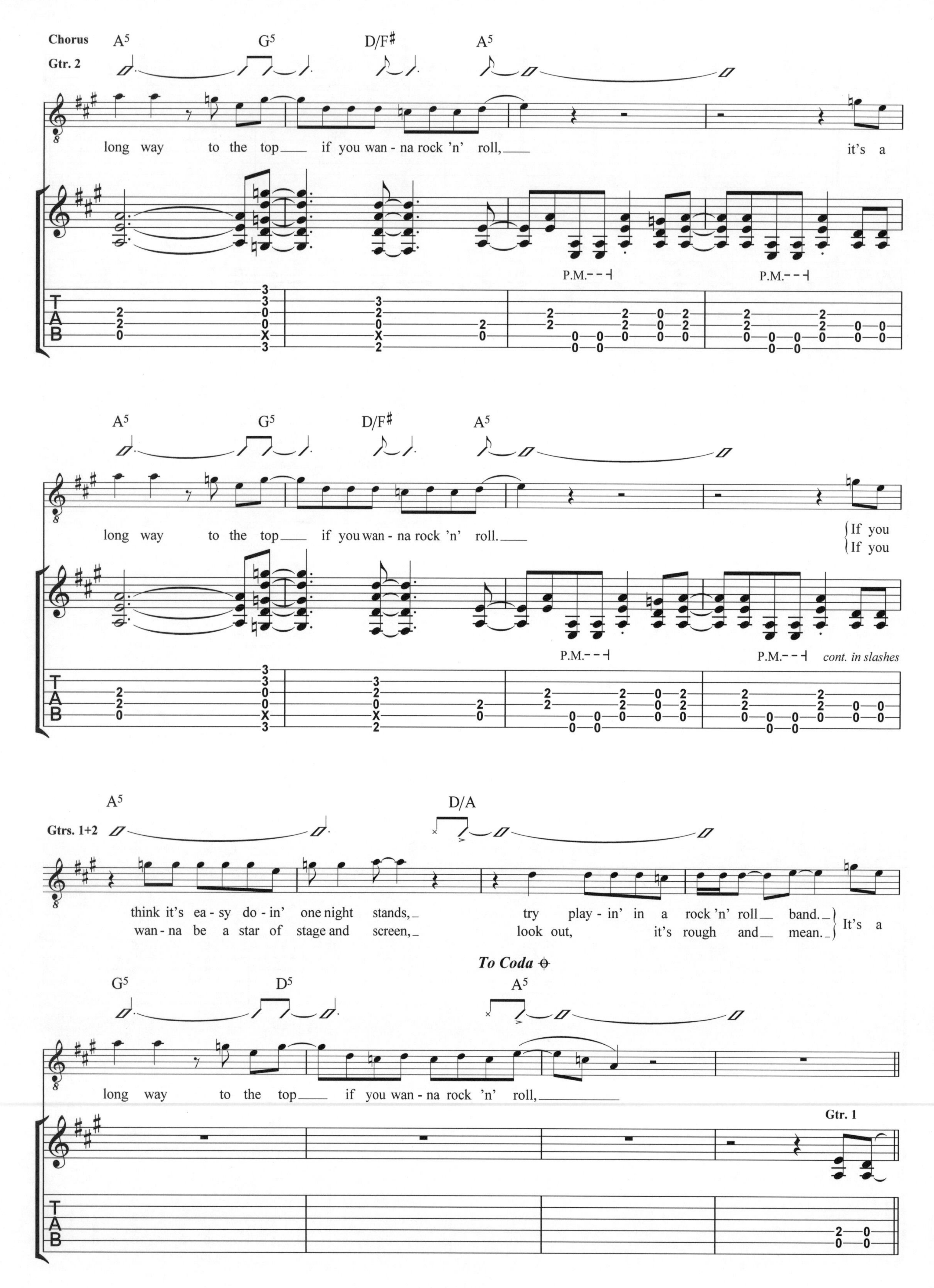
Chorus
Gtr. 2
A5 G5 D/F# A5
long way to the top if you wan - na rock 'n' roll, it's a
P.M.
P.M.
A5 G5 D/F# A5
long way to the top if you wan - na rock 'n' roll. If you If you
P.M.
P.M.
cont. in slashes
Gtrs. 1+2
A5 D/A
think it's ea - sy do - in' one night stands, try play - in' in a rock 'n' roll band.
wan - na be a star of stage and screen, look out, it's rough and mean.
It's a
To Coda
G5 D5 A5
long way to the top if you wan - na rock 'n' roll,
Gtr. 1

Interlude

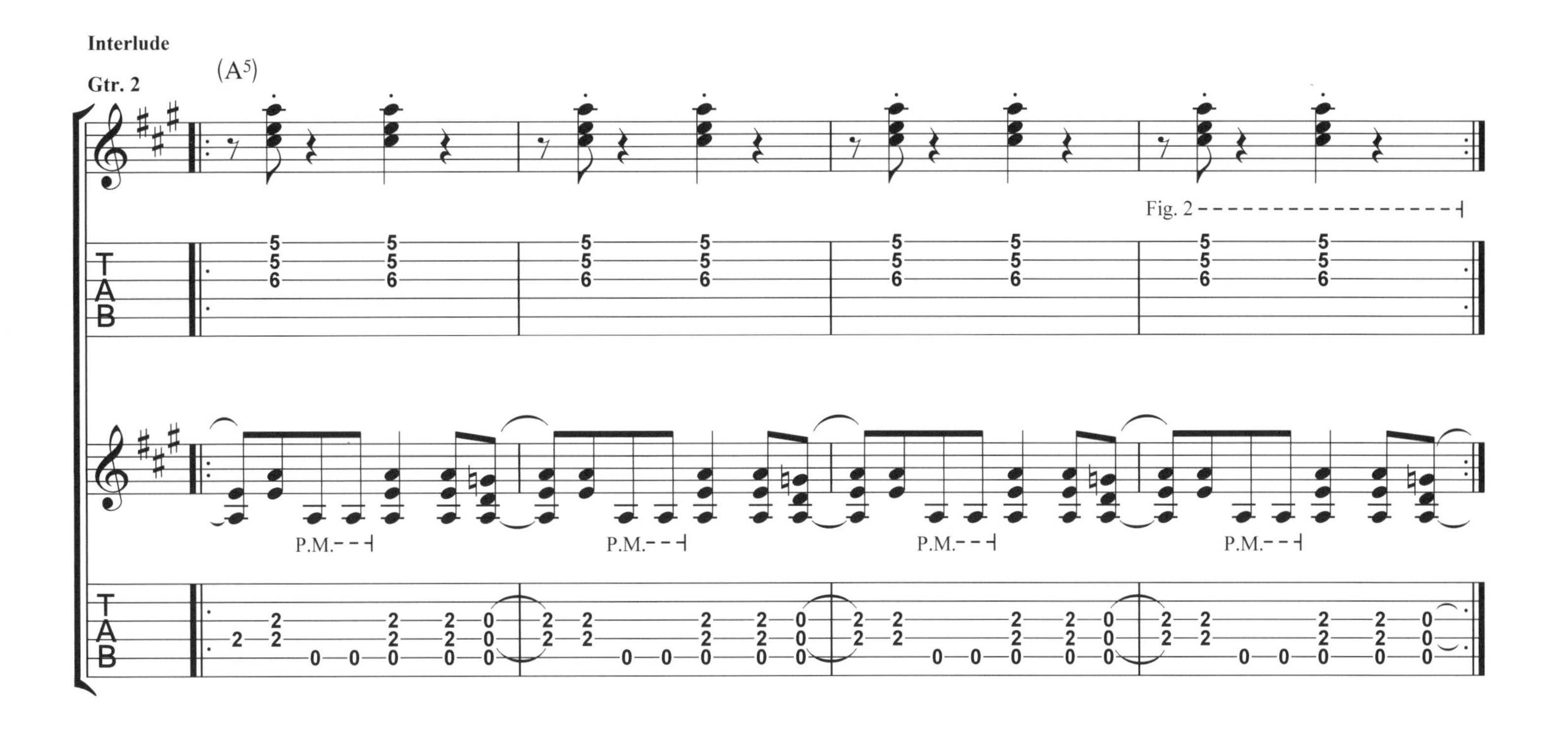
Gtr. 2
(A5)
Fig. 2
P.M.
P.M.
P.M.
P.M.

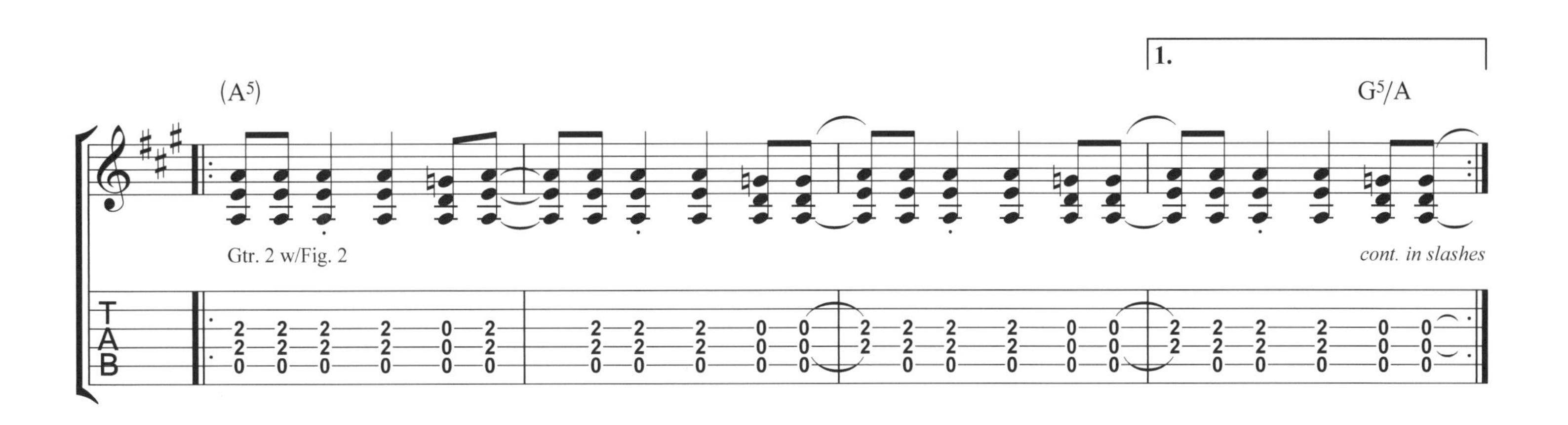
(A5)
1.
G5/A
Gtr. 2 w/Fig. 2
cont. in slashes

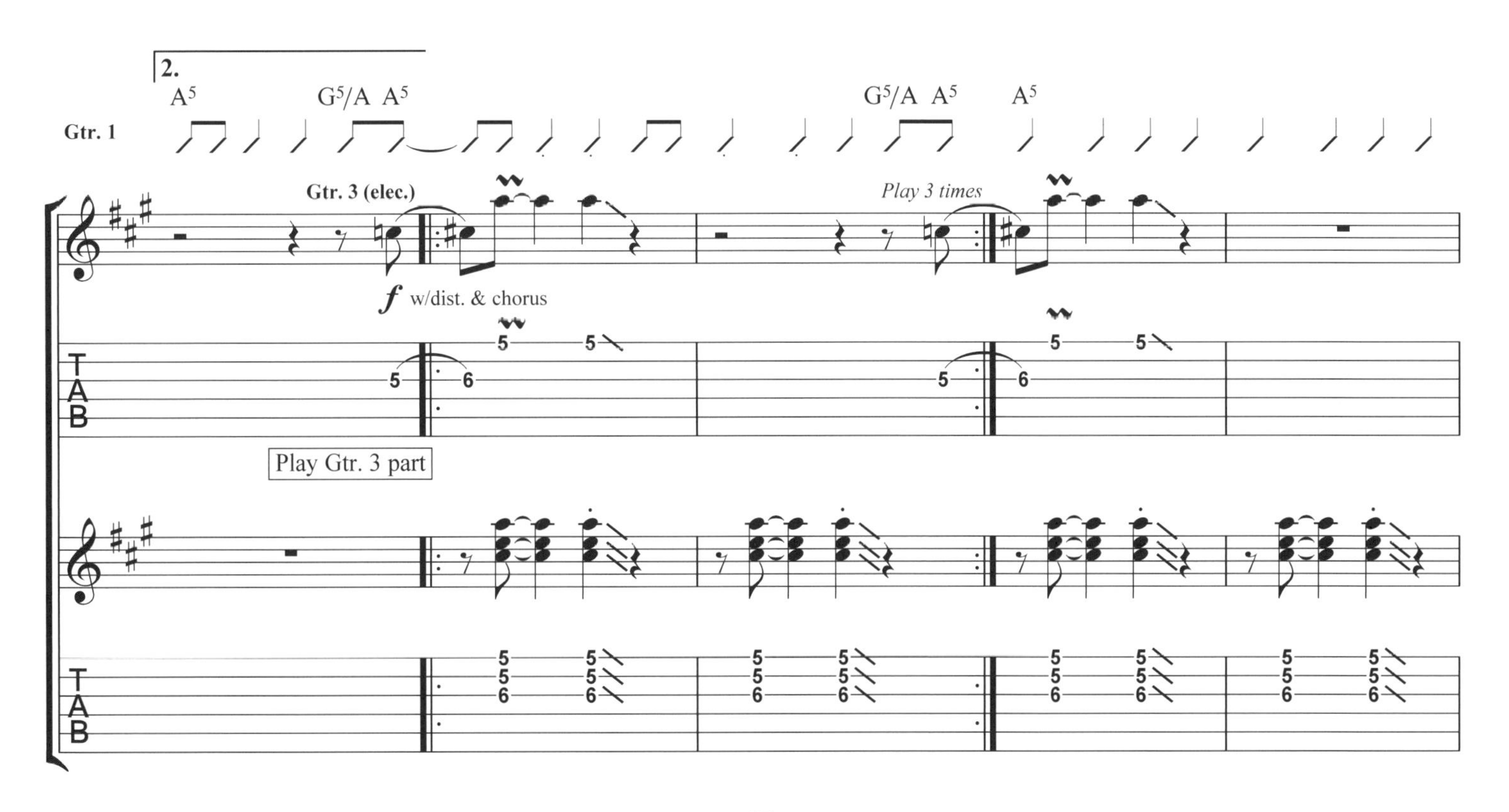
2.
A5
G5/A A5
G5/A A5
A5
Gtr. 1
Gtr. 3 (elec.)
Play 3 times
f w/dist. & chorus
Play Gtr. 3 part

(G5)
(D/F♯)
(A5)
(G5/A)
full
full
Gtrs. 1+2
(A5)
(G5/A)
(G5)
(D/F♯)
(A5)
G5/A
A5
G5/A
G5
D/F♯
8va
full
full
full

*D.S. al Coda*

2. Ho -

Gtr. 3 tacet

Gtr. 2 tacet

Play Gtr. 1 part

Coda
G5
D/F#
It's a long way to the top

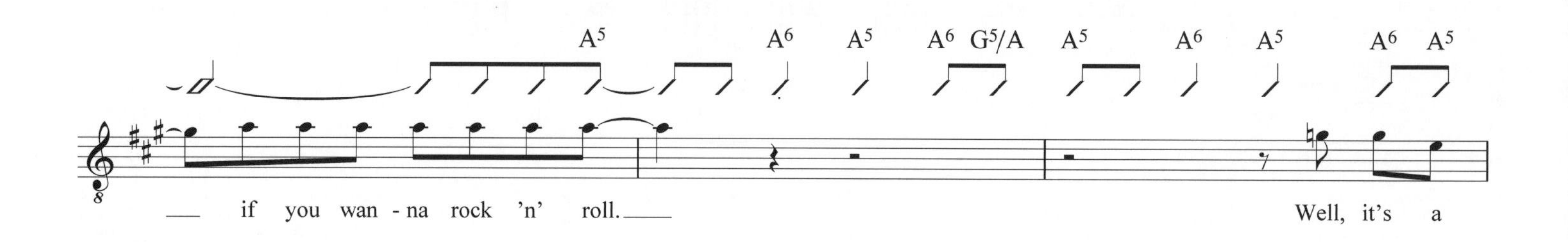
A5 A6 A5 A6 G5/A A5 A6 A5 A6 A5
if you wan - na rock 'n' roll.
Well, it's a

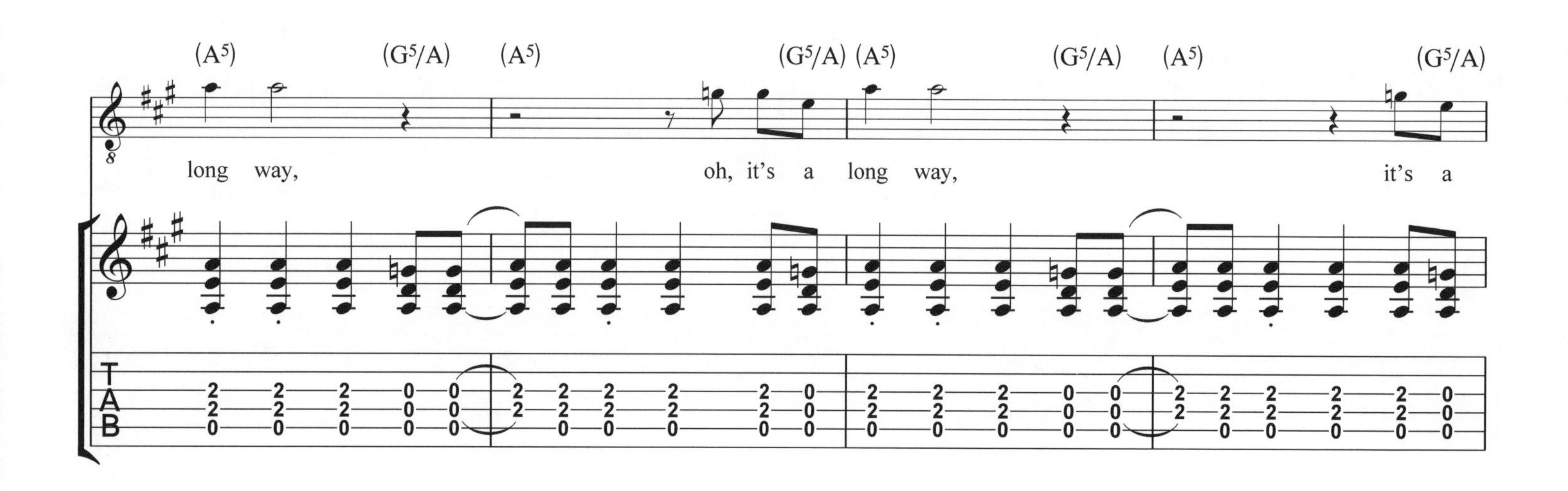
(A5) (G5/A) (A5) (G5/A) (A5) (G5/A) (A5) (G5/A)
long way, oh, it's a long way, it's a

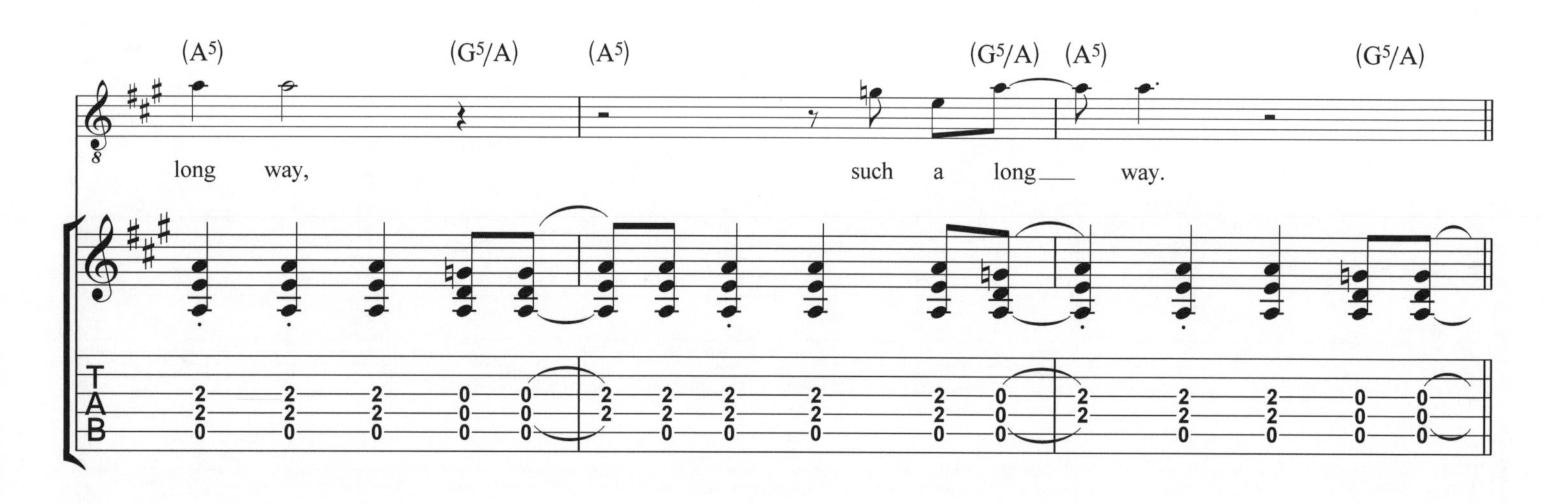
(A5) (G5/A) (A5) (G5/A) (A5) (G5/A)
long way, such a long way.

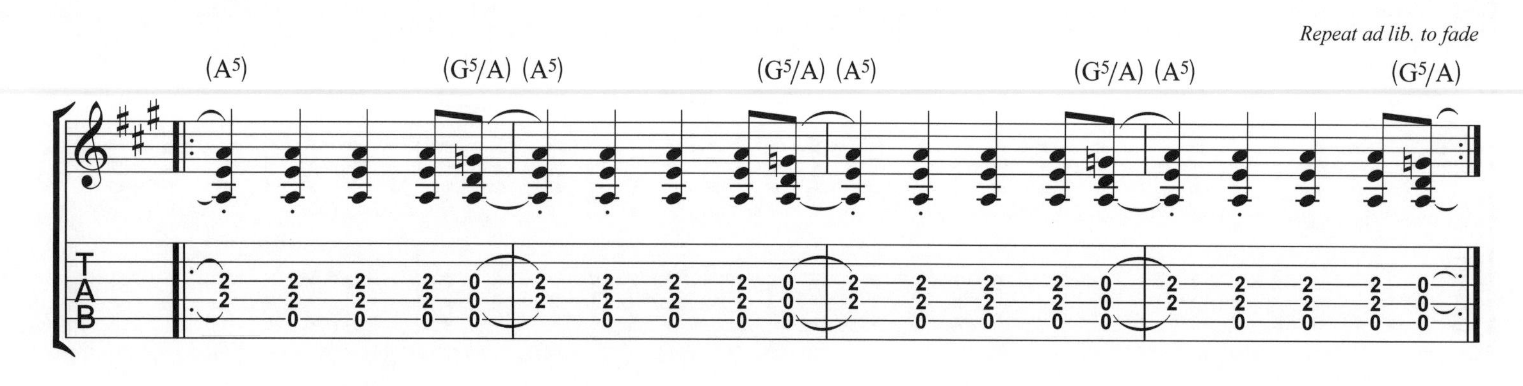
Repeat ad lib. to fade
(A5) (G5/A) (A5) (G5/A) (A5) (G5/A) (A5) (G5/A)

# let there be rock

**Words & Music by**
**Angus Young, Malcolm Young & Bon Scott**

nine - teen fif - ty five, man did - n't know 'bout a rock
rock 'n' roll was born, and all a - cross the land, ev - 'ry
'n' roll show, and all that jive. The white man had the schmaltz,
rock - ing band was blow - ing up a storm. And the gui - tar man got fa -
the black man had the blues, no - one knew what they was
- mous, the bus'- ness man got rich. And in ev - 'ry bar there was a
gon - na do but Tchai - kov - sky had the news. He said, "Let there be sound,"
su - per - star with a sev - en year itch. There were fif - ty mil - li - on fin -
and there was sound. "Let there be light,"
- gers learn - ing how to play, and you could hear the fin - gers pick -
3
and there was light. "Let there be drums,"
- ing, and this is what they had to say, "Let there be light,
there was drums. "Let there be gui - tar,"
sound, drums,
To Coda
A5
there was gui - tar. Oh, let there be rock.
gui - tar." Oh, let there be rock.
Gtrs. 1+2
T
A
B
2
2
0

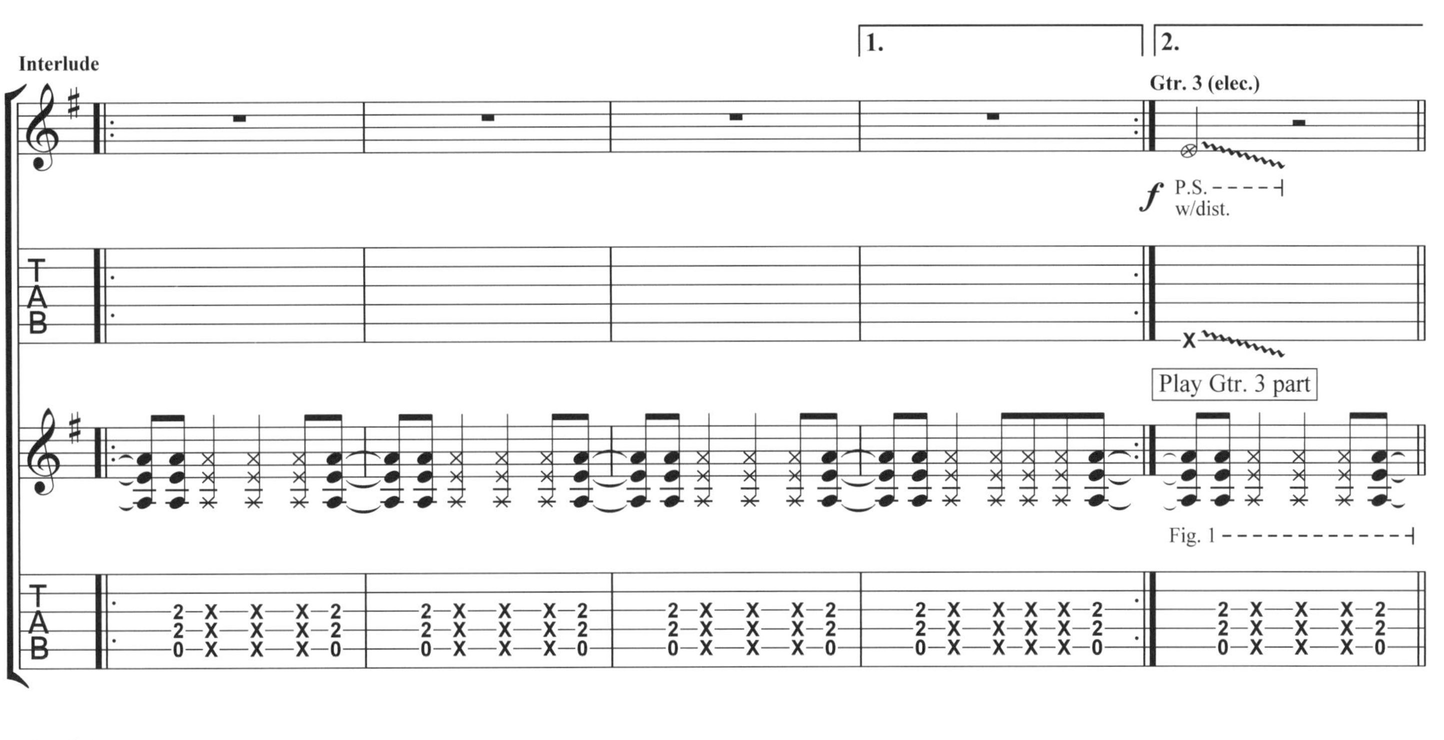

Interlude
1.
2.
Gtr. 3 (elec.)
P.S.
w/dist.
Play Gtr. 3 part
Fig. 1

Gtr. Solo
Gtrs. 1+2 w/Fig. 1


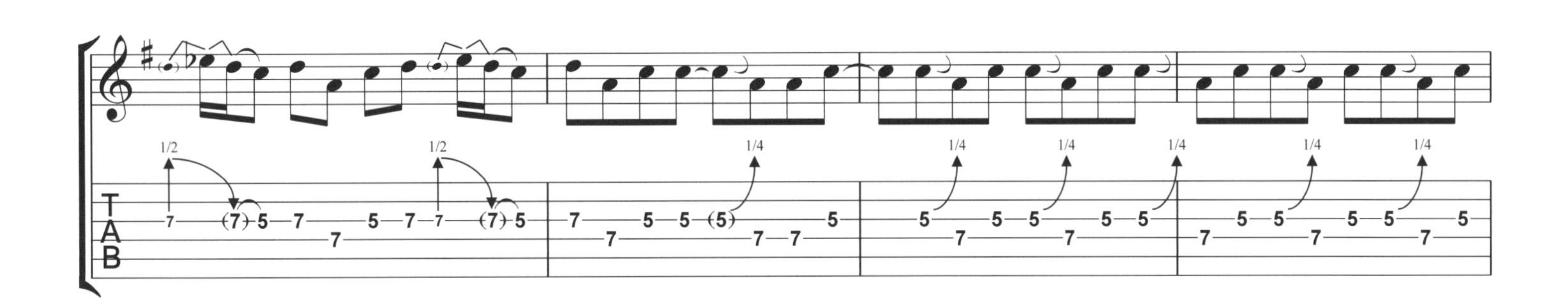

Gtrs. 1+2

8va
1/4
1/4
1/4
1/4
1/4
1/4
1/4
1/4
1/4
T
A
B
7
9
7
7
9
7
7
9
20
X
4
4
2


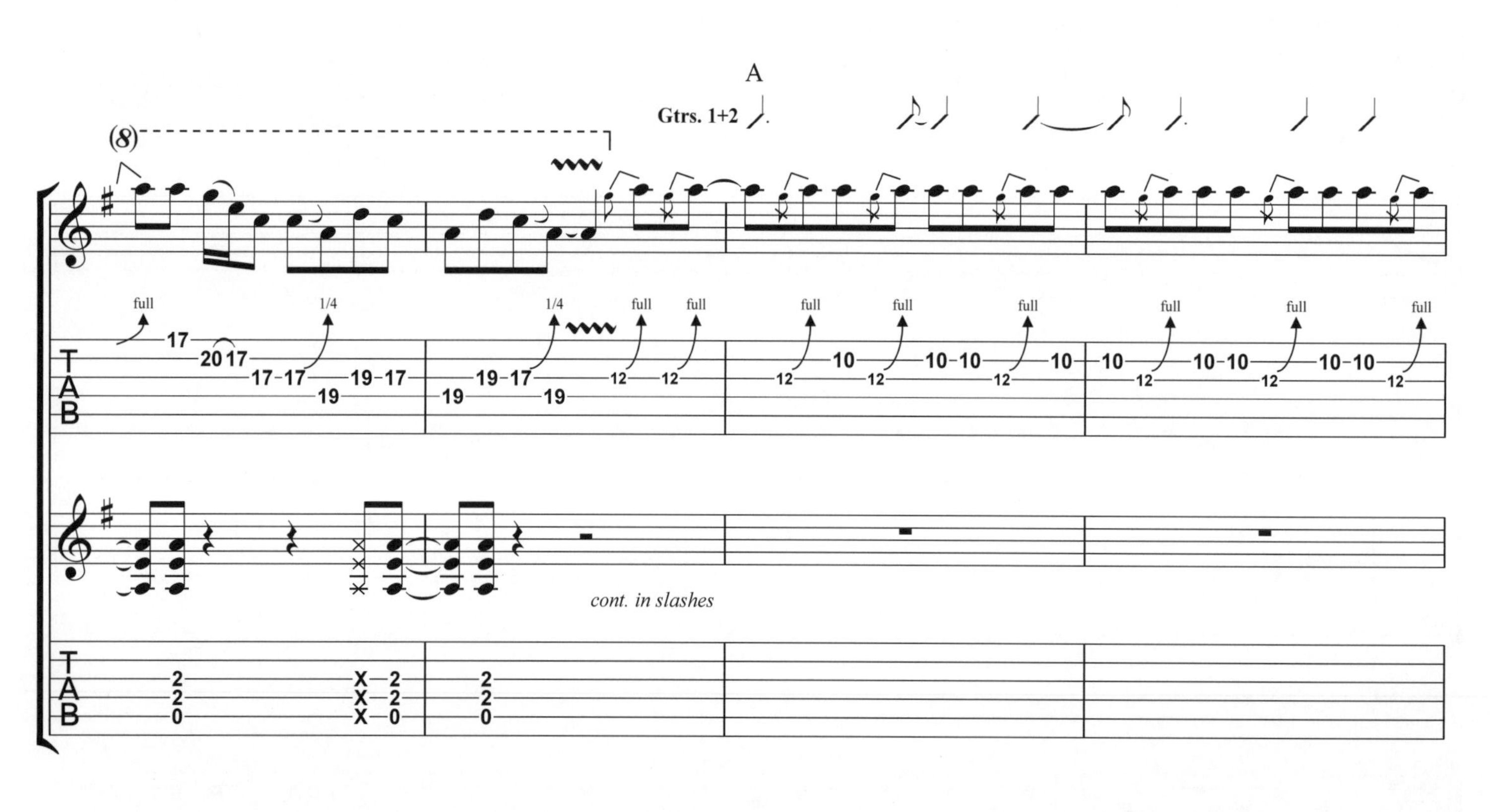
A
Gtrs. 1+2
(8)
full
1/4
full
full
cont. in slashes


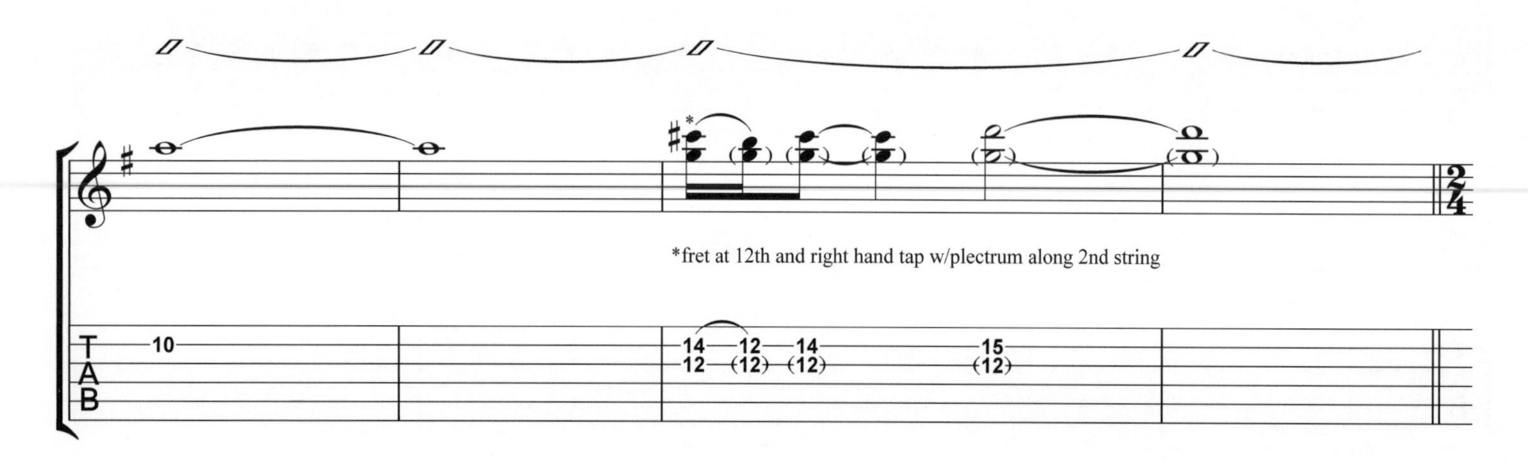
*fret at 12th and right hand tap w/plectrum along 2nd string

Interlude

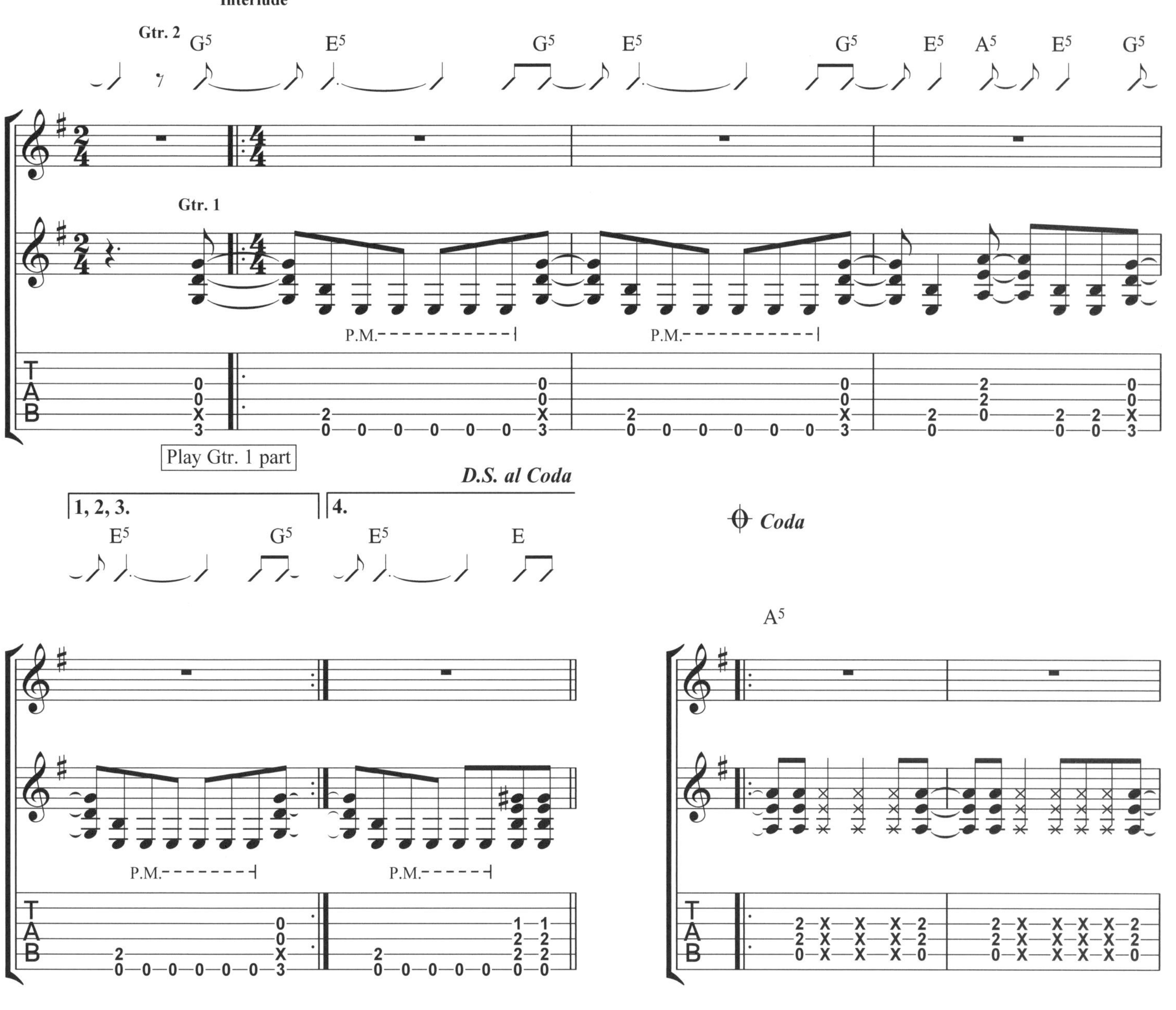
Gtr. 2
G5
E5
G5
E5
G5
E5
A5
E5
G5
Gtr. 1
P.M.
P.M.
Play Gtr. 1 part
1, 2, 3.
E5
G5
4.
D.S. al Coda
E5
E
P.M.
P.M.
Coda
A5

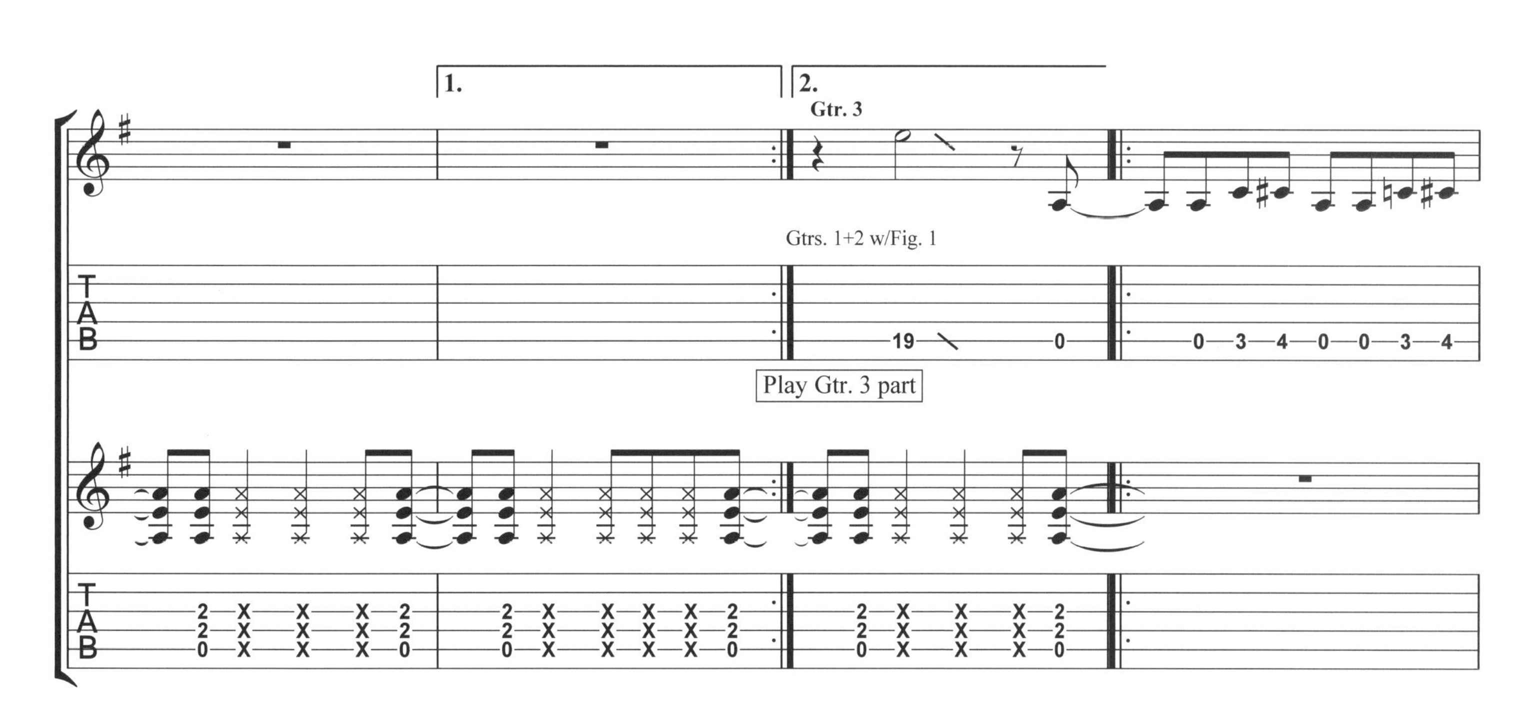
1.
2.
Gtr. 3
Gtrs. 1+2 w/Fig. 1
Play Gtr. 3 part

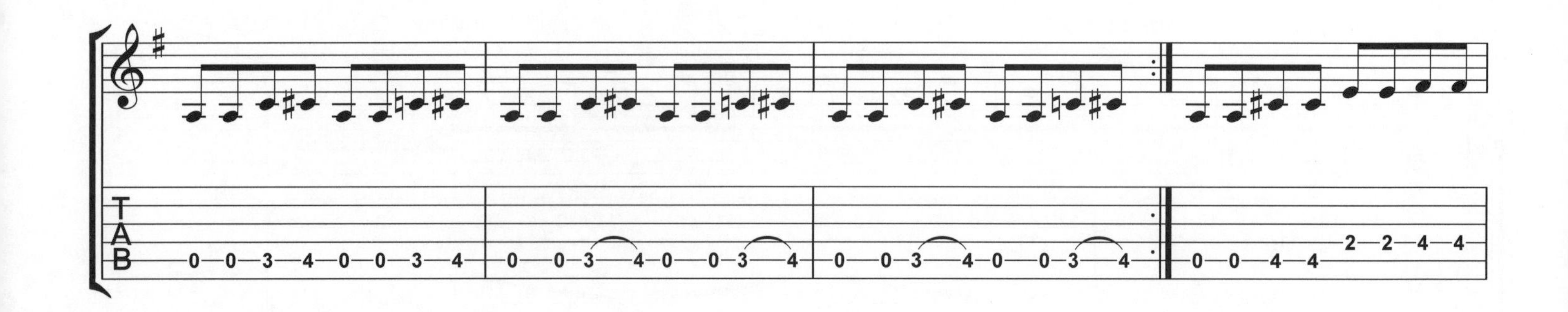

B5
Gtrs. 1+2

A5

A
Gtrs. 1+2
cont. in slashes
Gtr. 2
G5
E5
*fret at 12th and right hand tap w/plectrum along 2nd string
Gtr. 1
P.M.
Play Gtr. 1 part
1, 2, 3.
4.
A5
E
Verse
3.One night in the club called 'The
cont. in slashes

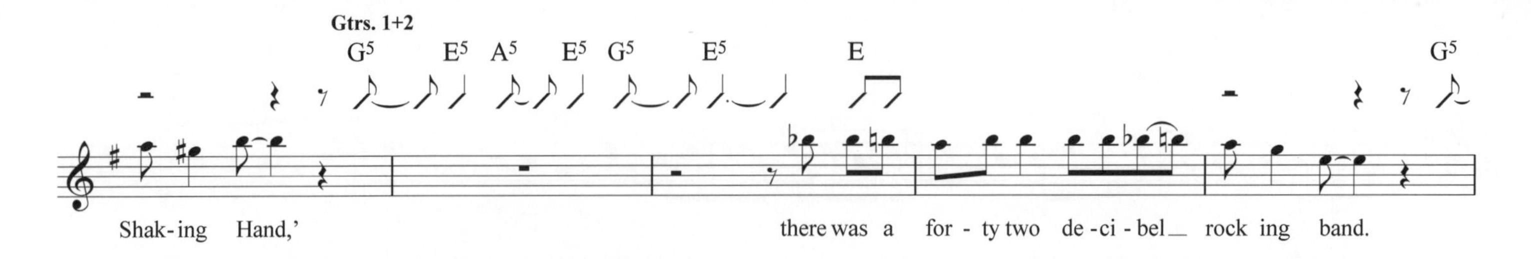
Gtrs. 1+2
G5 E5 A5 E5 G5 E5 E G5
Shak-ing Hand,' there was a for-ty two de-ci-bel rock ing band.

E5 A5 E5 G5 E5 E G5
And the mu - sic was good and the mu - sic was loud,

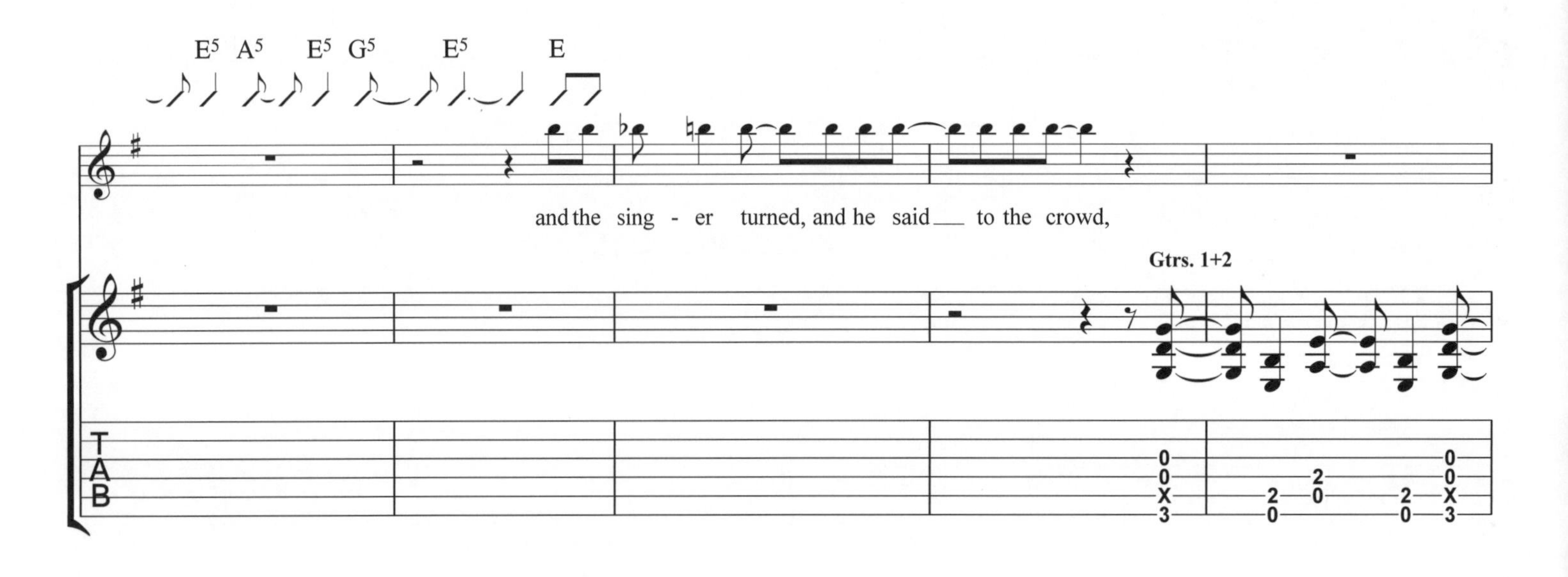
E5 A5 E5 G5 E5 E
and the sing - er turned, and he said to the crowd,
Gtrs. 1+2

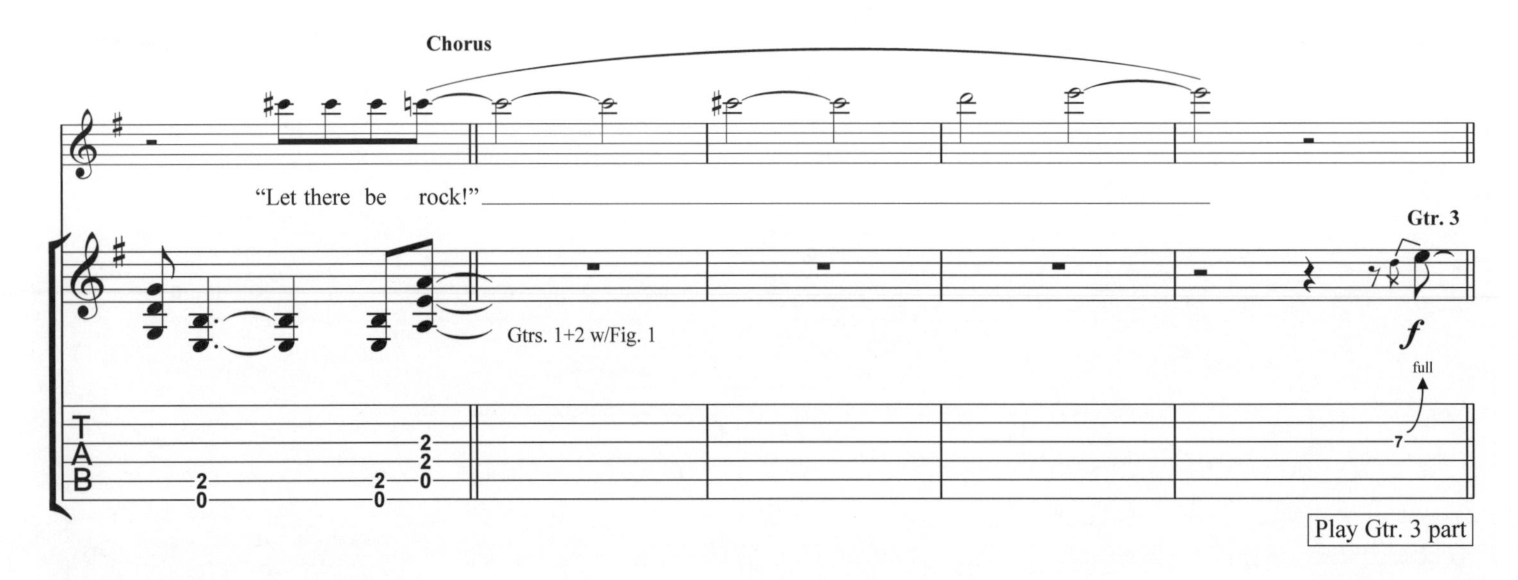
Chorus
"Let there be rock!"
Gtrs. 1+2 w/Fig. 1
Gtr. 3
full
Play Gtr. 3 part

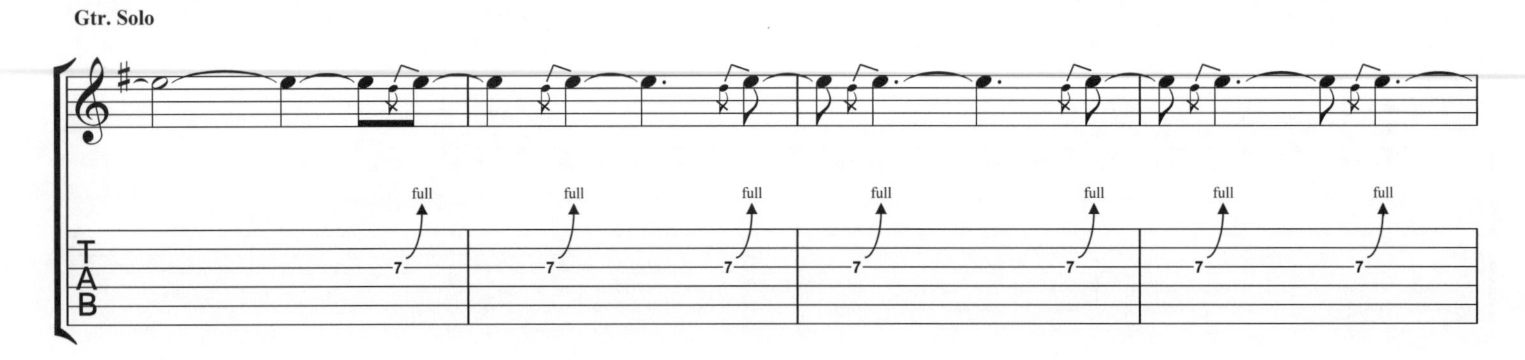
Gtr. Solo
full

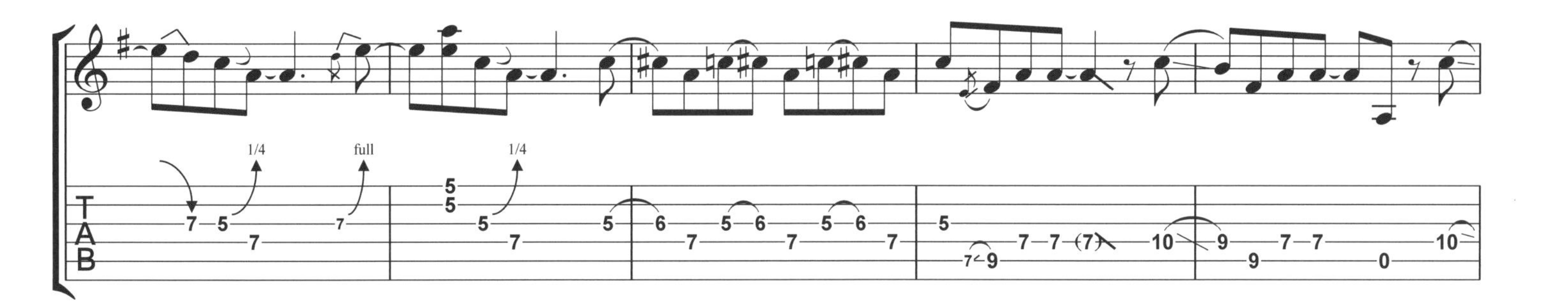
1/4
full
1/4

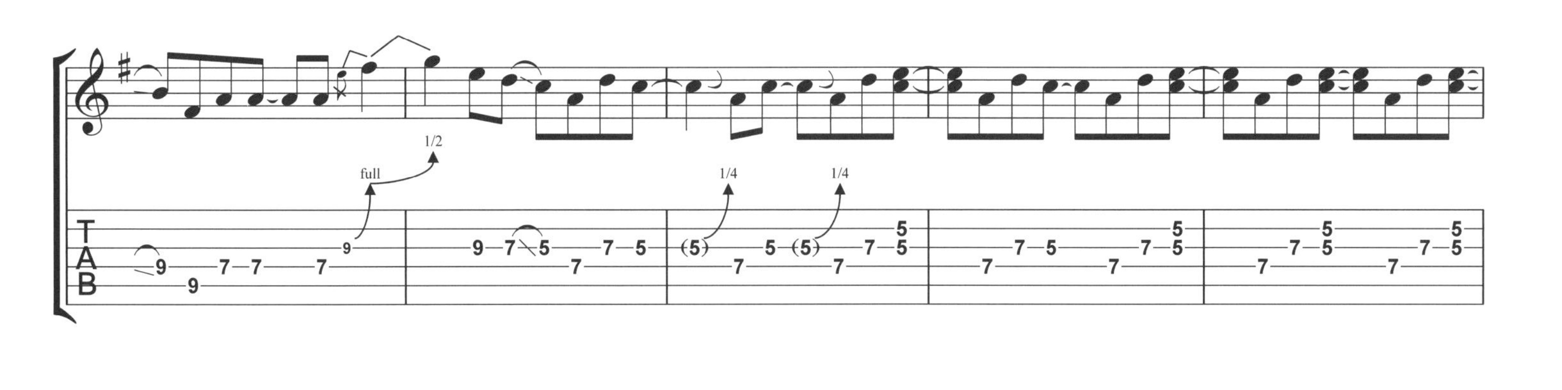
full
1/2
1/4
1/4

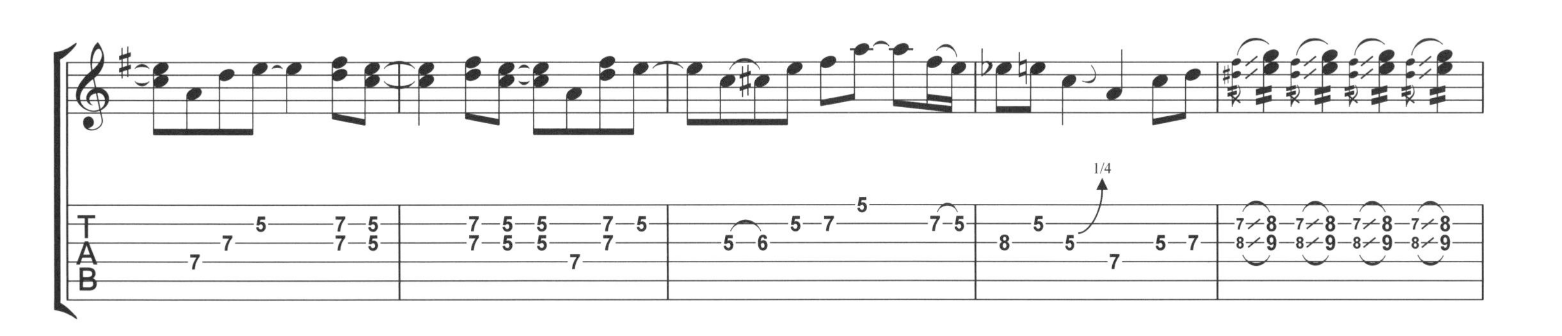
1/4

B5
full
full
1/4
Gtrs. 1+2
cont. in slashes

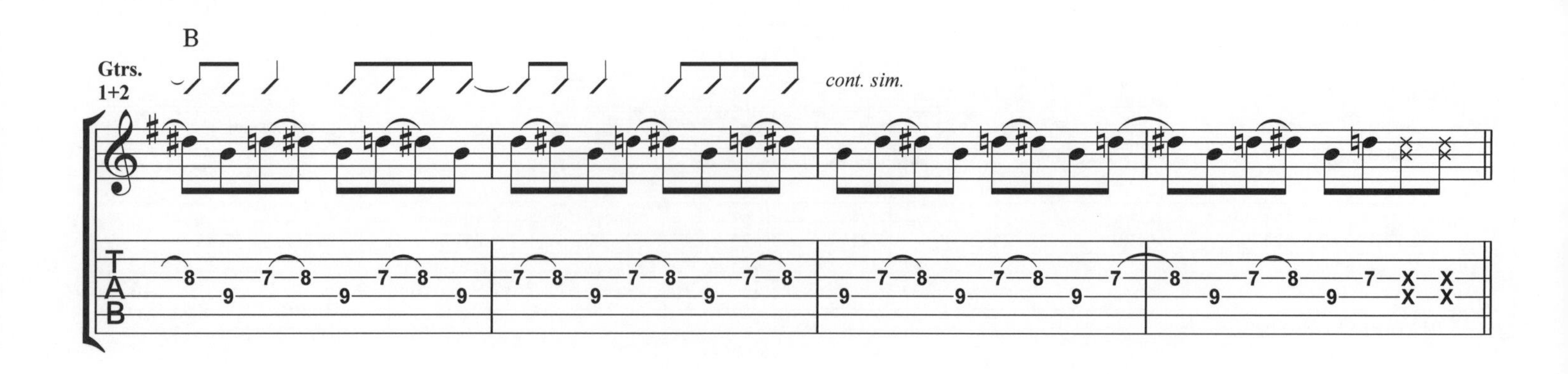
B
Gtrs. 1+2
cont. sim.

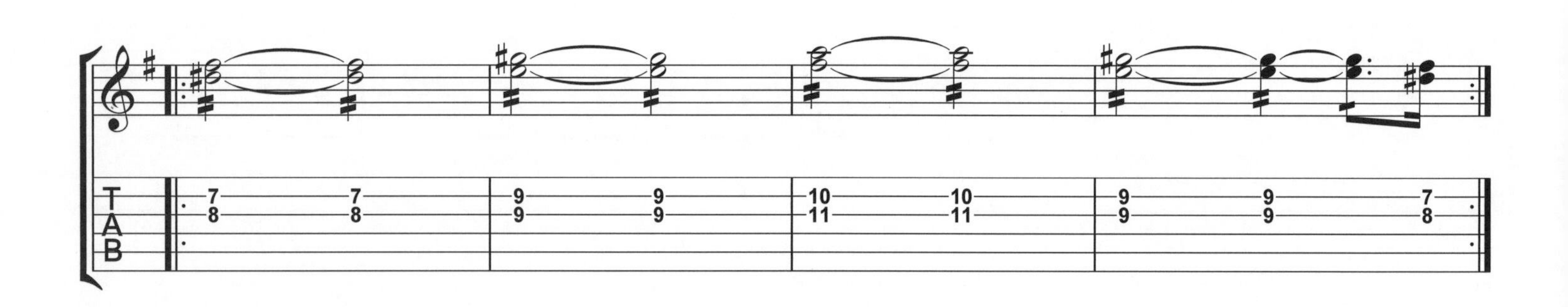

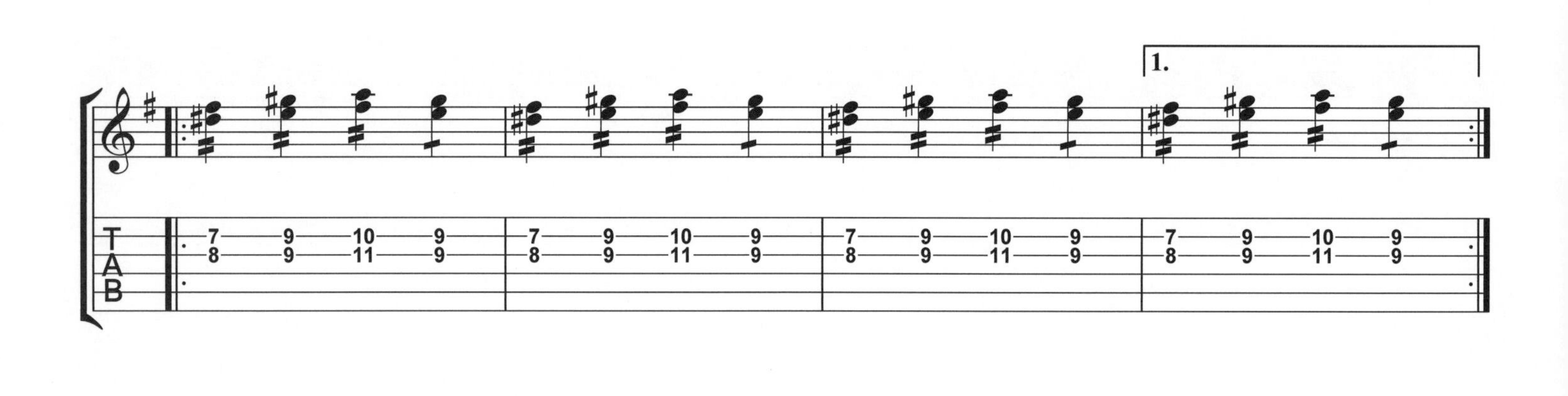
1.

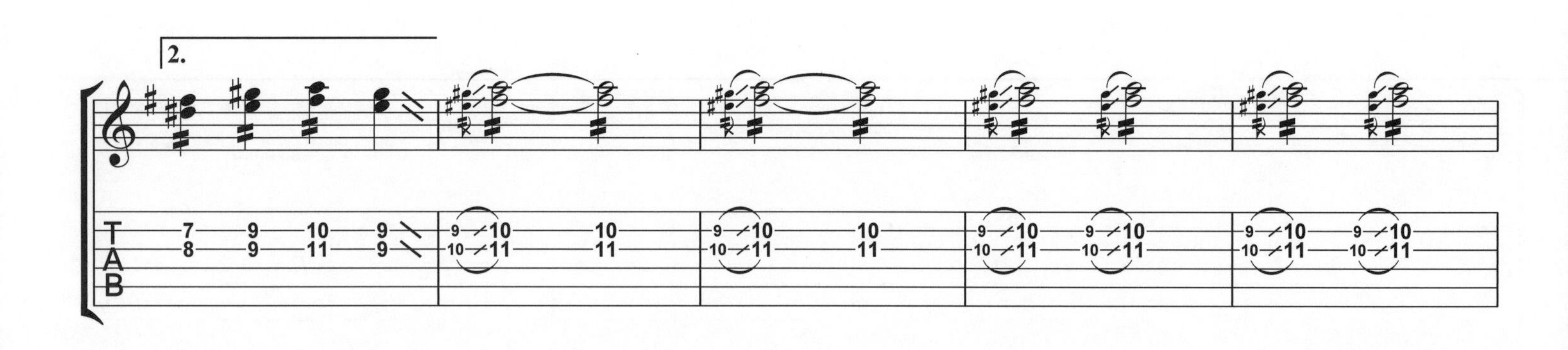
2.

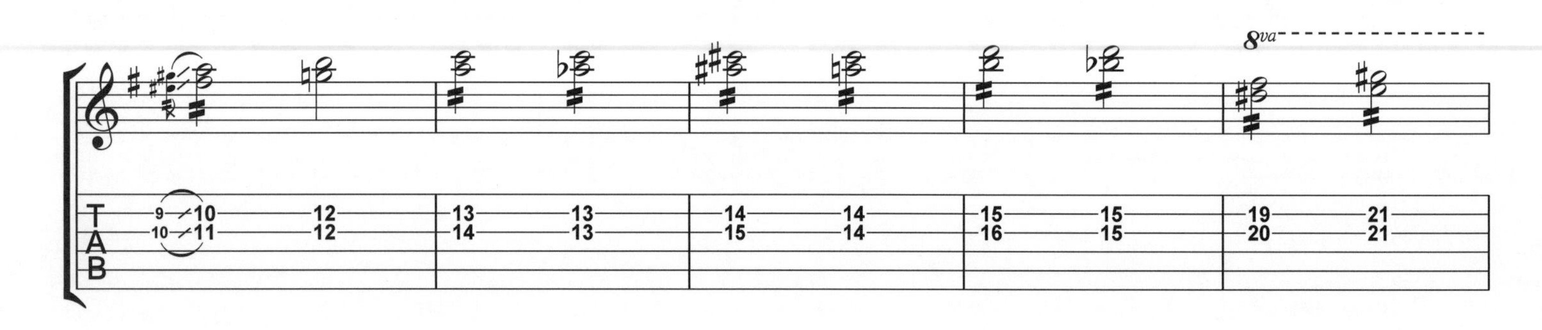
8va

(8)
B
Freely
B
full
E
B
full
1/2

# rock and roll ain't noise pollution

Words & Music by
Angus Young, Malcolm Young & Brian Johnson



**Full performance demo: CD 1 track 8**
**Backing only: CD 2 track 8**

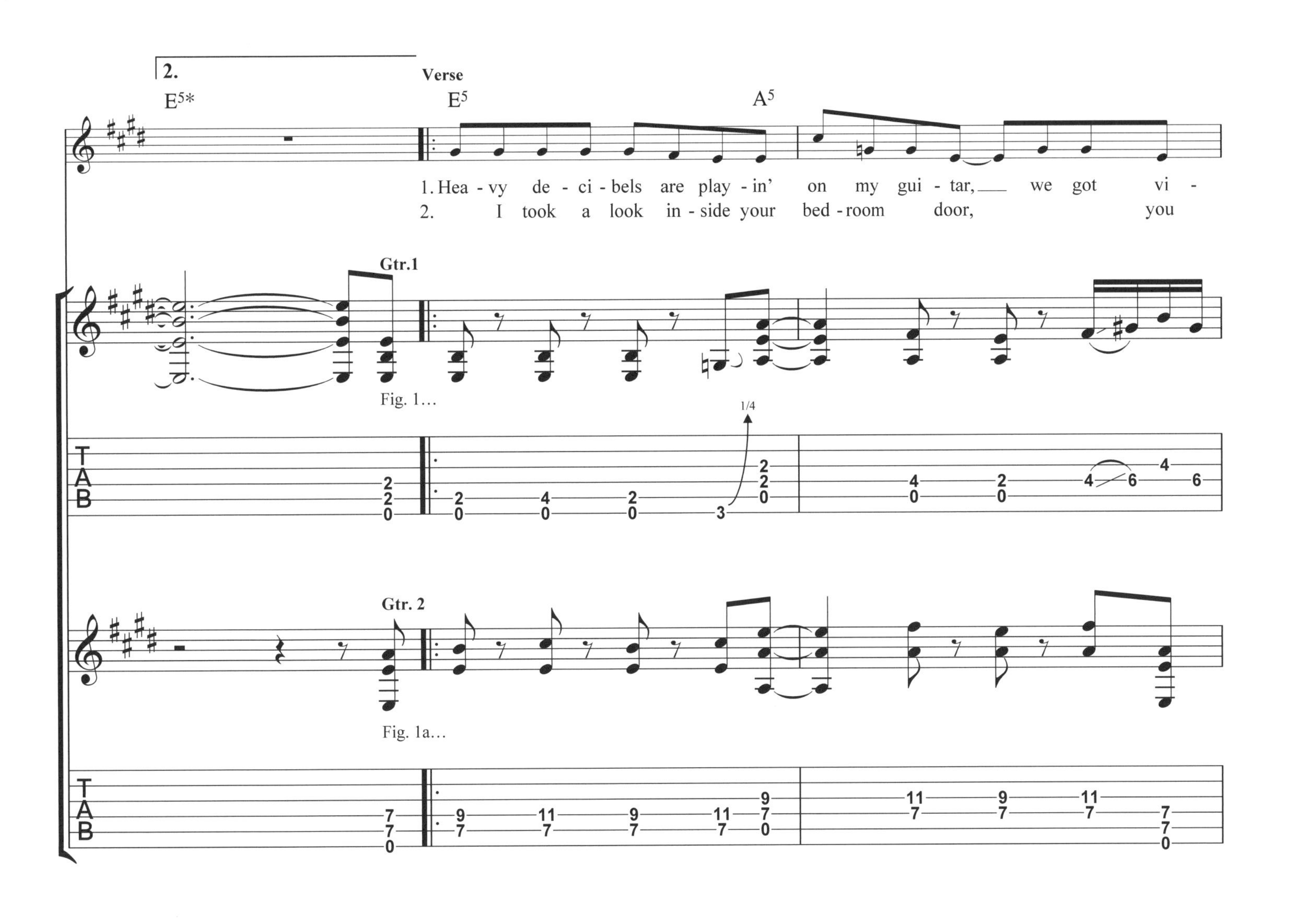
2.
Verse
E5*
E5
A5
1. Hea - vy de - ci - bels are play - in' on my gui - tar, we got vi -
2. I took a look in - side your bed - room door, you
Gtr.1
Fig. 1...
1/4
Gtr. 2
Fig. 1a...

E5
A5
E5
A5
-bra - tions com - in' up from the floor. Well, just lis - 'nin' to the rock that's giv - in'
looked so good ly - in' on your bed. Well, I asked you if you want - ed a - ny
1/4

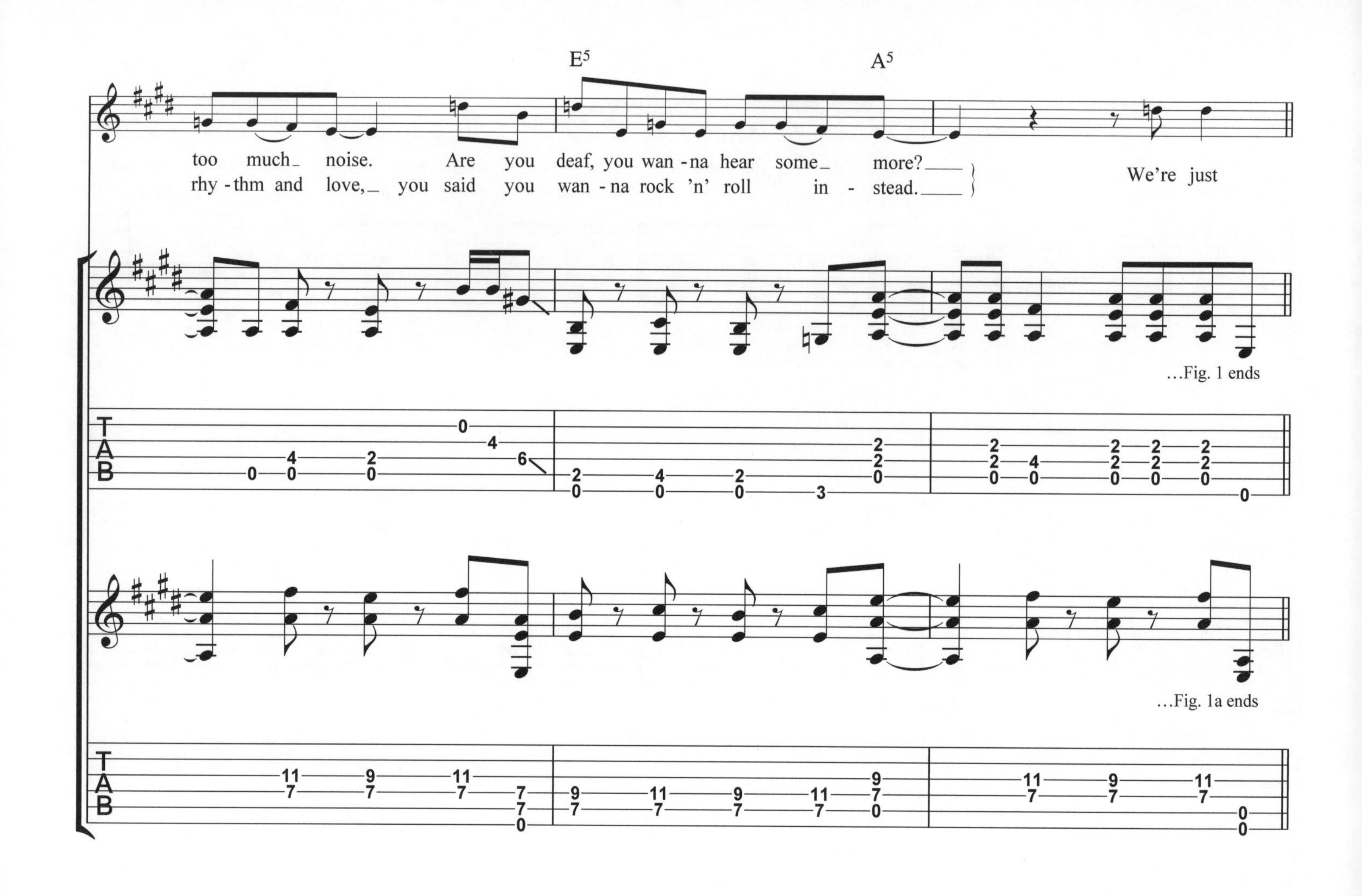
E5
A5
too much_ noise. Are you deaf, you wan-na hear some_ more?
rhy-thm and love,_ you said you wan-na rock 'n' roll in - stead.
We're just
...Fig. 1 ends
...Fig. 1a ends

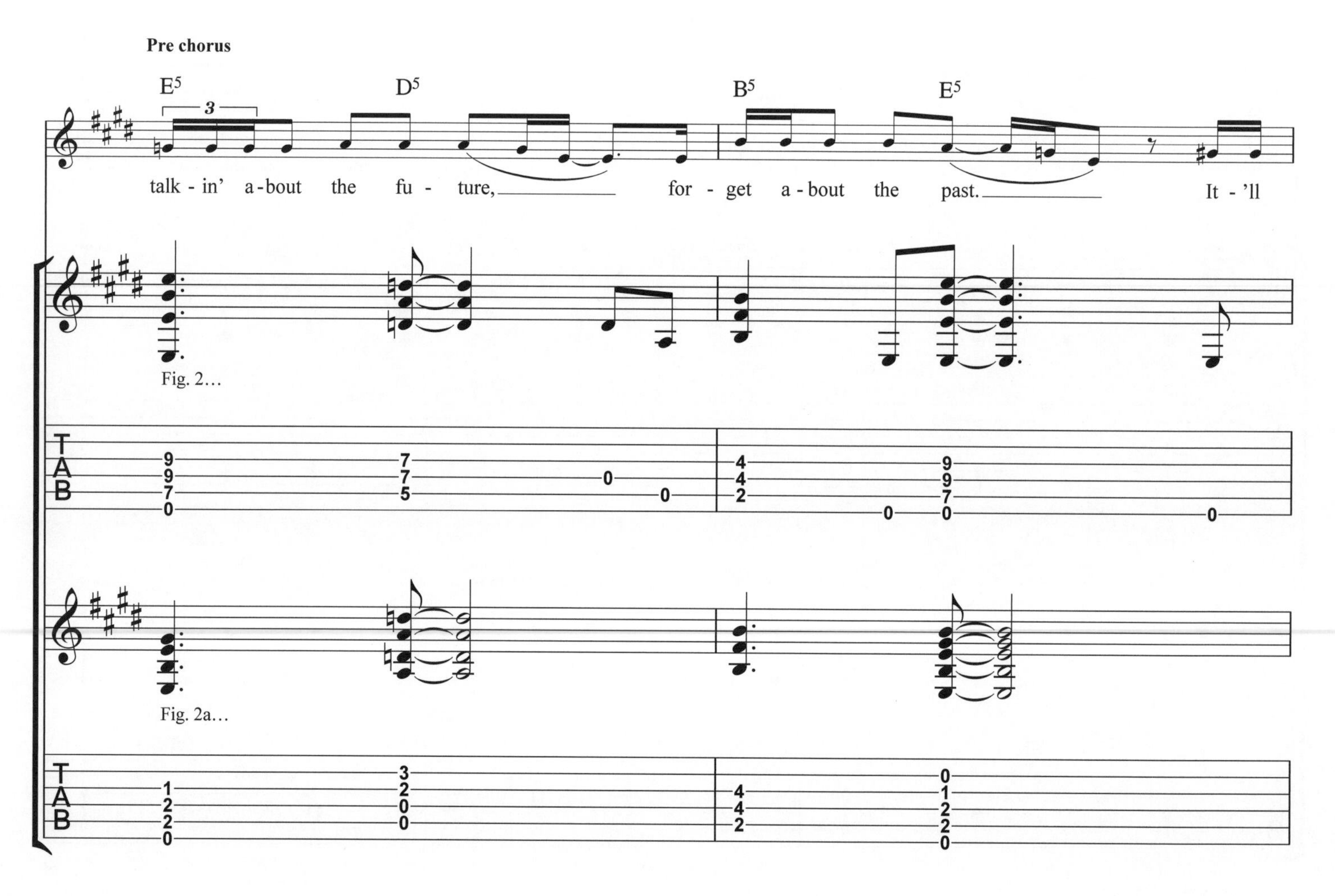
Pre chorus
E5
D5
B5
E5
talk - in' a-bout the fu - ture, for - get a - bout the past. It - 'll
Fig. 2...
Fig. 2a...

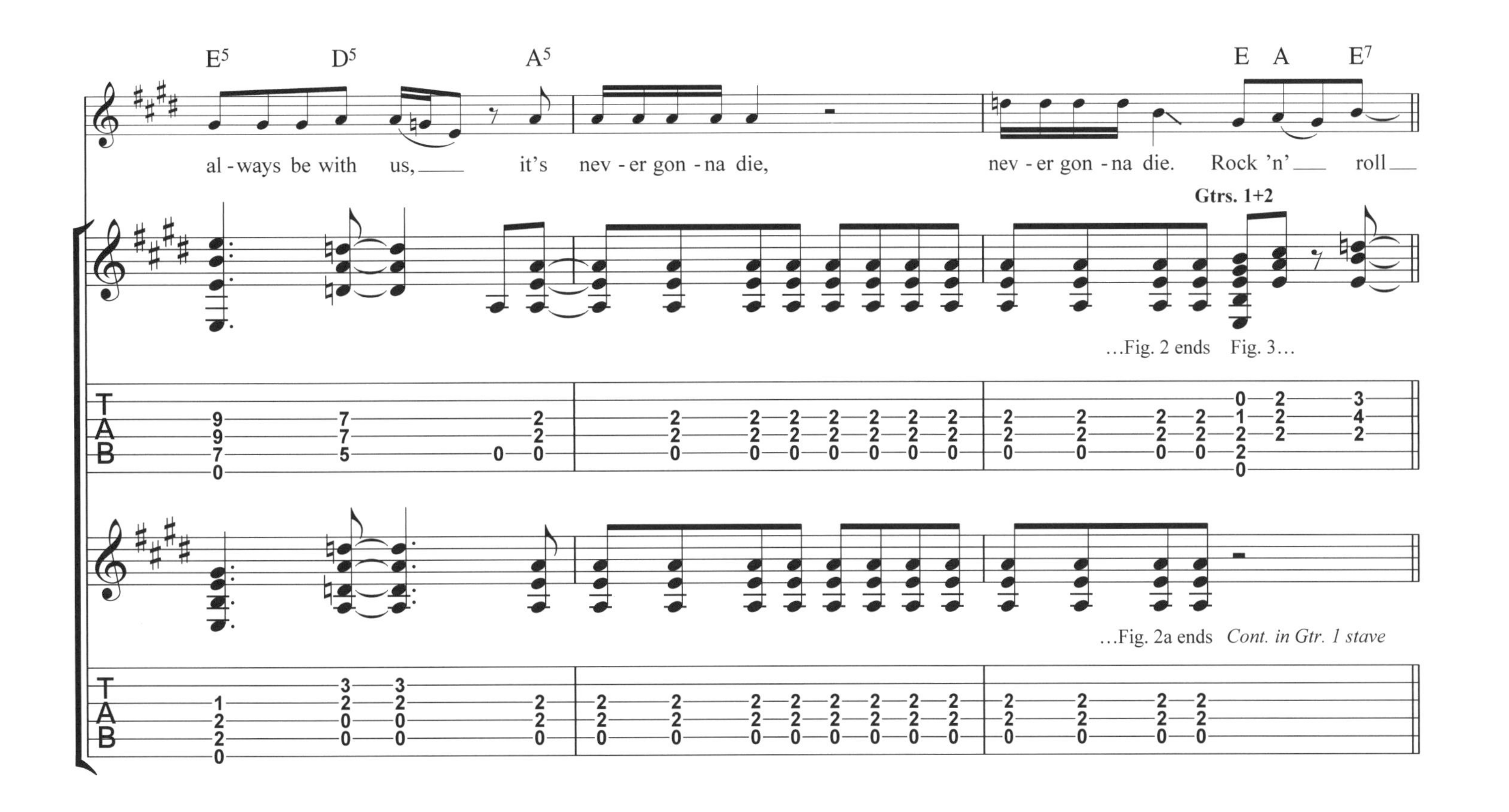
E5 D5 A5 E A E7
al-ways be with us, it's nev-er gon-na die, nev-er gon-na die. Rock 'n' roll
Gtrs. 1+2
…Fig. 2 ends Fig. 3…
…Fig. 2a ends Cont. in Gtr. 1 stave

Chorus

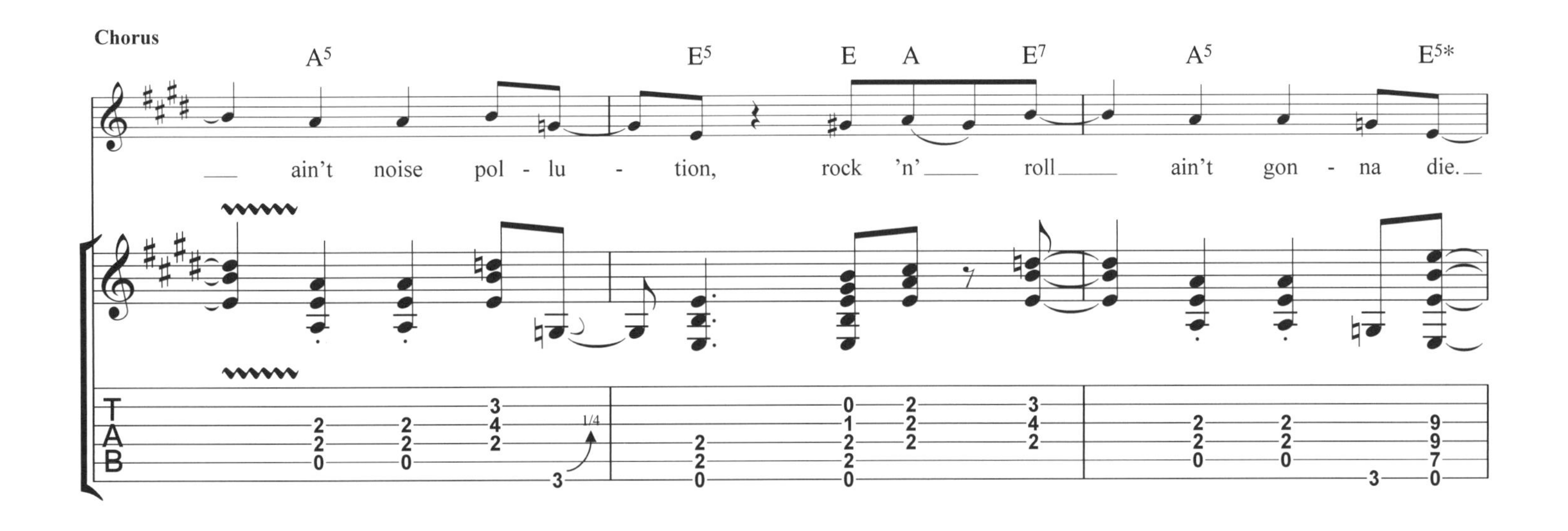
A5 E5 E A E7 A5 E5*
ain't noise pol-lu-tion, rock 'n' roll ain't gon-na die.
1/4

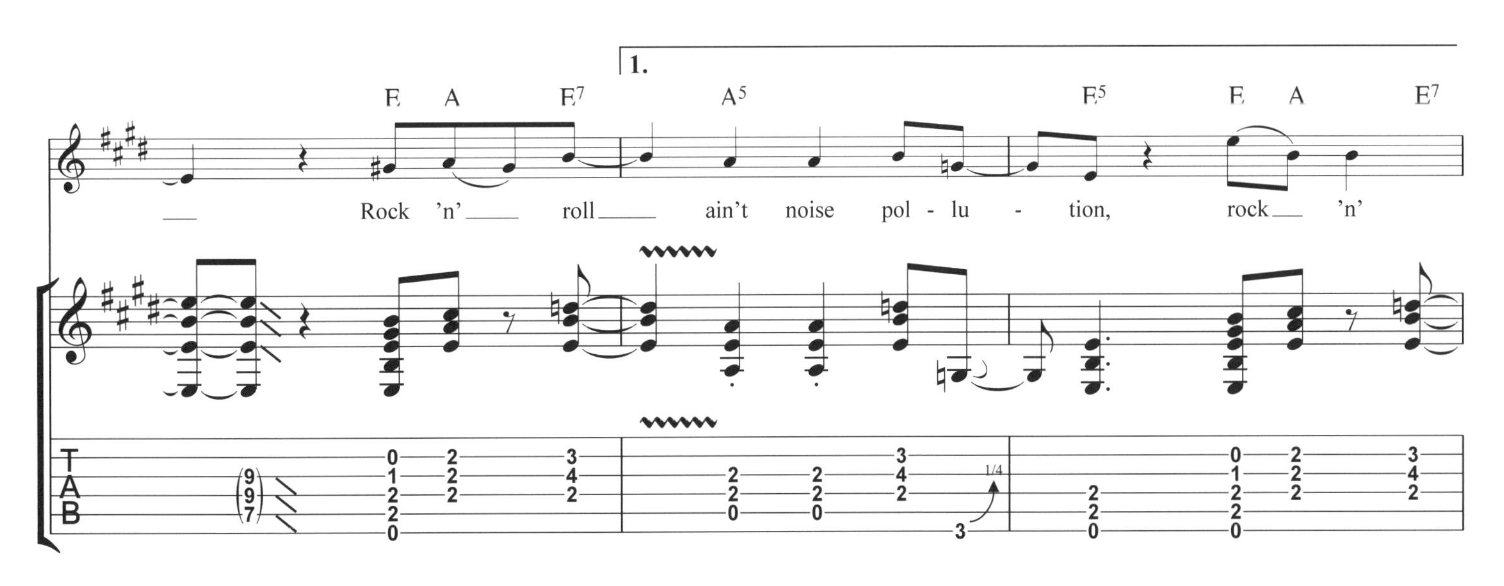
1.
E A E7 A5 E5 E A E7
Rock 'n' roll ain't noise pol-lu-tion, rock 'n'
1/4

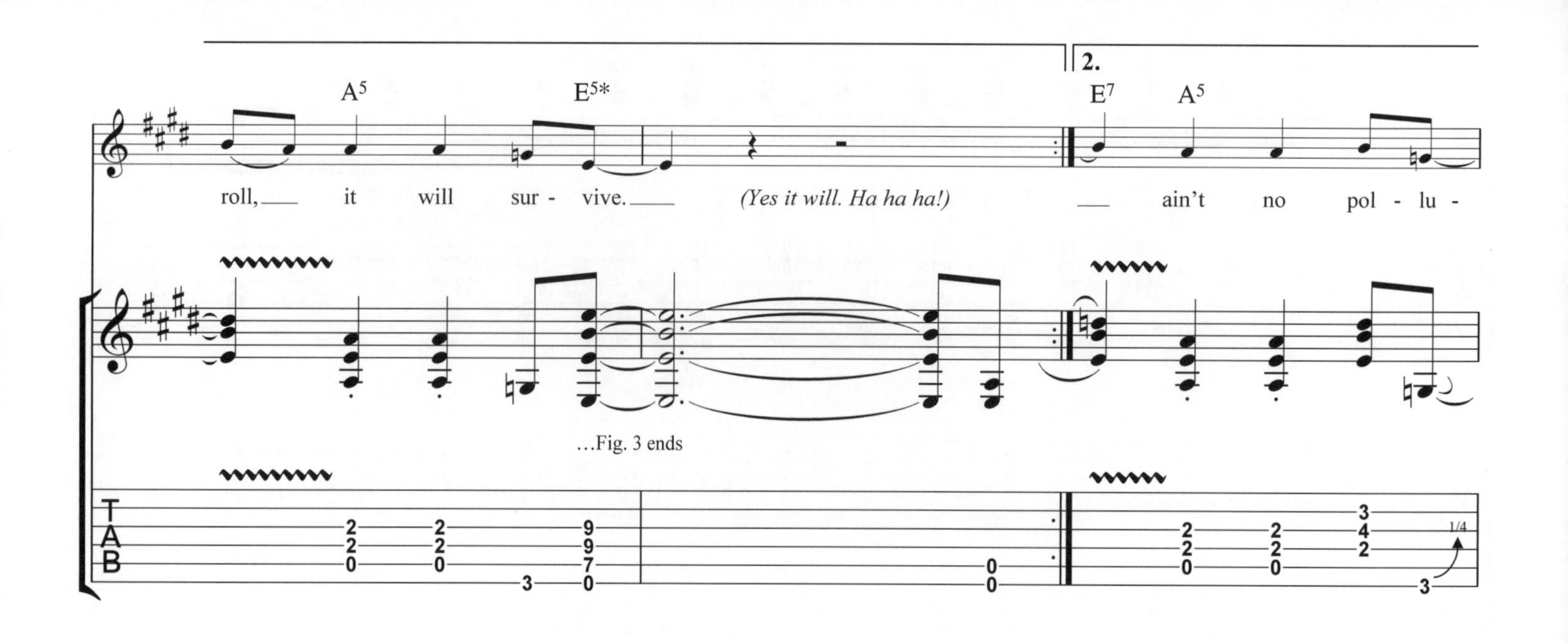
2.
A5
E5*
E7
roll, it will sur - vive.
(Yes it will. Ha ha ha!)
ain't no pol - lu -
…Fig. 3 ends
1/4

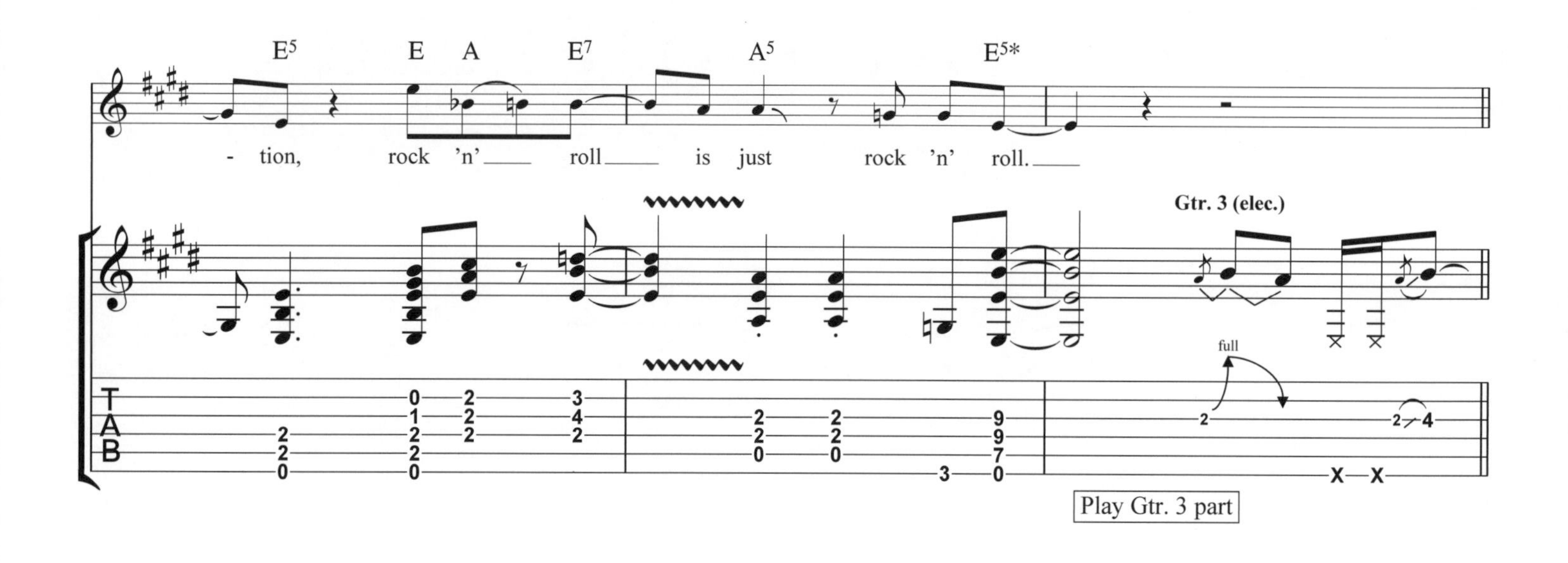
E5
E
A
E7
A5
E5*
- tion, rock 'n' roll is just rock 'n' roll.
Gtr. 3 (elec.)
full
Play Gtr. 3 part

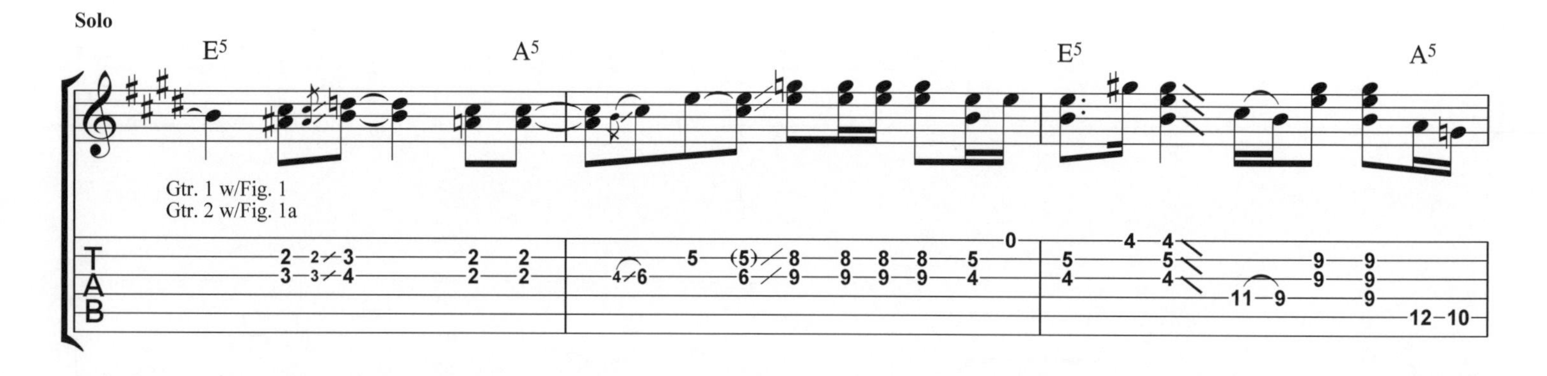
Solo
E5
A5
Gtr. 1 w/Fig. 1
Gtr. 2 w/Fig. 1a

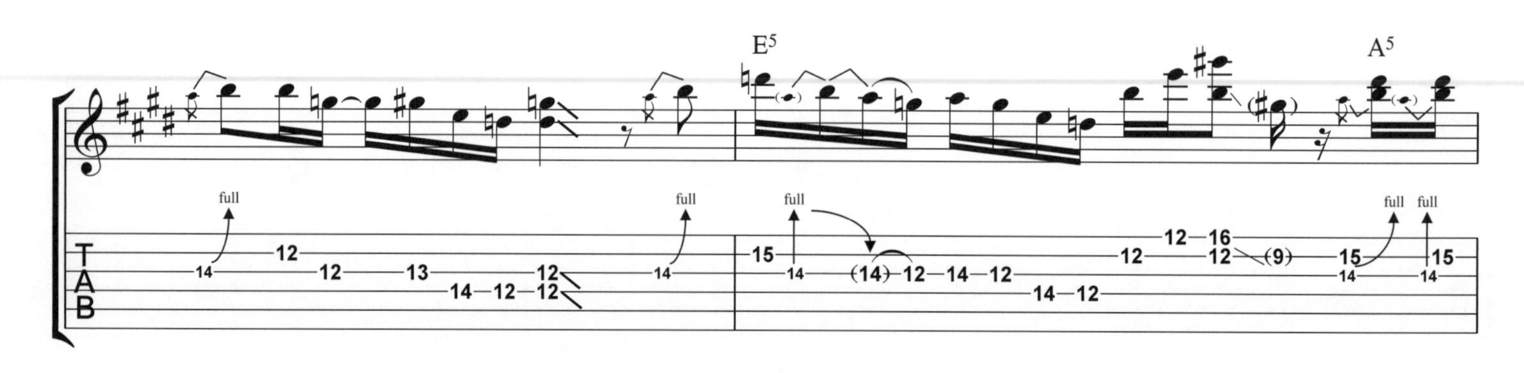
E5
A5
full

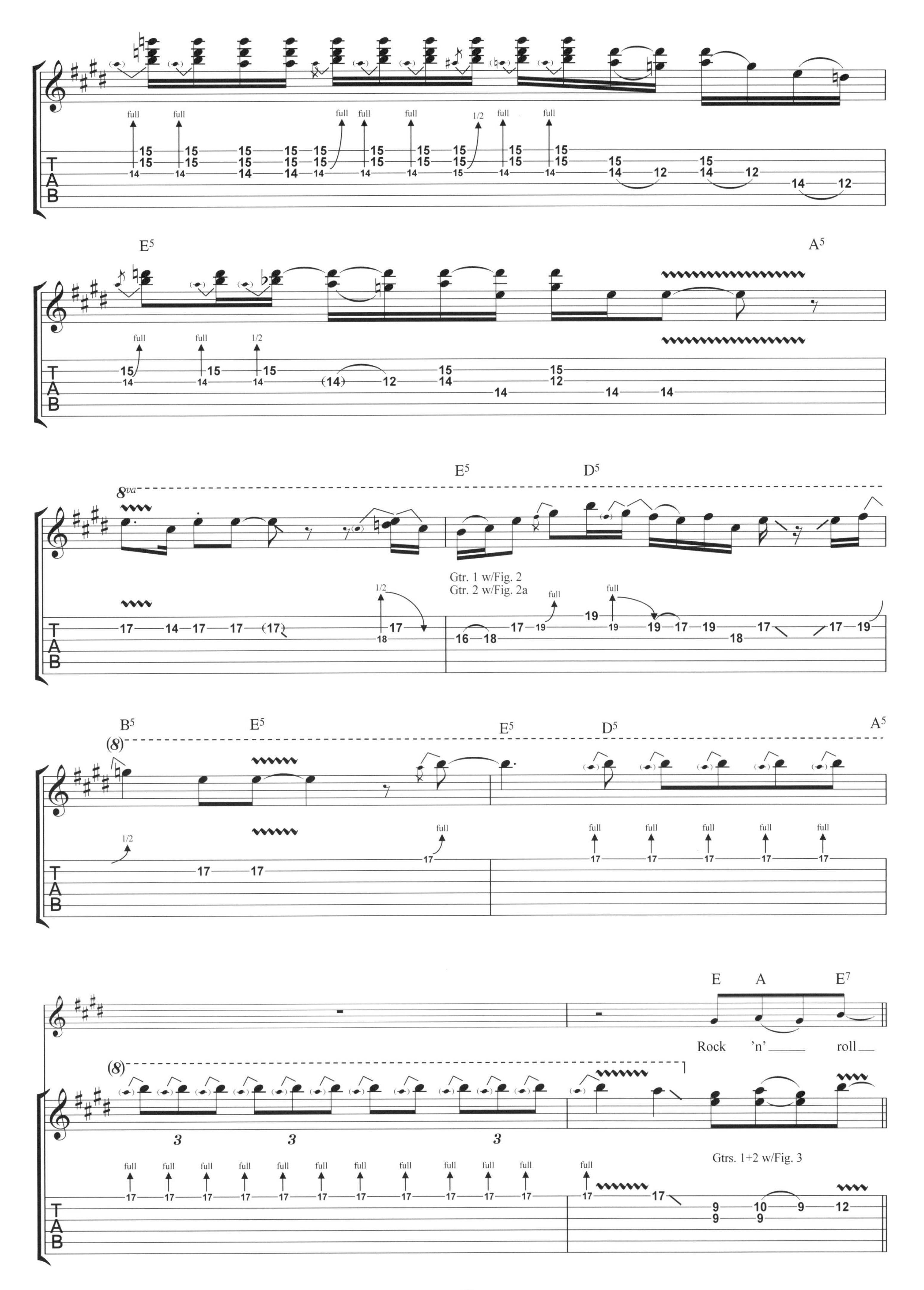
E5
A5
8va
E5
D5
Gtr. 1 w/Fig. 2
Gtr. 2 w/Fig. 2a
B5
E5
E5
D5
A5
E
A
E7
Rock 'n' roll
Gtrs. 1+2 w/Fig. 3

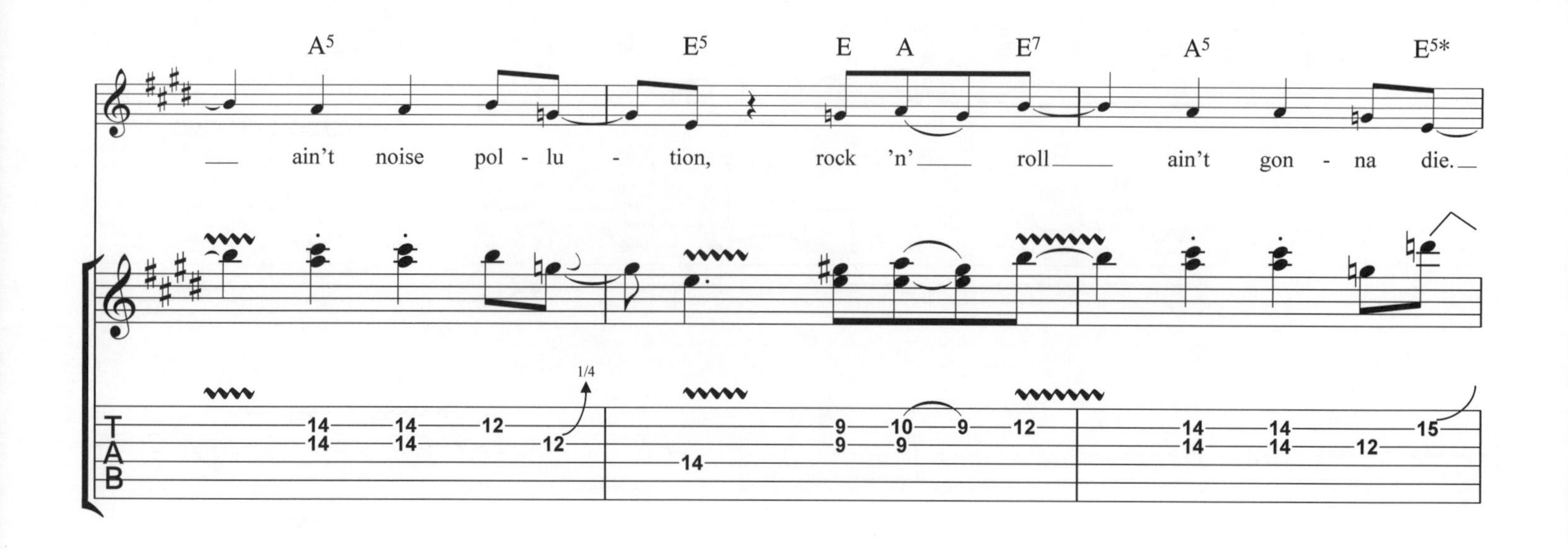
A5 E5 E A E7 A5 E5*
ain't noise pol - lu - tion, rock 'n' roll ain't gon - na die.
1/4
T
A
B

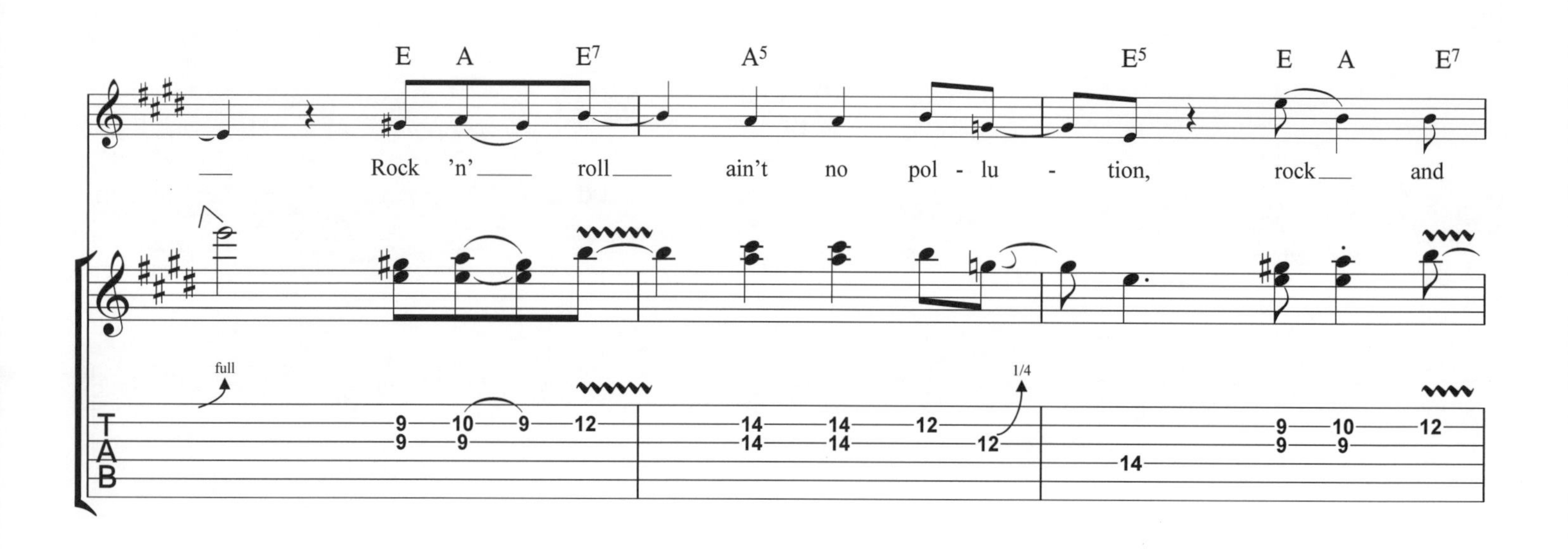
E A E7 A5 E5 E A E7
Rock 'n' roll ain't no pol - lu - tion, rock and
full
1/4
T
A
B

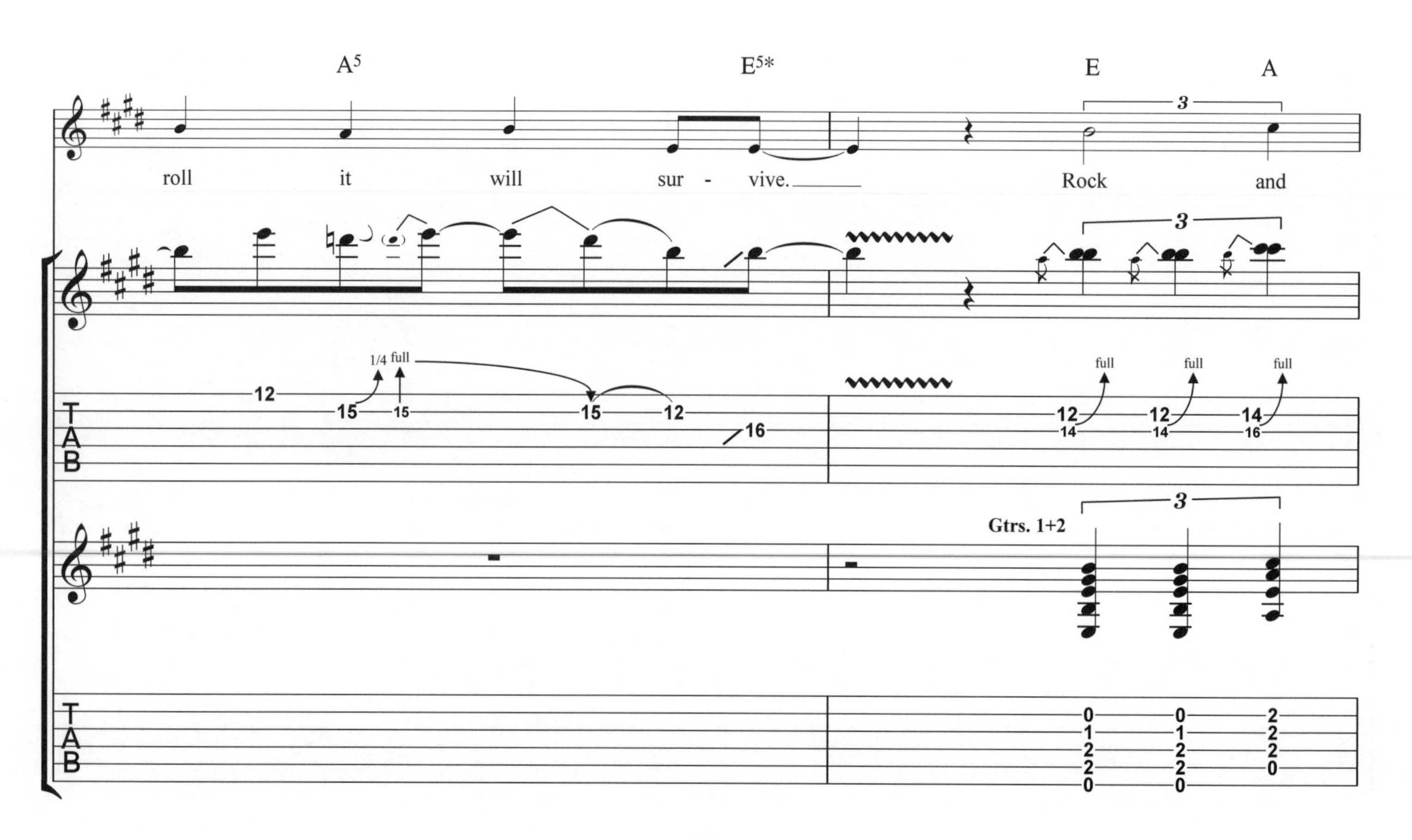
A5 E5* E A
roll it will sur - vive. Rock and
1/4 full
full full full
Gtrs. 1+2
T
A
B

E7
A5
E5
E
A
roll ain't no pol - lu - tion, rock and
full
TAB
1/4

E7
A5
E5*
E
A
roll, it - 'll nev - er die. Rock and
full
TAB

roll ain't no pol - lu - tion, rock and roll, ah
full full 1/2 full
full full full full
1/4

E5*
rock 'n' roll, is just a rock 'n' roll, yeah.
gradual bend
1/2

# rock 'n' roll train

**Words & Music by**
**Angus Young & Malcolm Young**



***Full performance demo: CD 1 track 9***
***Backing only: CD 2 track 9***

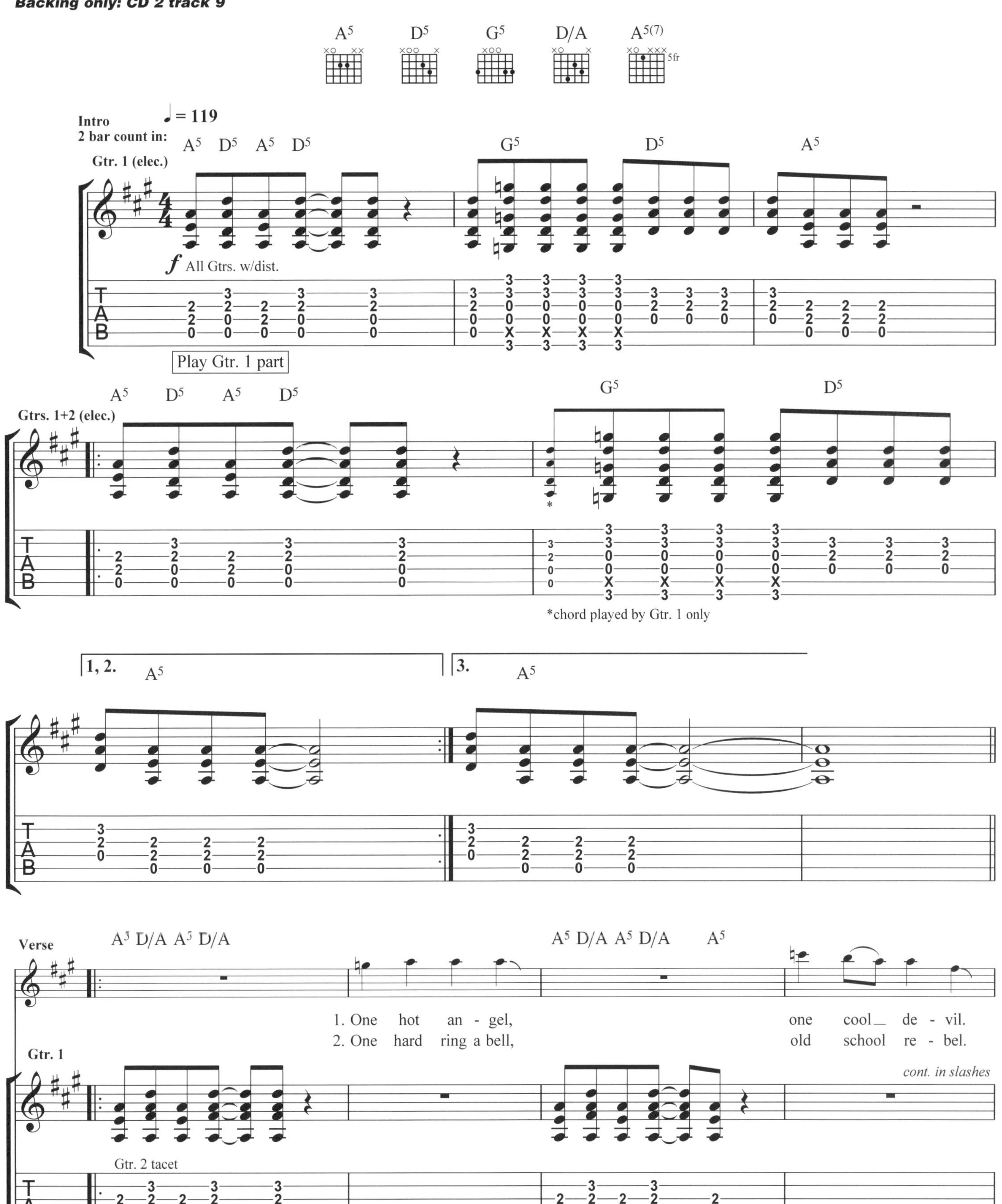

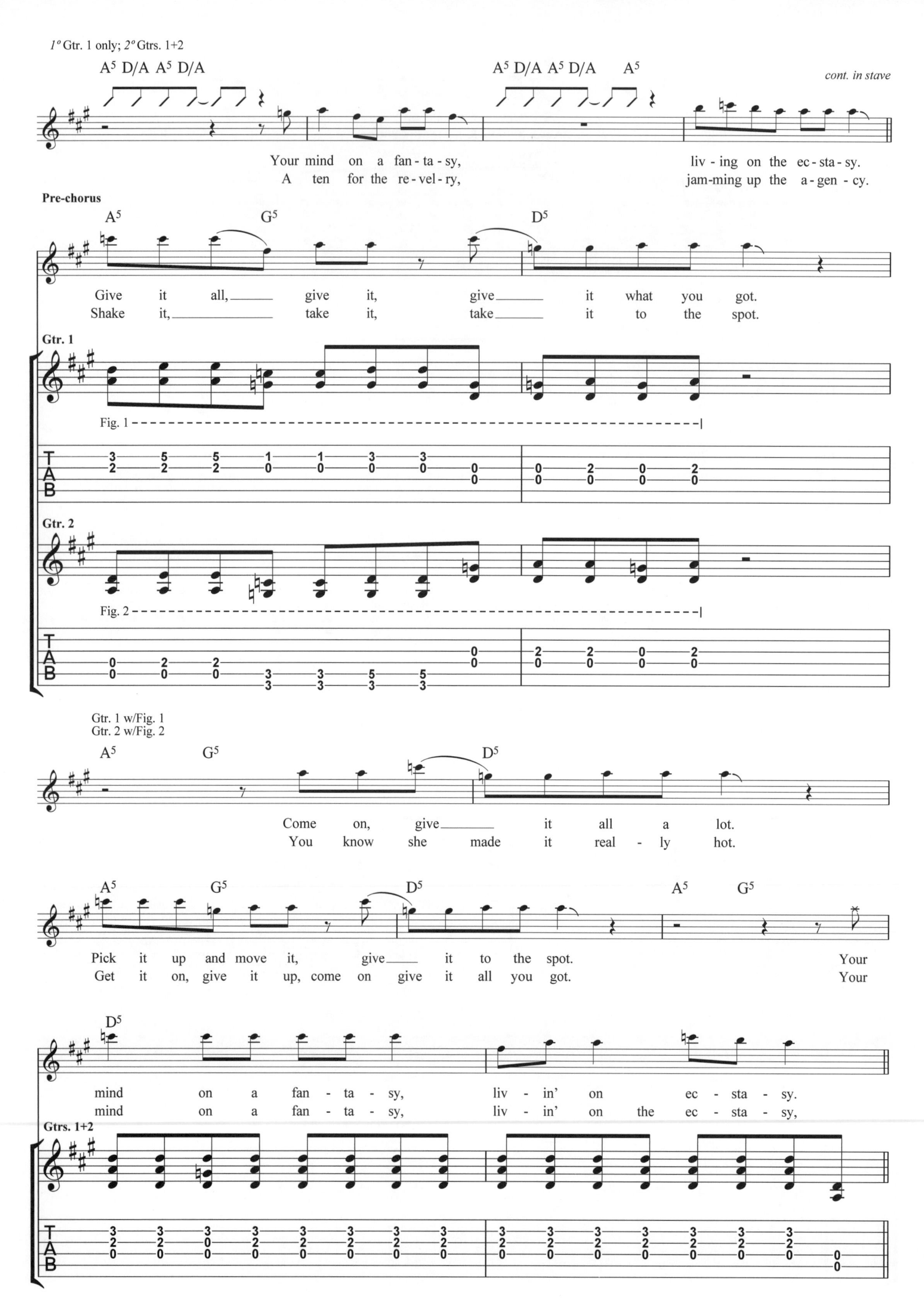
1° Gtr. 1 only; 2° Gtrs. 1+2
A5 D/A A5 D/A
A5 D/A A5 D/A A5
cont. in stave
Your mind on a fan - ta - sy,
A ten for the re - vel - ry,
liv - ing on the ec - sta - sy.
jam-ming up the a - gen - cy.
Pre-chorus
A5
G5
D5
Give it all, give it, give it what you got.
Shake it, take it, take it to the spot.
Gtr. 1
Fig. 1
Gtr. 2
Fig. 2
Gtr. 1 w/Fig. 1
Gtr. 2 w/Fig. 2
Come on, give it all a lot.
You know she made it real - ly hot.
Pick it up and move it, give it to the spot.
Get it on, give it up, come on give it all you got.
Your
Your
mind on a fan - ta - sy, liv - in' on ec - sta - sy.
mind on a fan - ta - sy, liv - in' on the ec - sta - sy,
Gtrs. 1+2

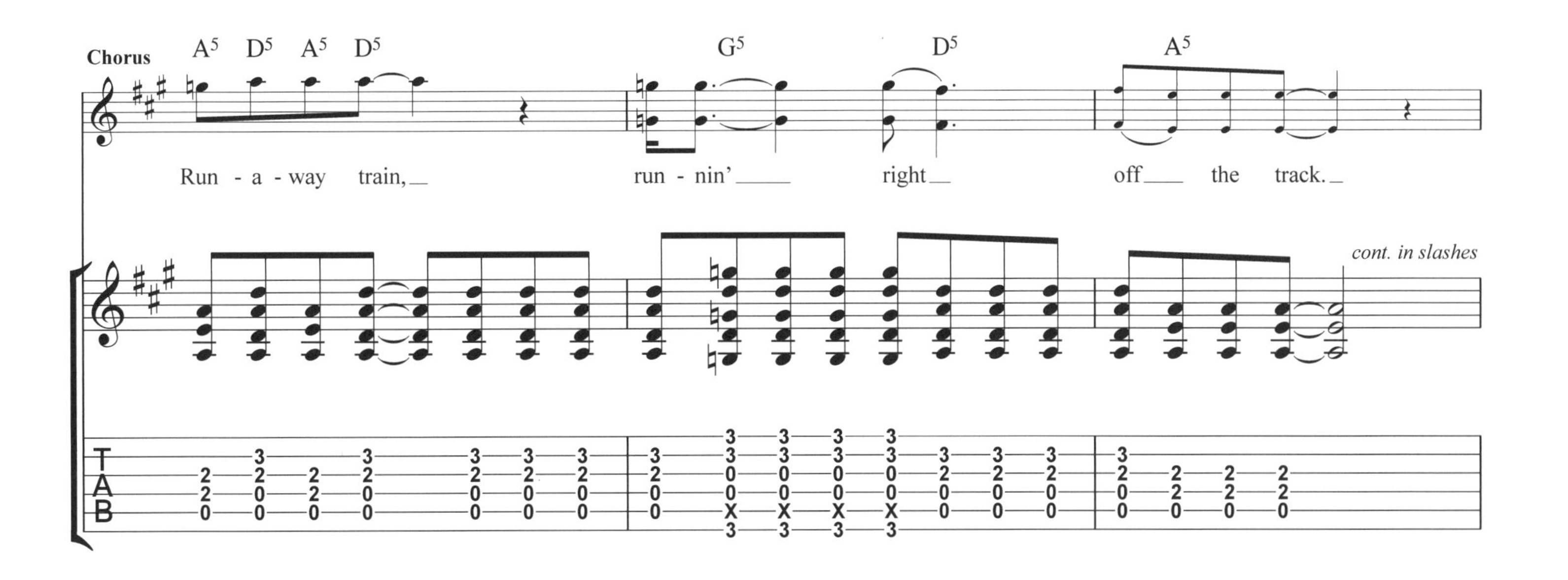
Chorus
A5 D5 A5 D5
G5
D5
A5
Run - a - way train,
run - nin'
right
off the track.
cont. in slashes
TAB

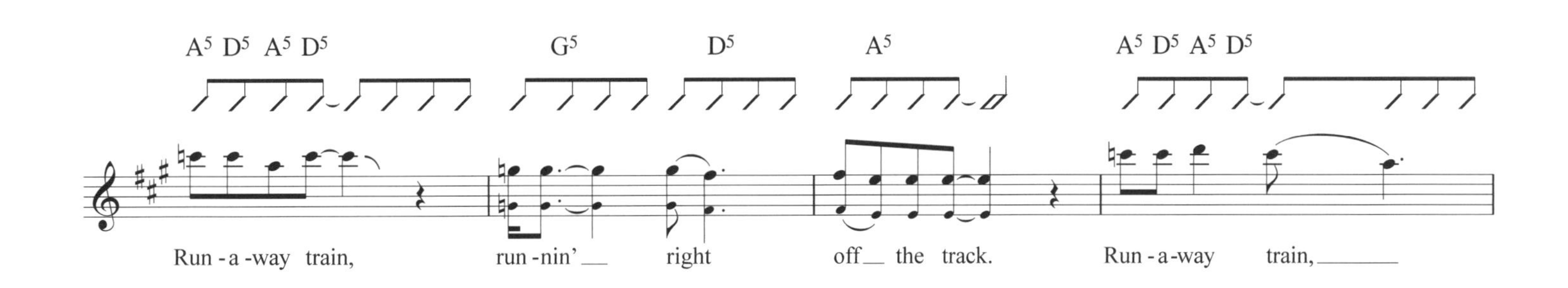
A5 D5 A5 D5
G5
D5
A5
A5 D5 A5 D5
Run - a - way train,
run - nin'
right
off the track.
Run - a - way train,

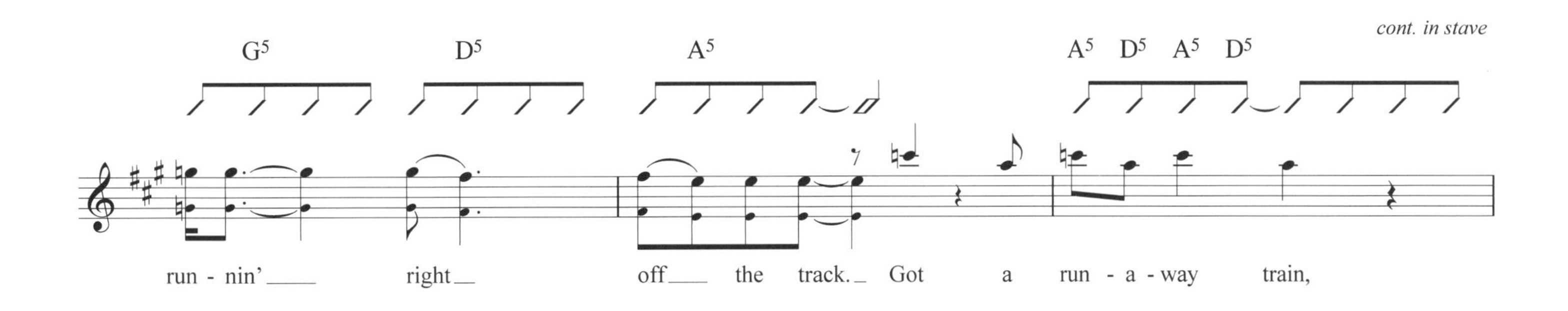
cont. in stave
G5
D5
A5
A5 D5 A5 D5
run - nin'
right
off the track. Got a run - a - way train,

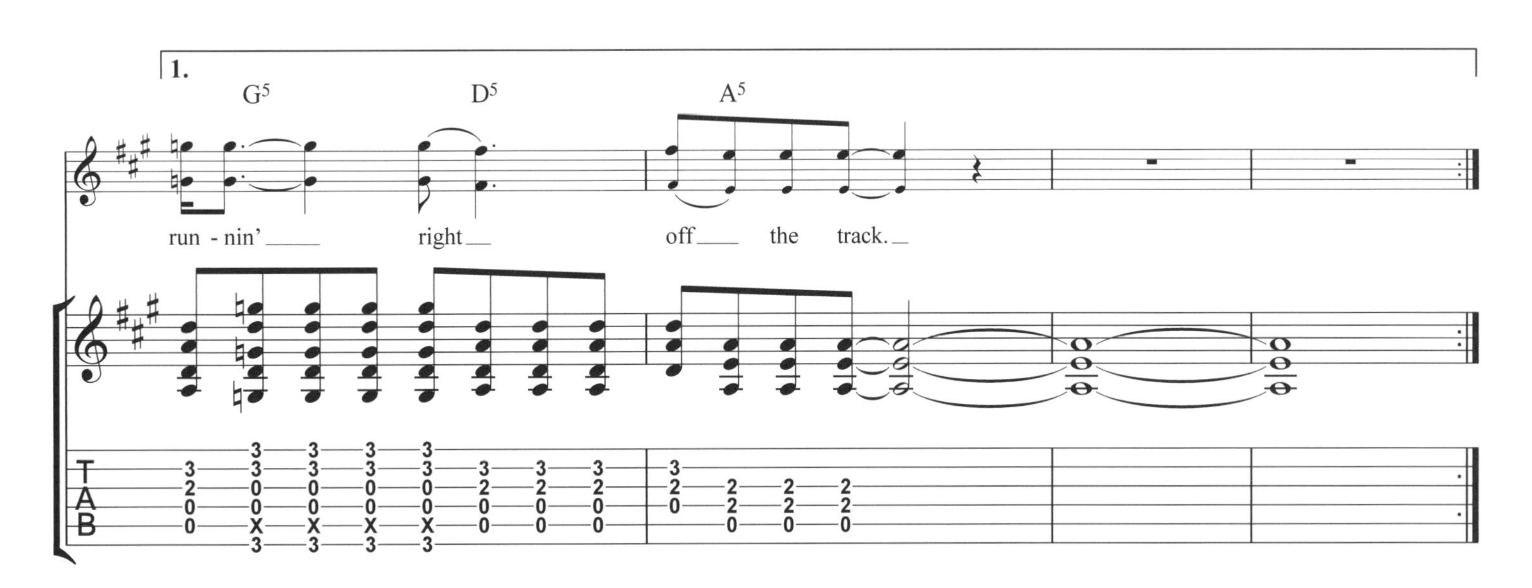
1.
G5
D5
A5
run - nin'
right
off the track.
TAB

2.
G5
D5
A5
G5
D5
run - nin'
right
off
the
track.
Gtr. 3 (elec.)
ff
P.S.
3
full
1/4
full
full
full
Play Gtr. 3 part
Gtrs. 1+2
cont. in slashes
A5
G5
D5
A5
G5
D5
1/2
1/4
1/4
1/4
1/4
1/4
1/4
1/4
D5 A5
gradual slide
1/2
A5 D/A A5 D/A
A5 D/A A5 D/A
A5
Verse
Gtr. 3 tacet
Play rhythm slashes
3. One hot South-ern Belle,
son of a de - vil,

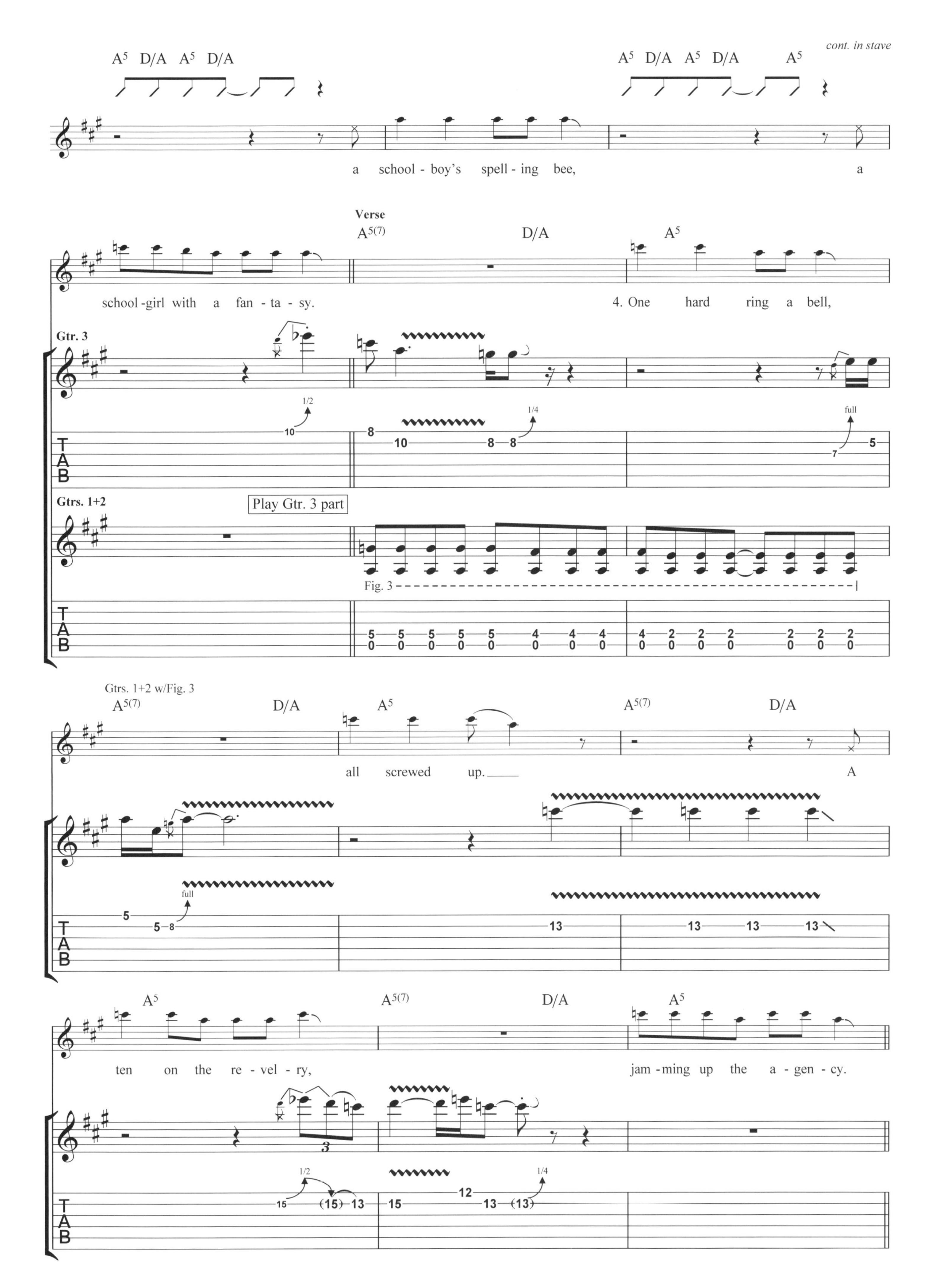
cont. in stave
A5 D/A A5 D/A
A5 D/A A5 D/A A5
a school - boy's spell - ing bee, a
Verse
A5(7) D/A A5
school - girl with a fan - ta - sy. 4. One hard ring a bell,
Gtr. 3
Gtrs. 1+2
Play Gtr. 3 part
Fig. 3
Gtrs. 1+2 w/Fig. 3
A5(7) D/A A5 A5(7) D/A
all screwed up. A
A5 A5(7) D/A A5
ten on the re - vel - ry, jam - ming up the a - gen - cy.

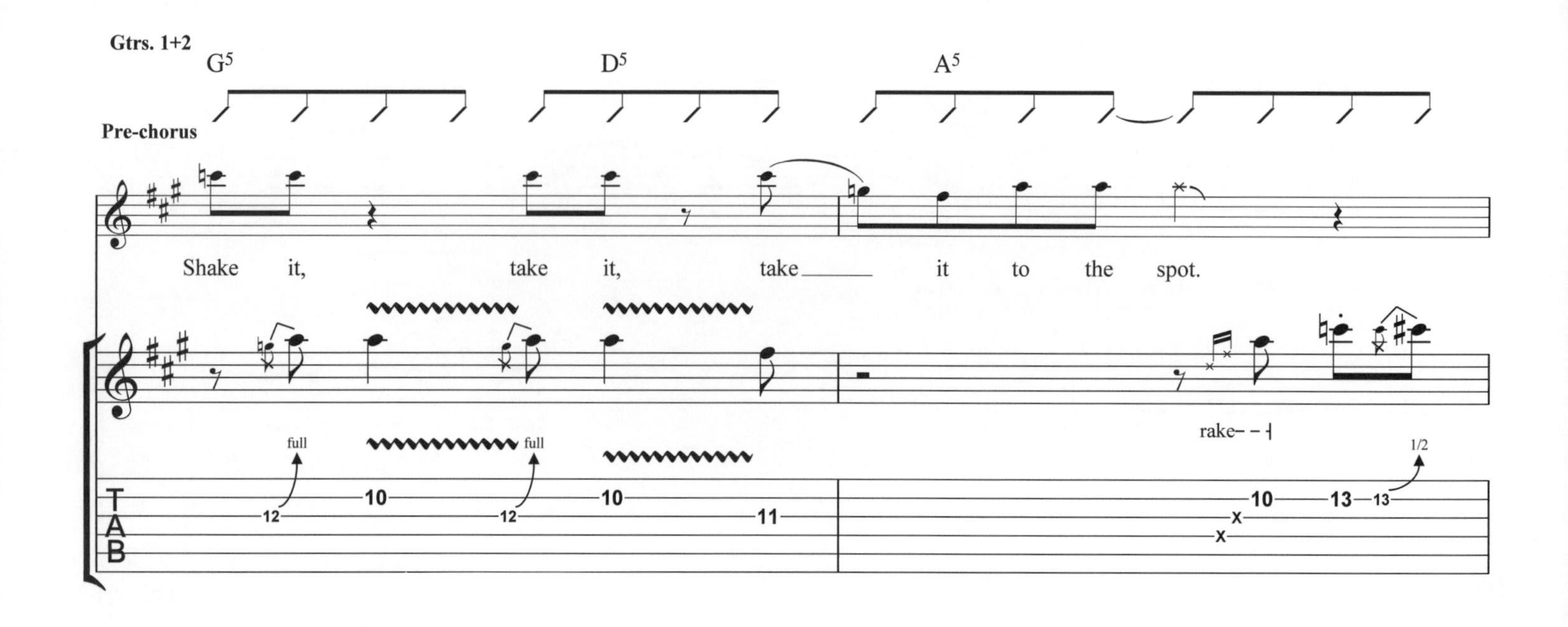
Gtrs. 1+2
G5
D5
A5
Pre-chorus
Shake it, take it, take it to the spot.
full
full
rake
1/2

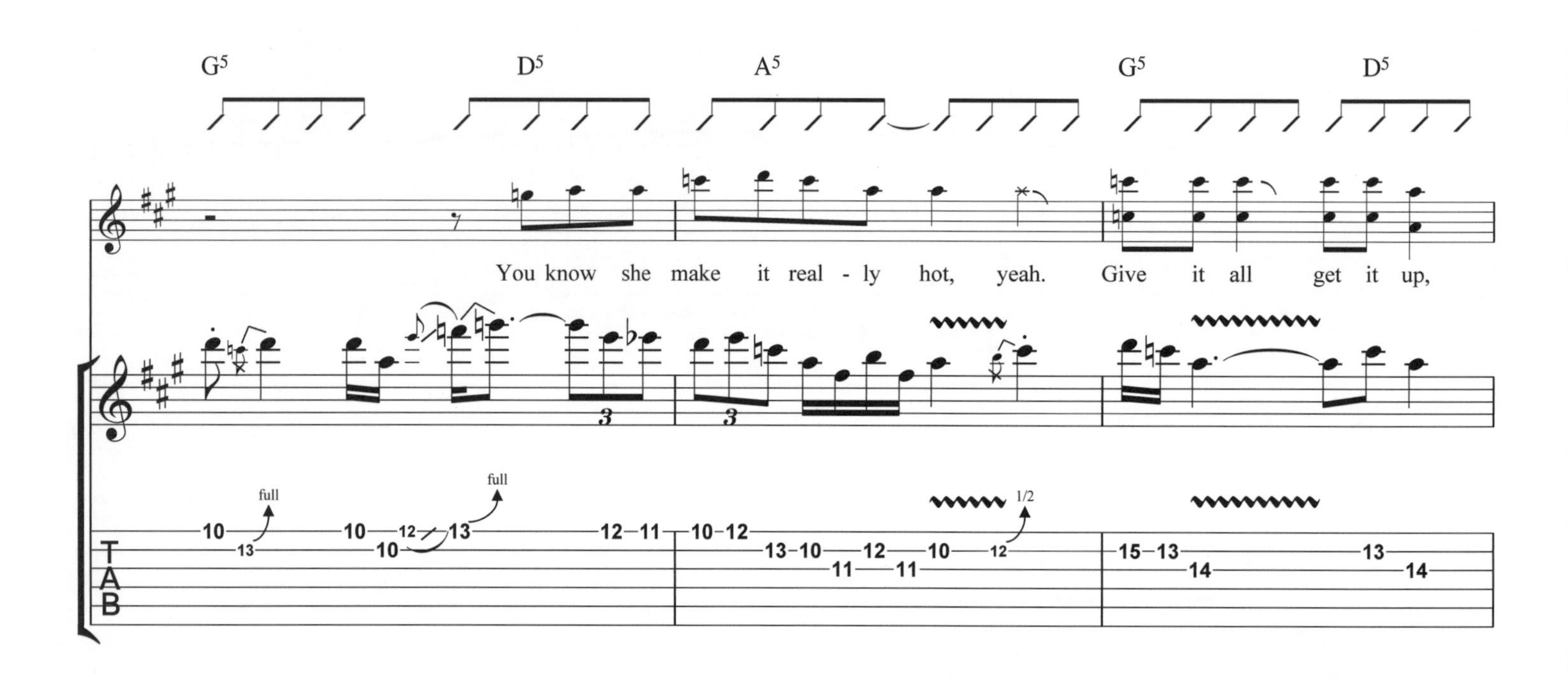
G5
D5
A5
G5
D5
You know she make it real - ly hot, yeah. Give it all get it up,
full
full
1/2

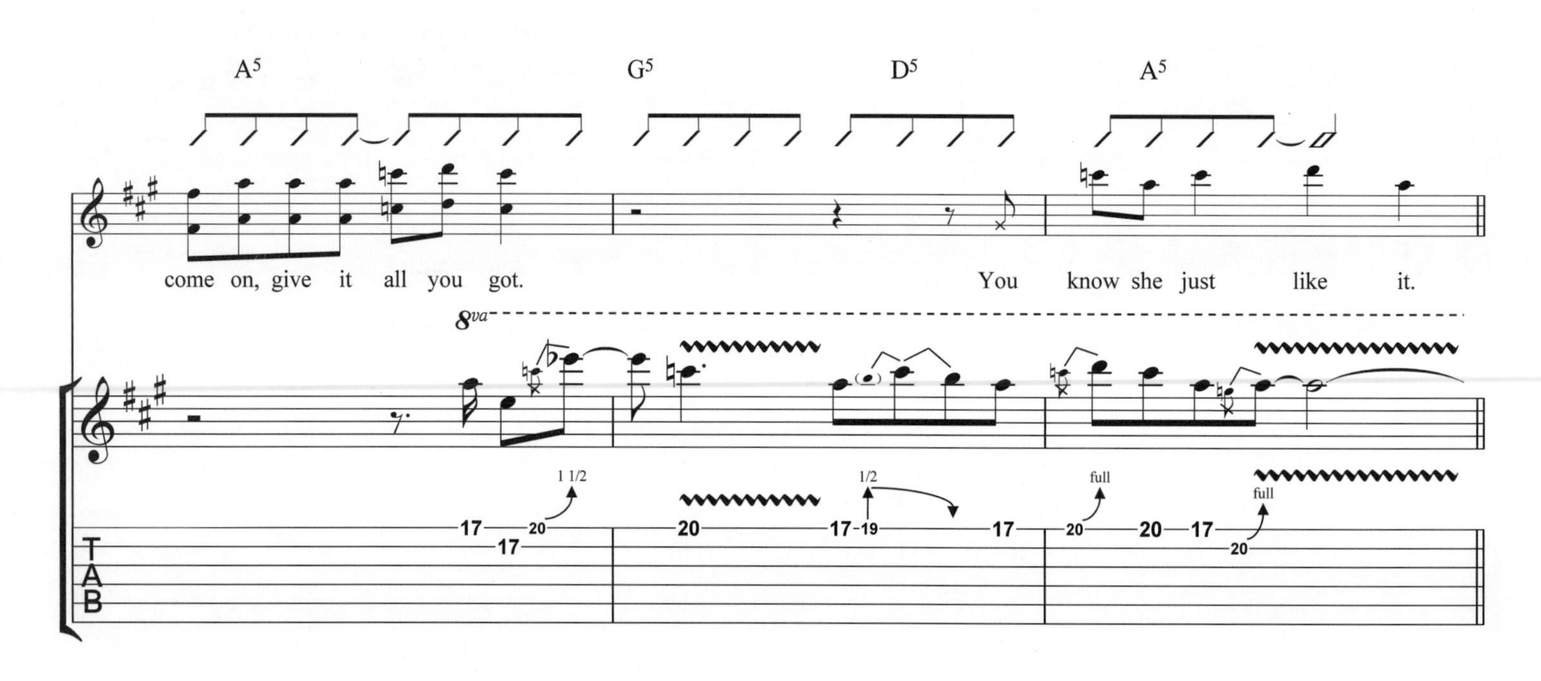
A5
G5
D5
A5
come on, give it all you got. You know she just like it.
1 1/2
1/2
full
full

Gtrs. 1+2
Outro chorus
A5 D/A A5 D/A
G5
D5
A5
Run - a - way train,
she's run - nin' off the track.
(run - nin' right off the track.)
(8)
full
P.M.
(20)
9 7
X

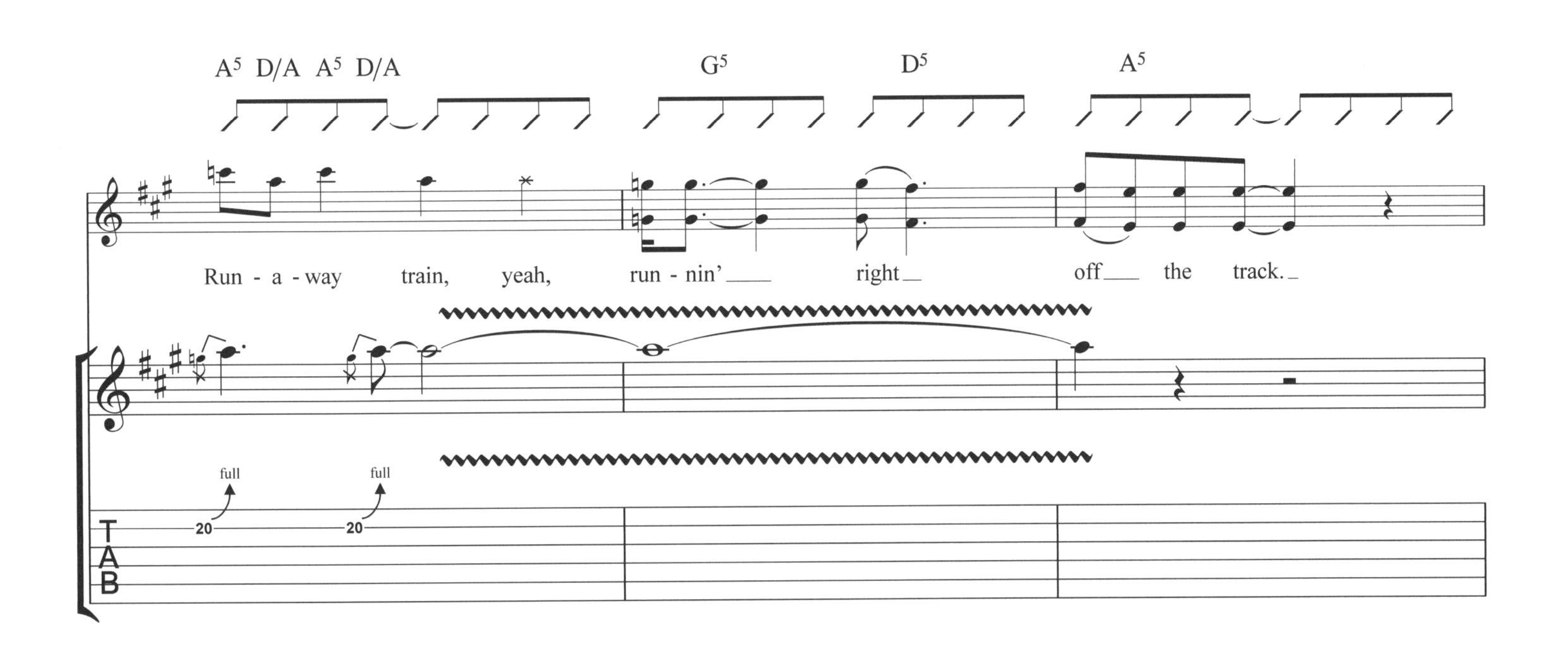
A5 D/A A5 D/A
G5
D5
A5
Run - a - way train, yeah, run - nin' right off the track.
full
full
20
20

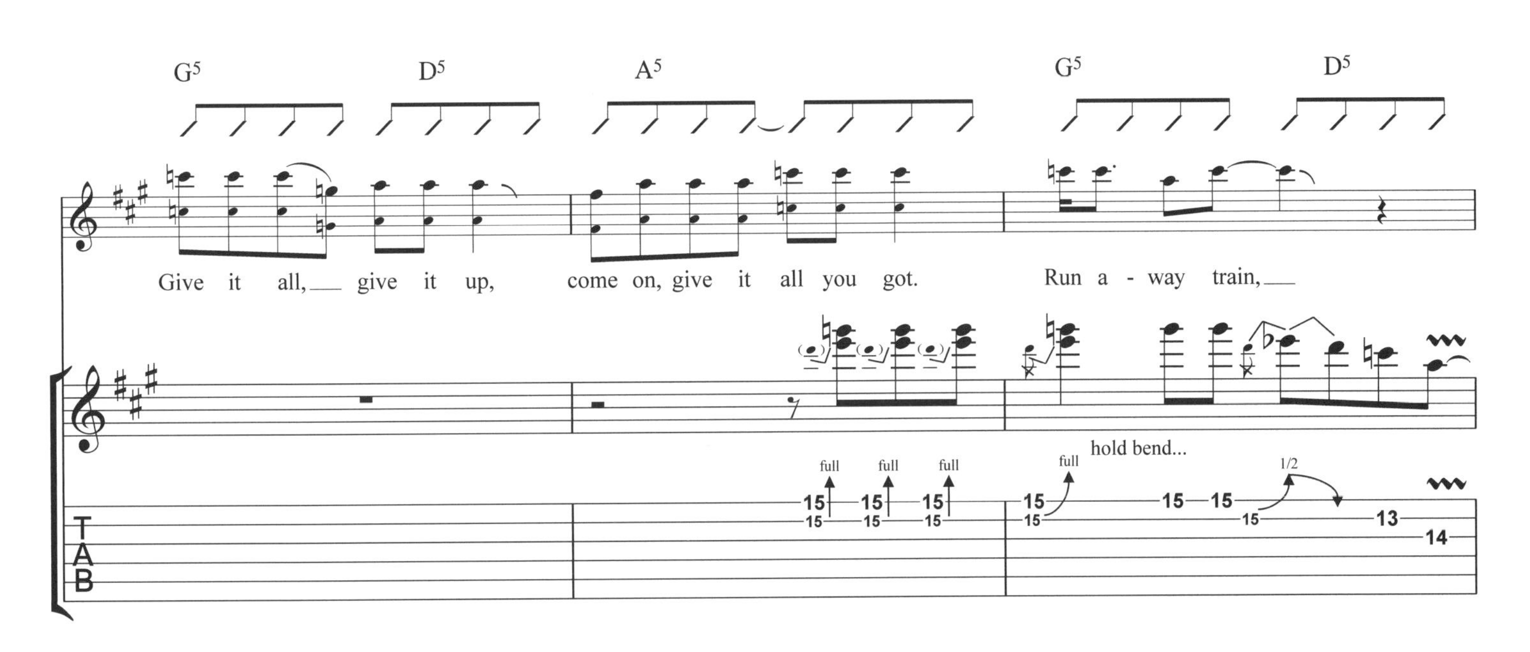
G5
D5
A5
G5
D5
Give it all, give it up, come on, give it all you got. Run a - way train,
full full full full
hold bend...
1/2
15 15 15 15 15 15 15
15 15 15 15 15 13
14

A5
G5
D5
A5
run - nin'
right
off
the
track.
8va
1/4
1/4
1/4
full
full
full
G5
D5
A5
Run - a - way
train,
full
full
G5
D5
A5
run - nin'
right
off
the
track.
rake
full
8va
G5
D5
A5
(8)
full
1/2
1/4

# thunderstruck

**Words & Music by**
**Angus Young & Malcolm Young**



***Full performance demo: CD 1 track 10***
***Backing only: CD 2 track 10***

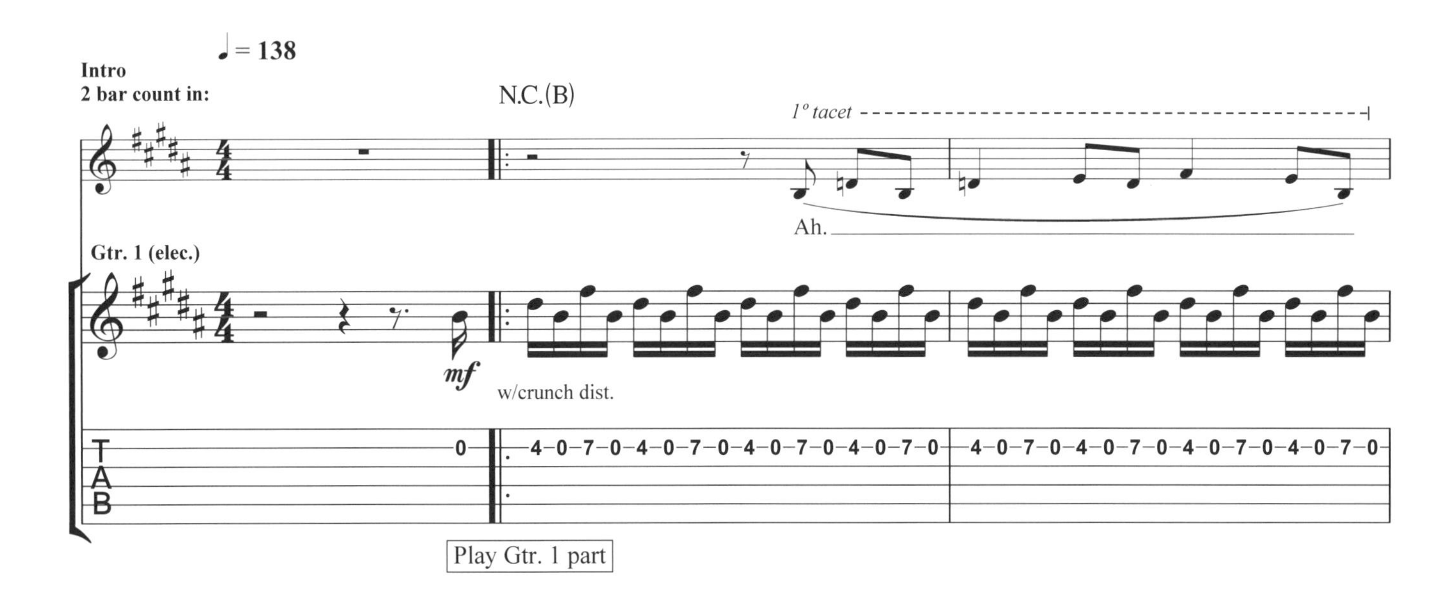


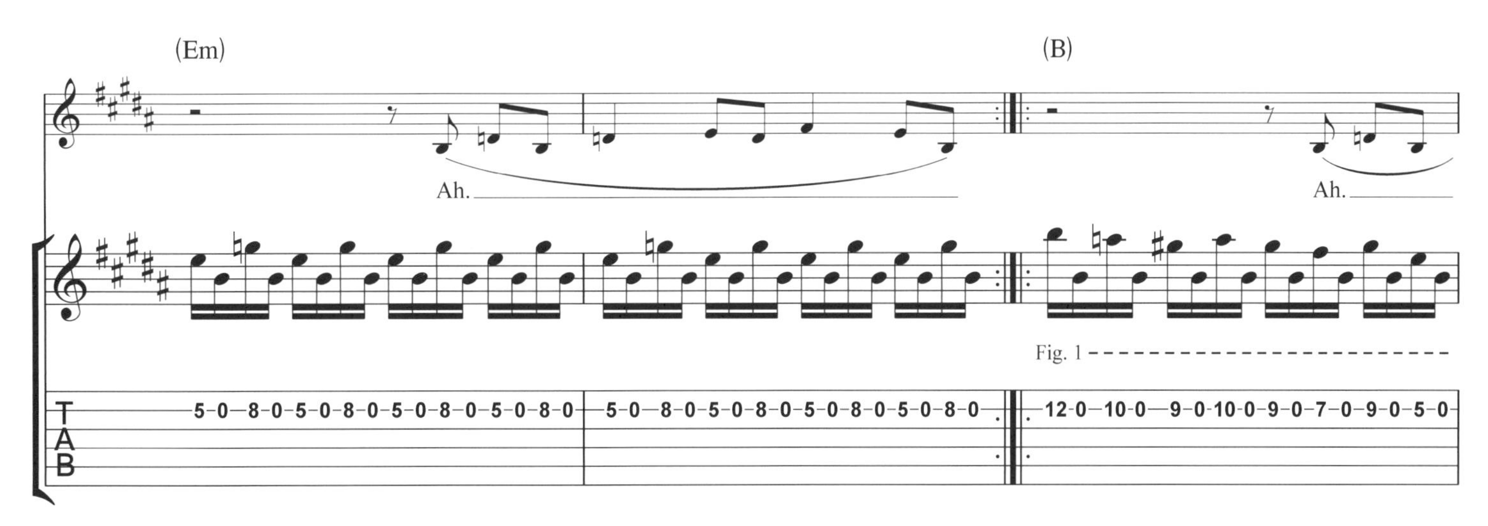


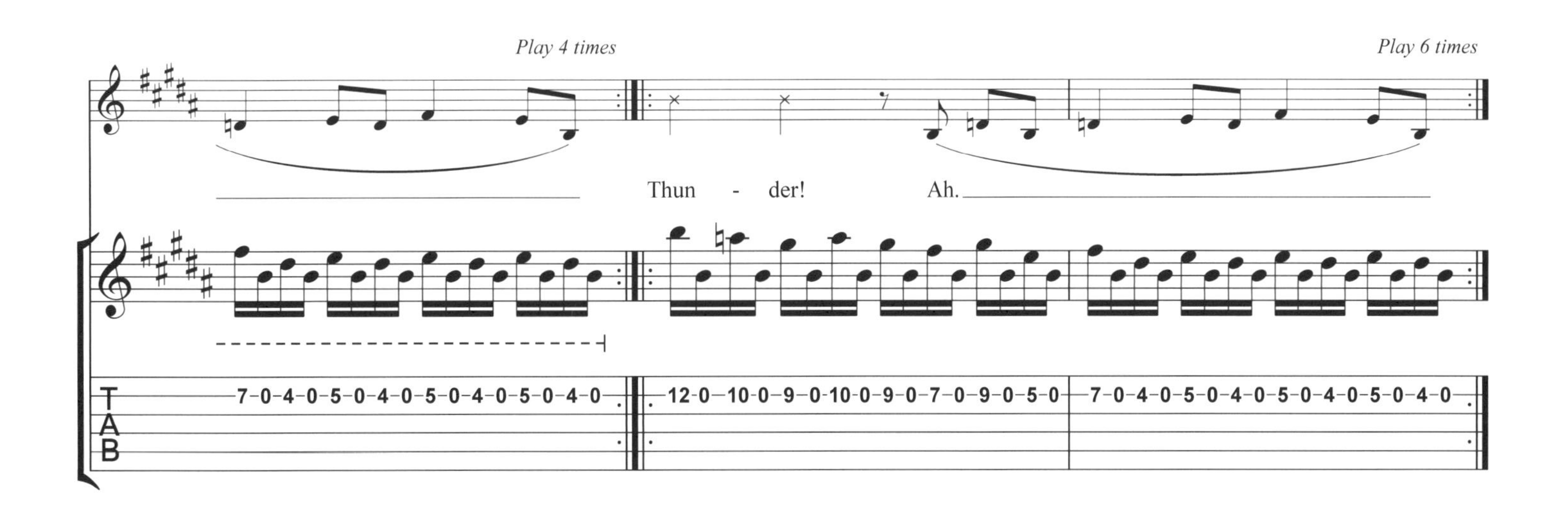

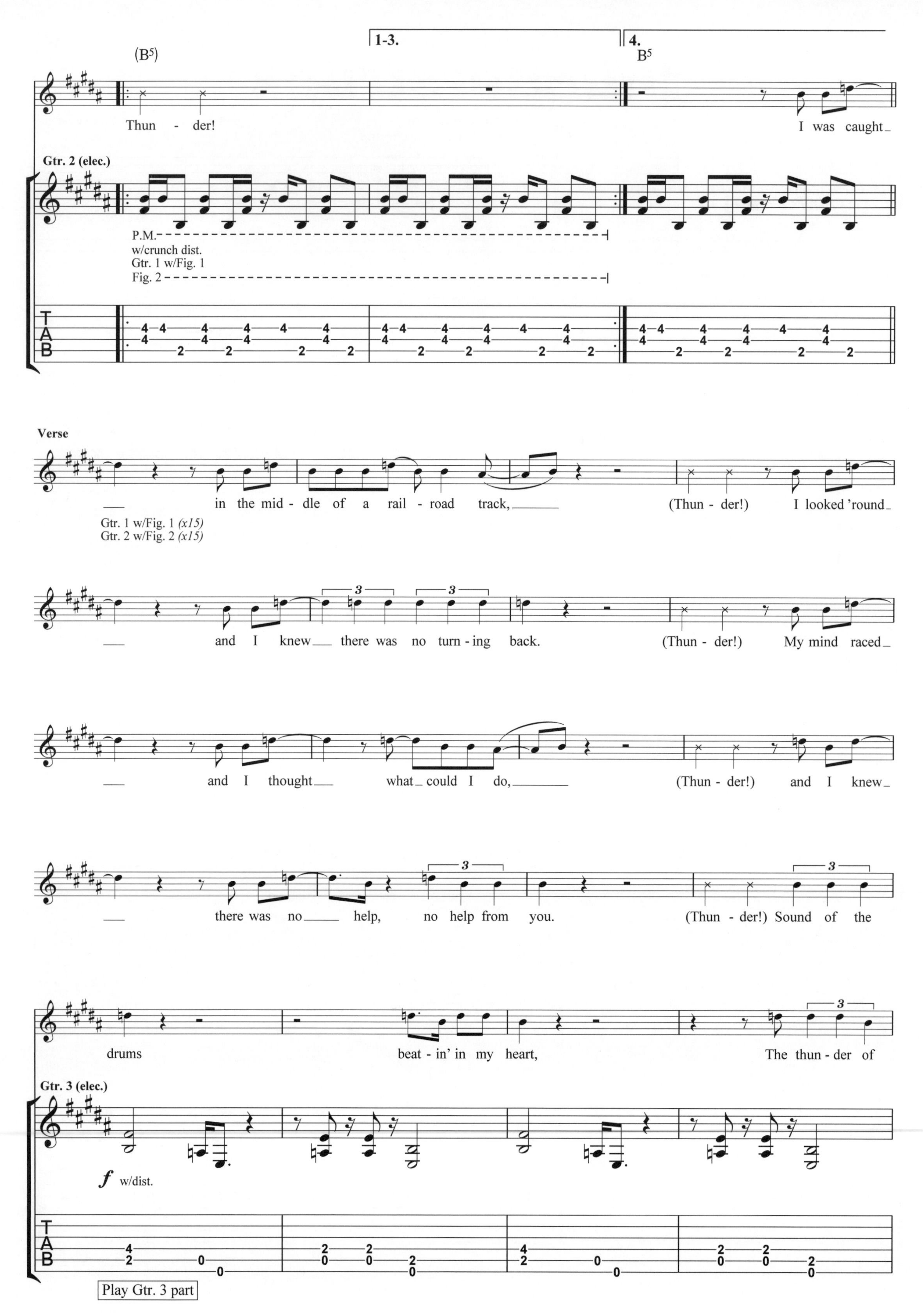
1-3.
4.
(B5)
B5
Thun - der!
I was caught
Gtr. 2 (elec.)
P.M.
w/crunch dist.
Gtr. 1 w/Fig. 1
Fig. 2
Verse
in the mid - dle of a rail - road track,
(Thun - der!) I looked 'round
Gtr. 1 w/Fig. 1 (x15)
Gtr. 2 w/Fig. 2 (x15)
and I knew there was no turn - ing back.
(Thun - der!) My mind raced
and I thought what could I do,
(Thun - der!) and I knew
there was no help, no help from you.
(Thun - der!) Sound of the
drums beat - in' in my heart,
The thun - der of
Gtr. 3 (elec.)
f w/dist.
Play Gtr. 3 part

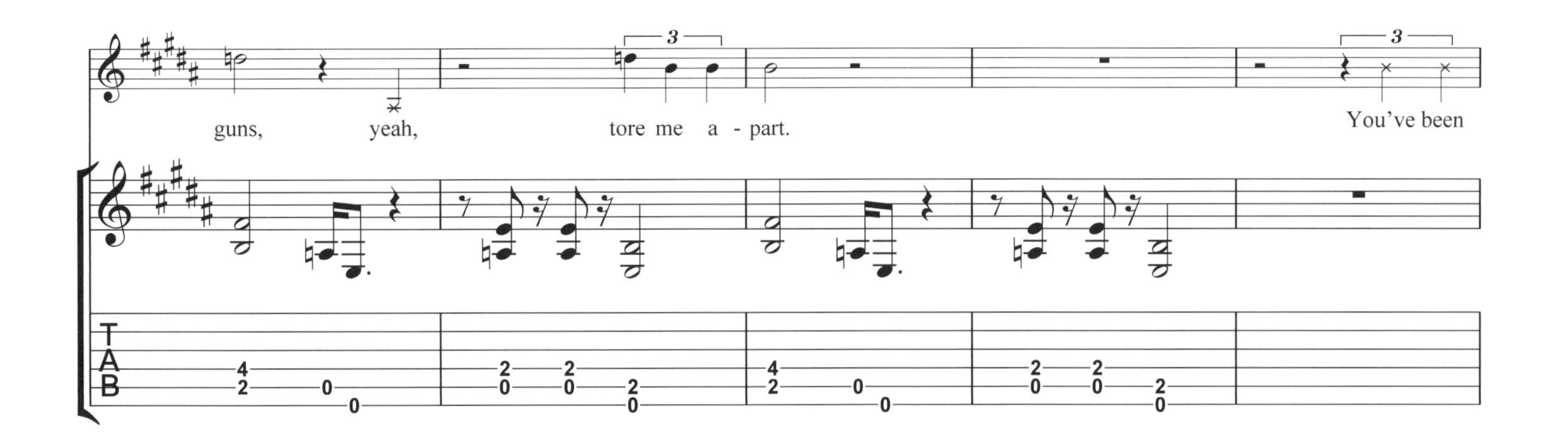
guns, yeah, tore me a - part. You've been
T
A
B
4
2
0
0
2
0
2
0
2
0
4
2
0
0
2
0
2
0
2
0

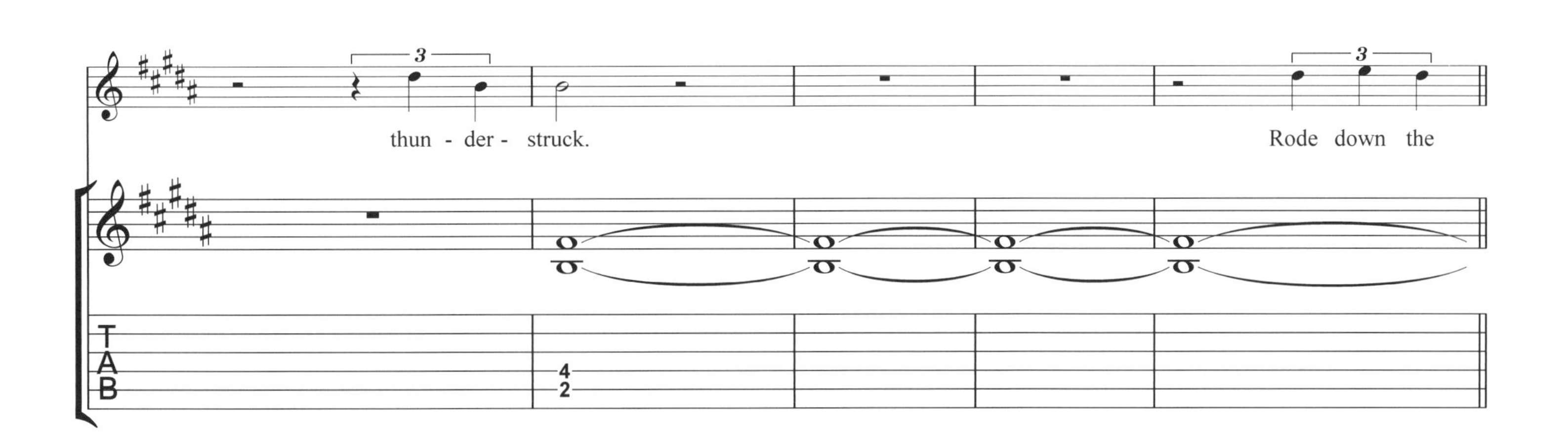
thun - der - struck. Rode down the
T
A
B
4
2

Verse

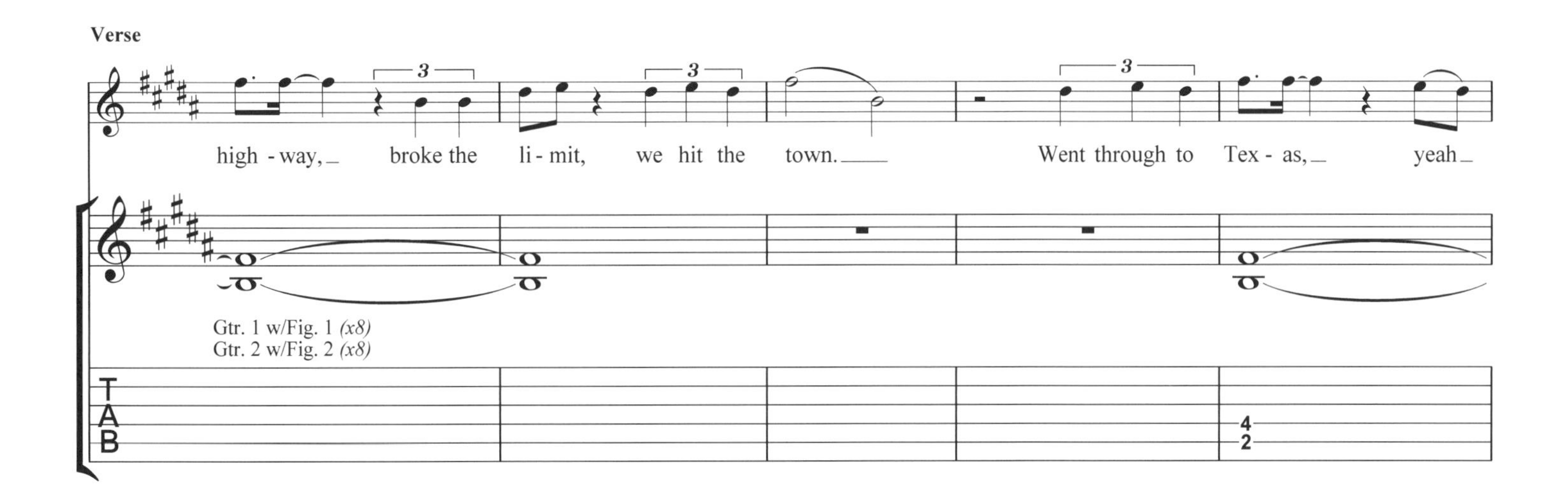
high - way, broke the li - mit, we hit the town. Went through to Tex - as, yeah
Gtr. 1 w/Fig. 1 (x8)
Gtr. 2 w/Fig. 2 (x8)
T
A
B
4
2

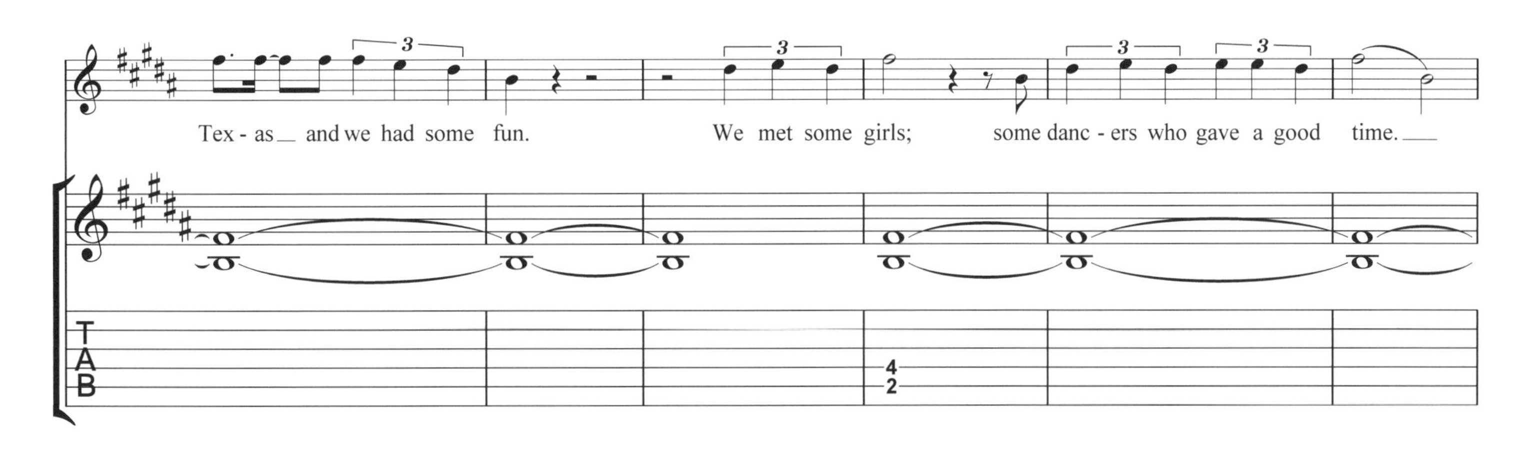
Tex - as and we had some fun. We met some girls; some danc - ers who gave a good time.
T
A
B
4
2

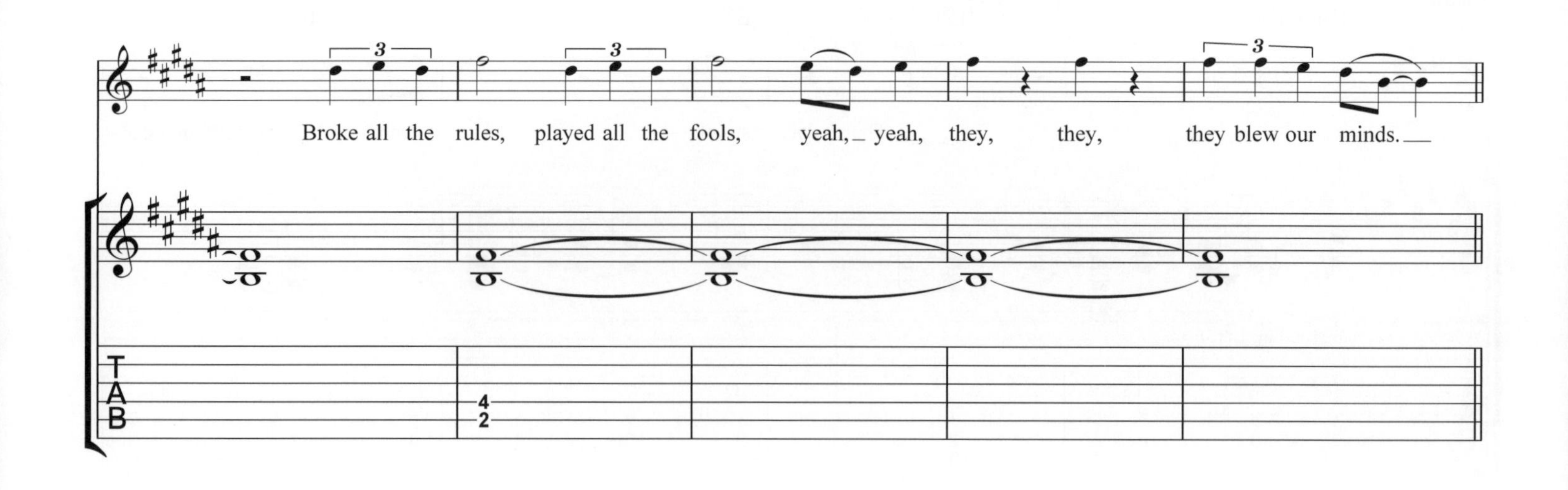
Broke all the rules, played all the fools, yeah, yeah, they, they, they blew our minds.
T
A
B
4
2

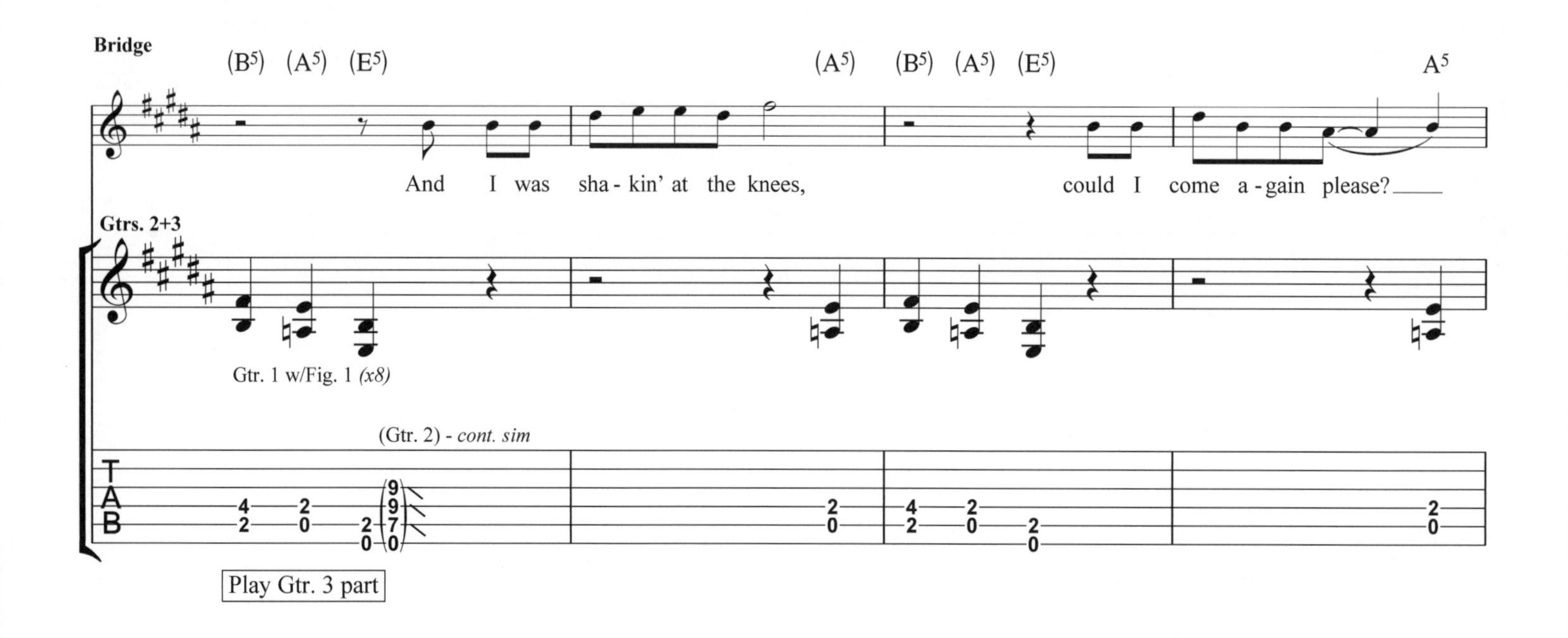
Bridge
(B5) (A5) (E5) (A5) (B5) (A5) (E5) A5
And I was sha - kin' at the knees, could I come a - gain please?
Gtrs. 2+3
Gtr. 1 w/Fig. 1 (x8)
(Gtr. 2) - cont. sim
T
A
B
Play Gtr. 3 part

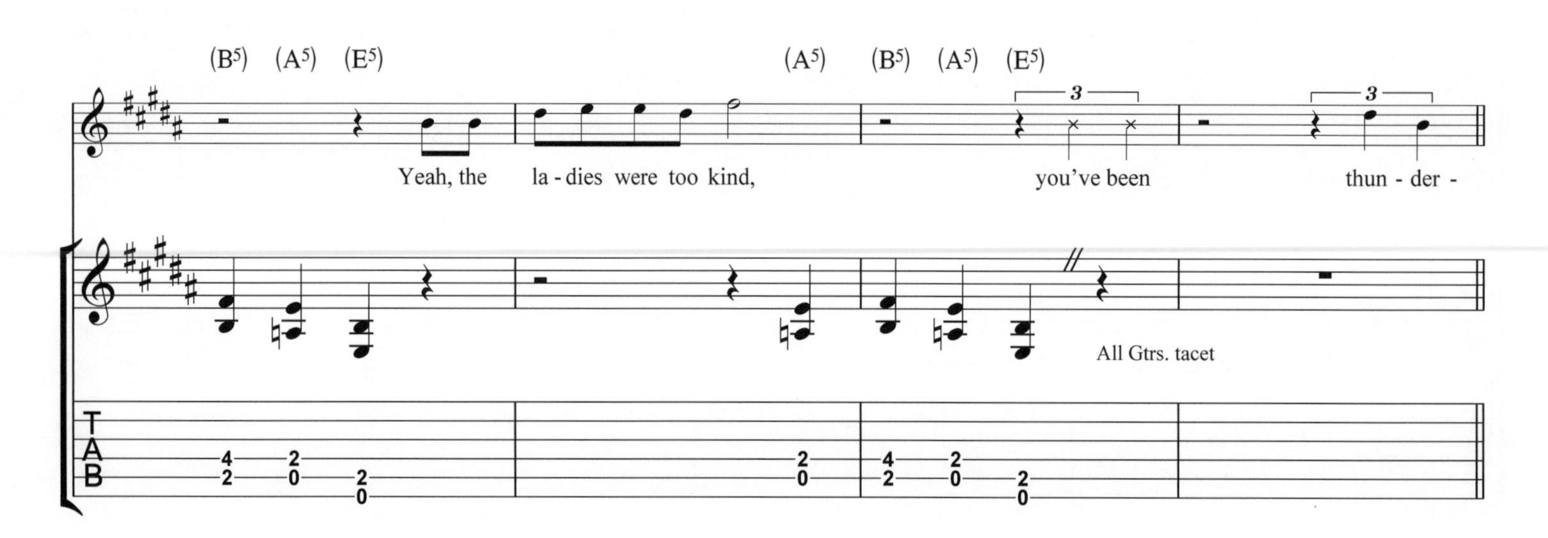
(B5) (A5) (E5) (A5) (B5) (A5) (E5)
Yeah, the la - dies were too kind, you've been thun - der -
All Gtrs. tacet
T
A
B

Chorus

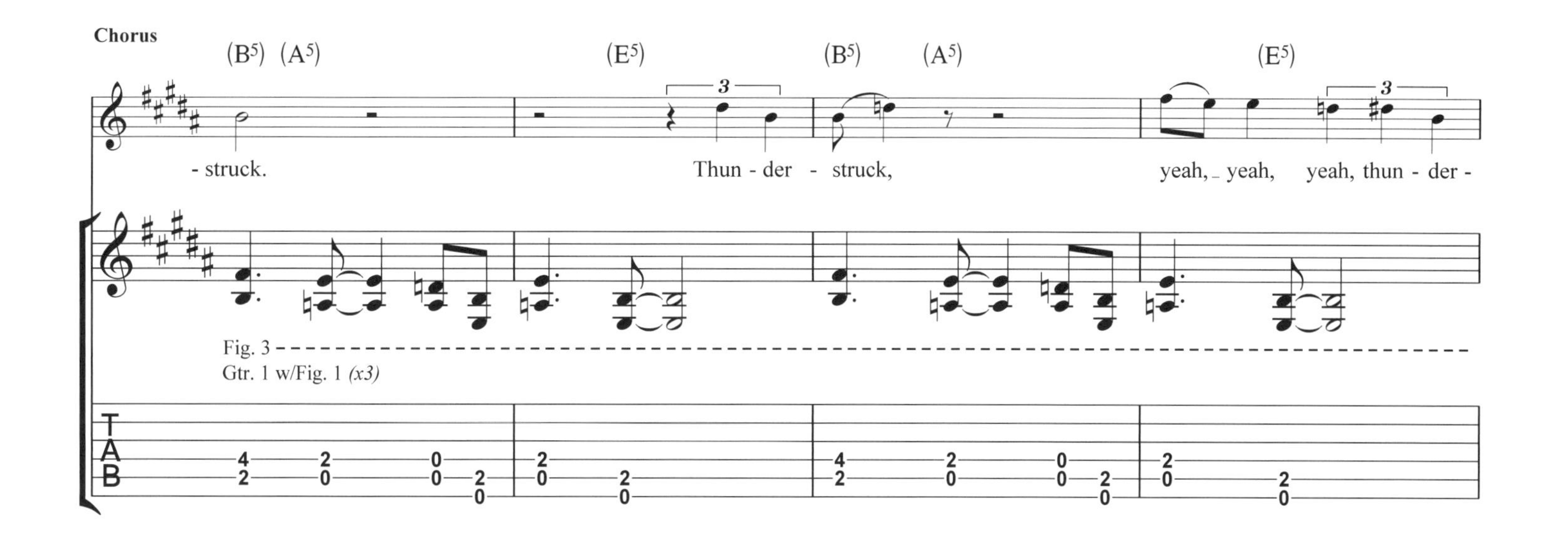
(B5) (A5)
(E5)
(B5) (A5)
(E5)
- struck.
Thun - der - struck,
yeah, yeah, yeah, thun - der -
Fig. 3
Gtr. 1 w/Fig. 1 (x3)
TAB

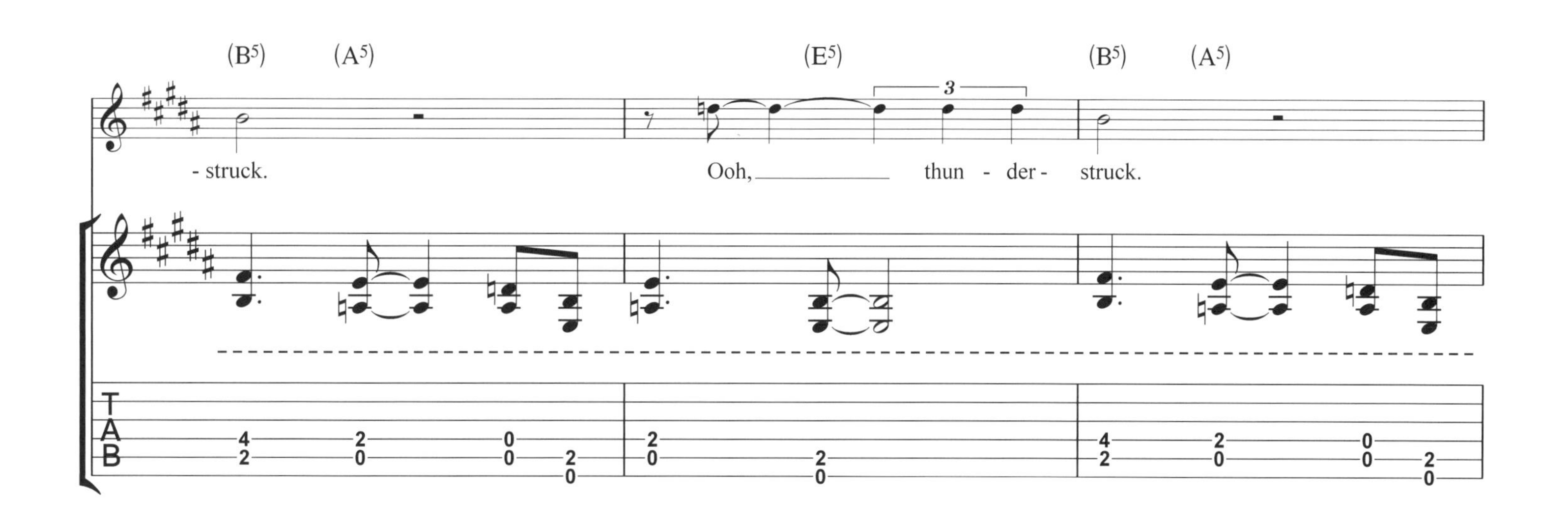
(B5) (A5)
(E5)
(B5) (A5)
- struck.
Ooh, thun - der - struck.
TAB

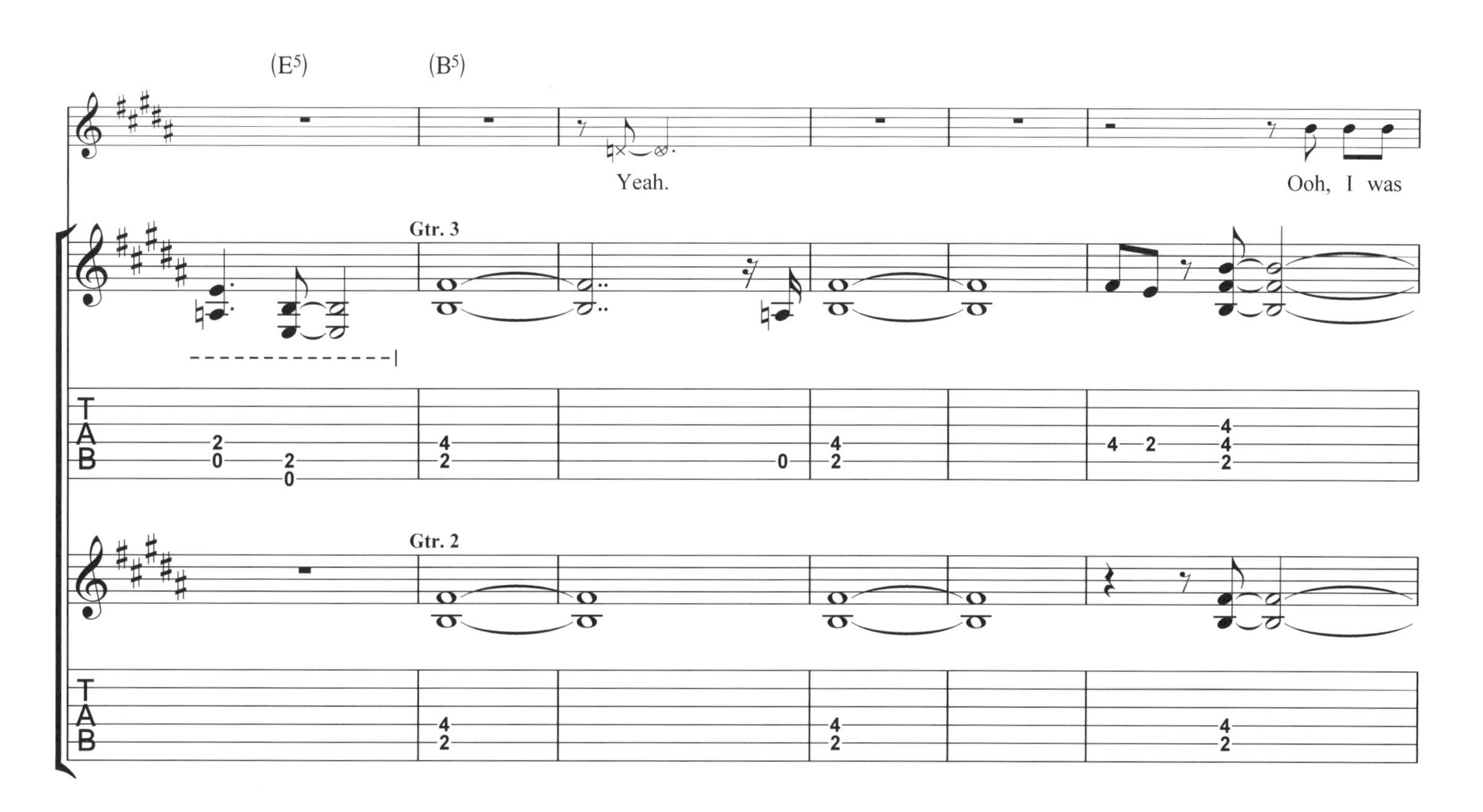
(E5) (B5)
Yeah.
Ooh, I was
Gtr. 3
TAB
Gtr. 2
TAB

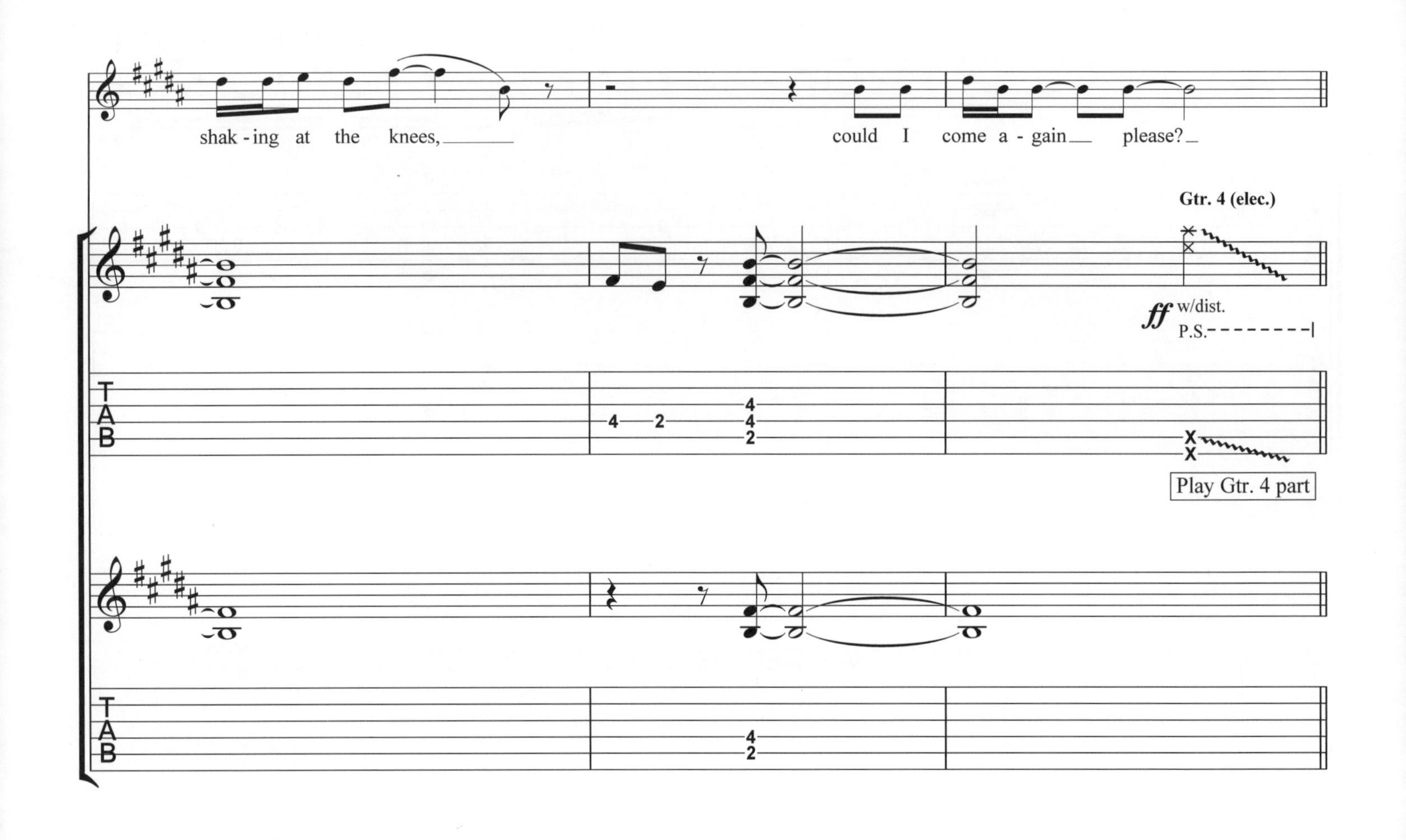
shak - ing at the knees,
could I come a - gain please?
Gtr. 4 (elec.)
ff w/dist.
P.S.
Play Gtr. 4 part

Gtr. solo
(E5) (B5) (A5) (E5) (E5) (B5)
full
Gtrs. 2+3

(A5) (E5) (E5) (B5)
full
P.H.
(A5) (E5) (E5) (B5) (A5) (E5)
8va
1/4 full 1/2 full full 1/2 full full
(B5) (A5) (B5) (A5)
Ah.
Ah.
Gtr. 1 w/Fig. 1
full
Gtr. 1 w/Fig. 1
Gtrs. 2+3

Ow!
Ooh,
thun - der -
Gtr. 1 w/Fig. 1 (x5)
P.S.
Chorus
(B5) (A5)
(E5)
(B5) (A5)
(E5)
- struck,
thun - der - struck,
yeah, yeah, yeah, thun - der -
Gtrs. 2+3 w/Fig. 3
Play Gtr. 3 part
B5 A5
E5
B5 A5
E5
- struck.
Thun - der - struck,
yeah, yeah, yeah. Said
full
full
full
1.
2.
(B5)
(E5)
(B5)
(E5)
yeah, it's all right,
we're
do - ing fine.
fine so fine. Thun - der -
Gtr. 1 w/Fig.1 (x2)
Gtrs. 2+3

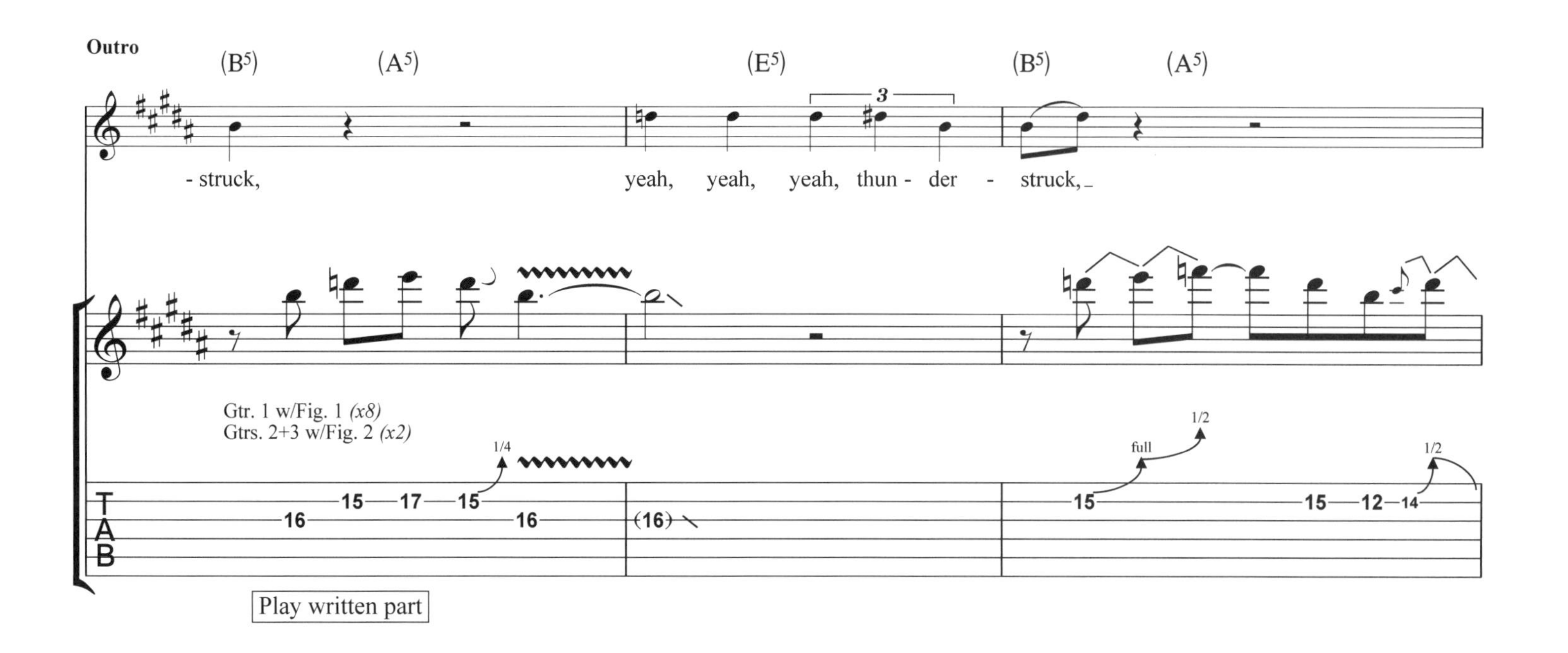

Outro
(B5) (A5) (E5) (B5) (A5)
-struck, yeah, yeah, yeah, thun - der - struck,
Gtr. 1 w/Fig. 1 (x8)
Gtrs. 2+3 w/Fig. 2 (x2)
Play written part


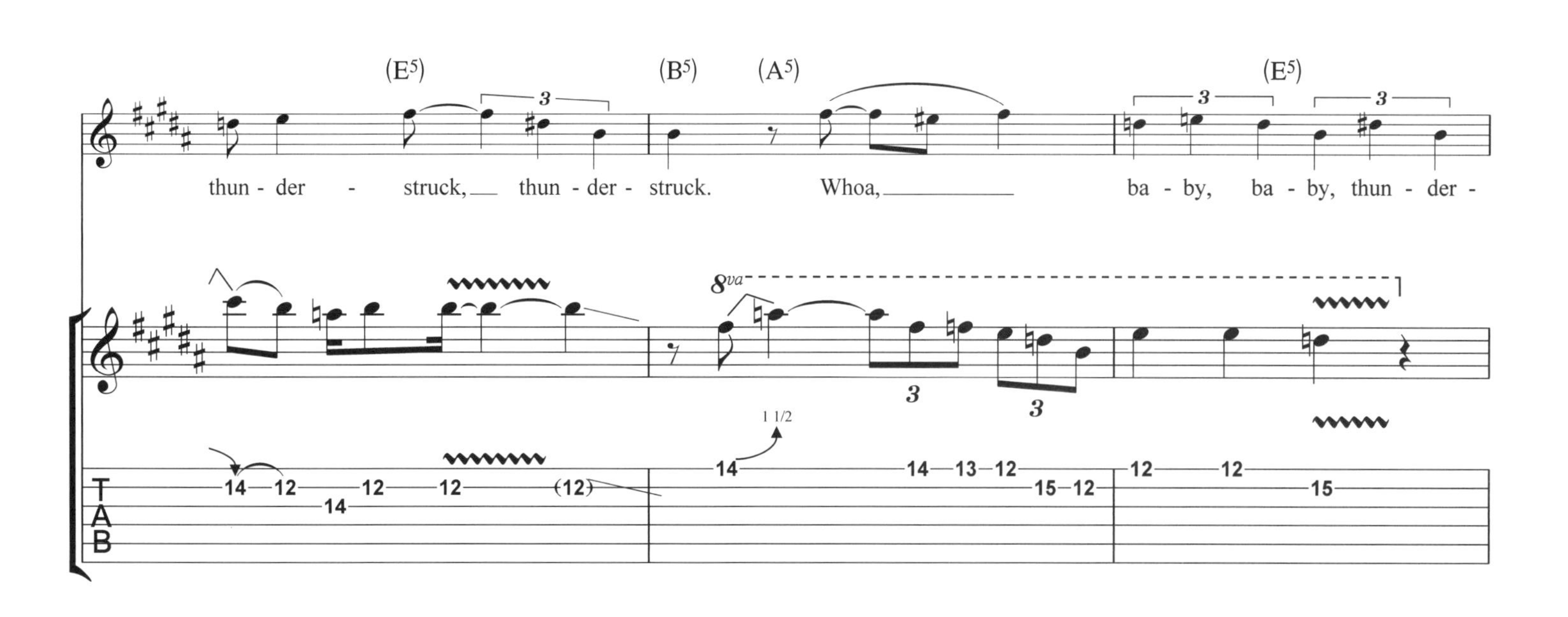

(E5) (B5) (A5) (E5)
thun - der - struck, thun - der - struck. Whoa, ba - by, ba - by, thun - der -


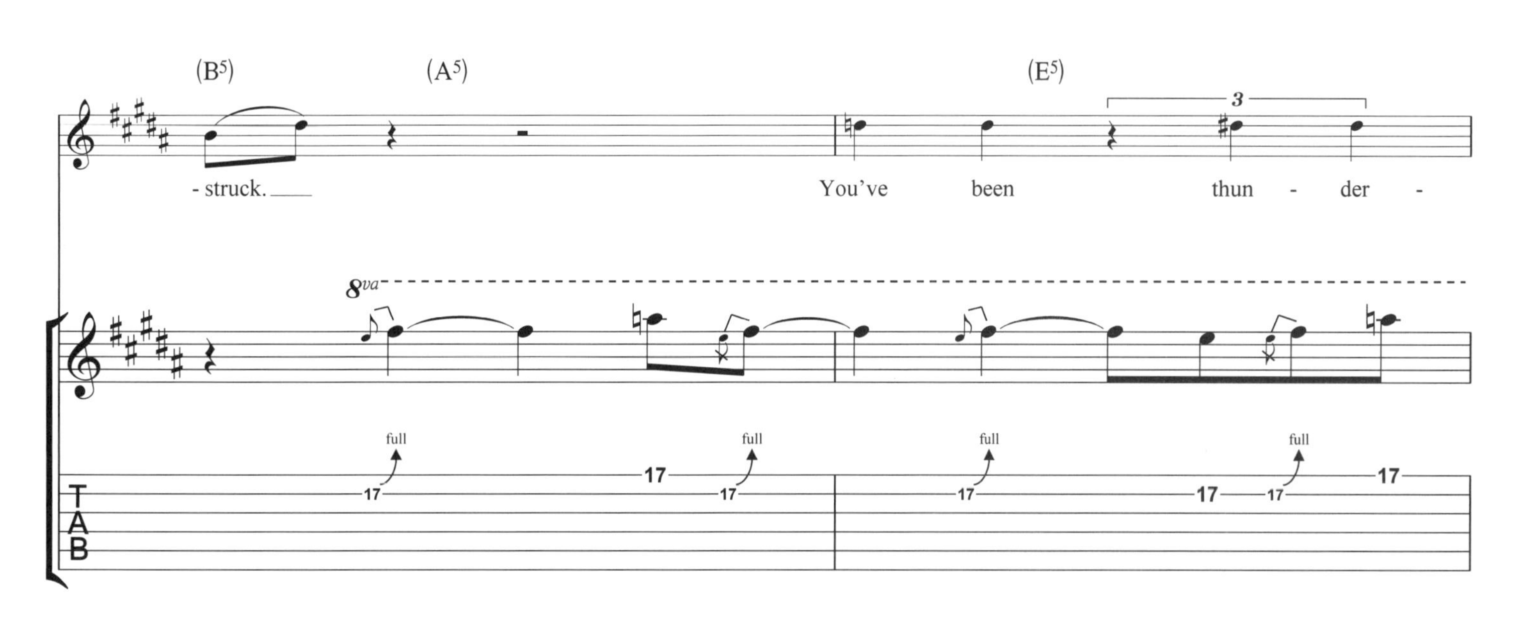

(B5) (A5) (E5)
-struck. You've been thun - der -

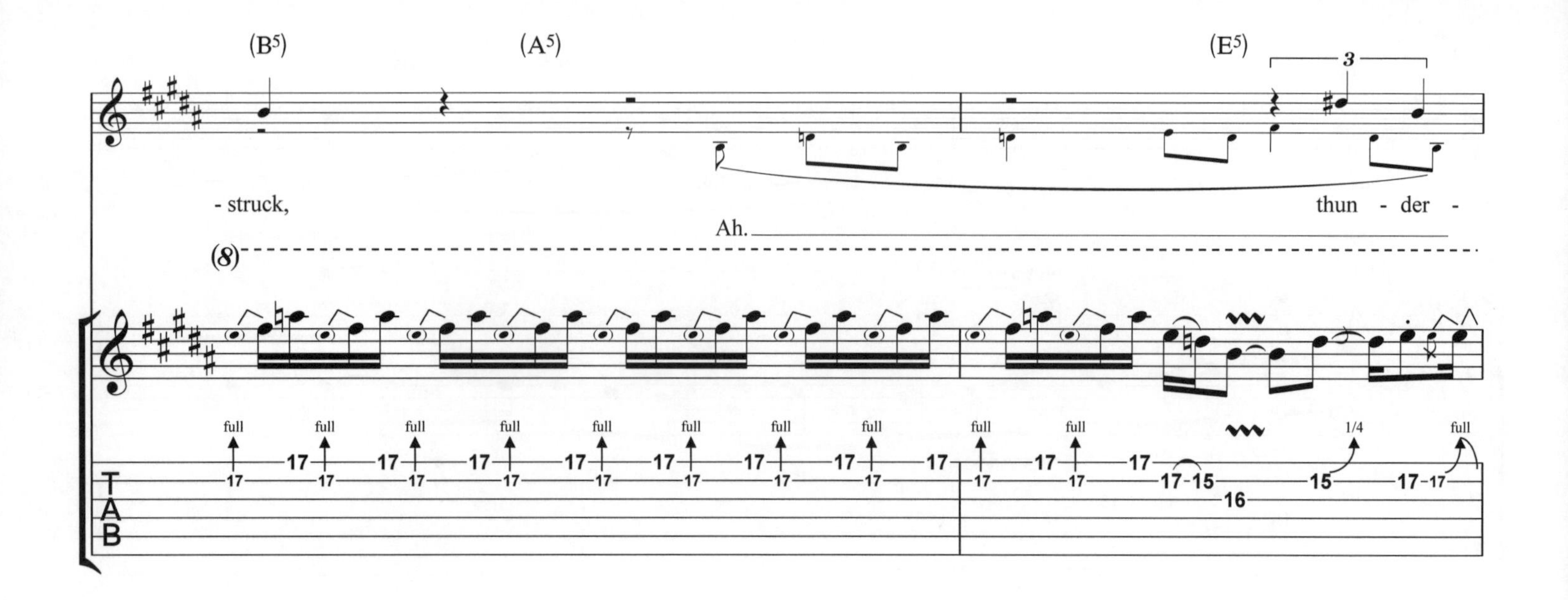
(B5)
(A5)
(E5)
- struck,
thun - der -
Ah.
full
1/4


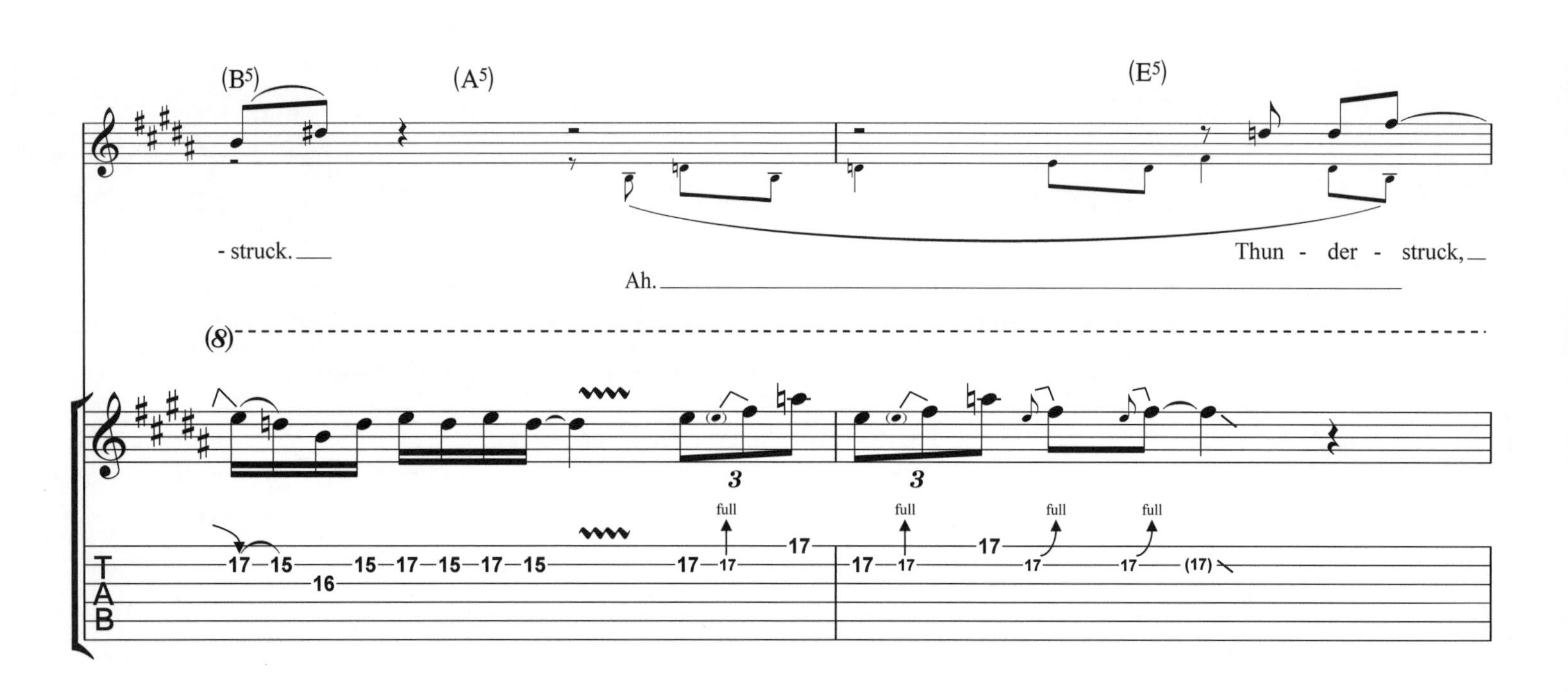
(B5)
(A5)
(E5)
- struck.
Thun - der - struck,
Ah.
full


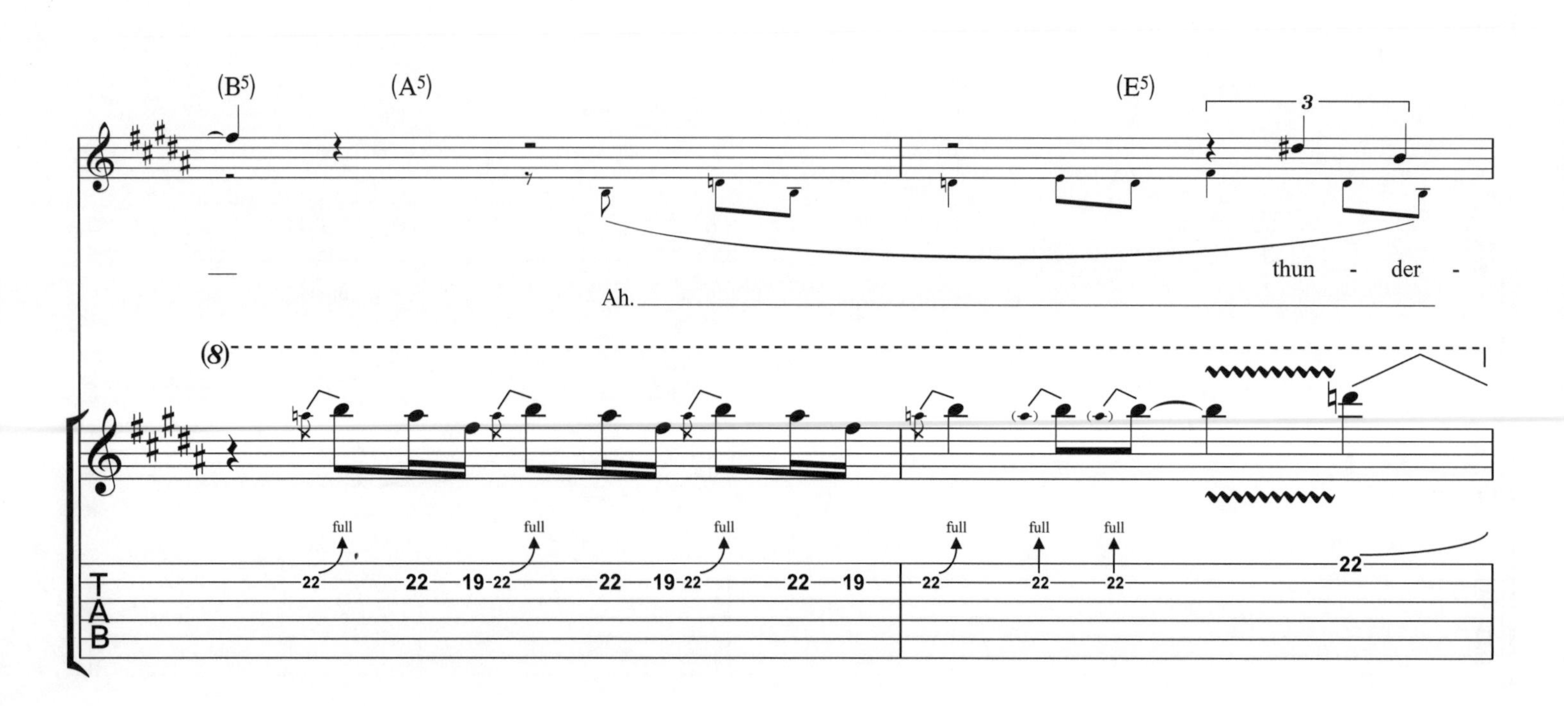
(B5)
(A5)
(E5)
thun - der -
Ah.
full

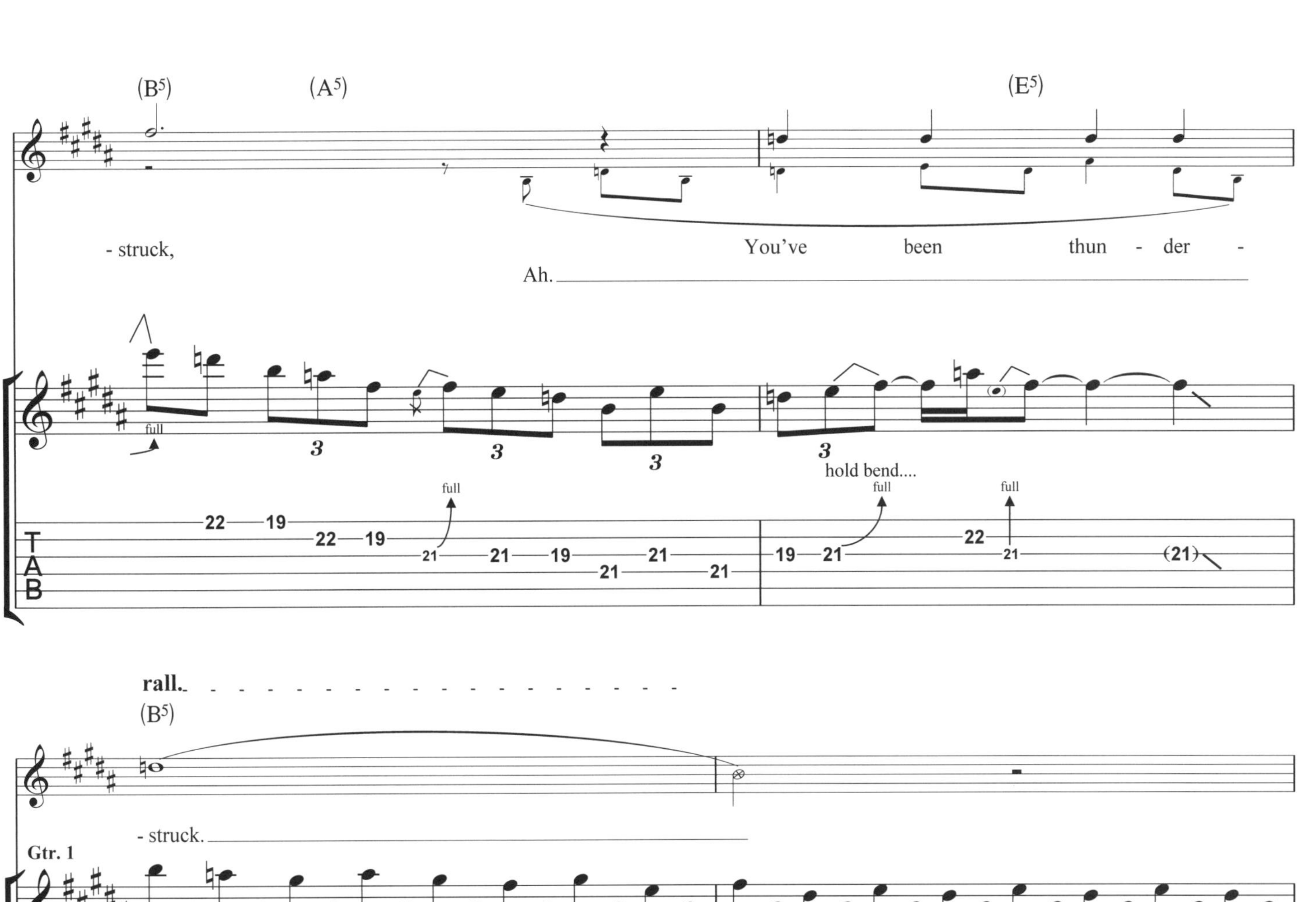

(B5)
(A5)
(E5)
- struck,
You've been thun - der -
Ah.
full
hold bend....
full
full


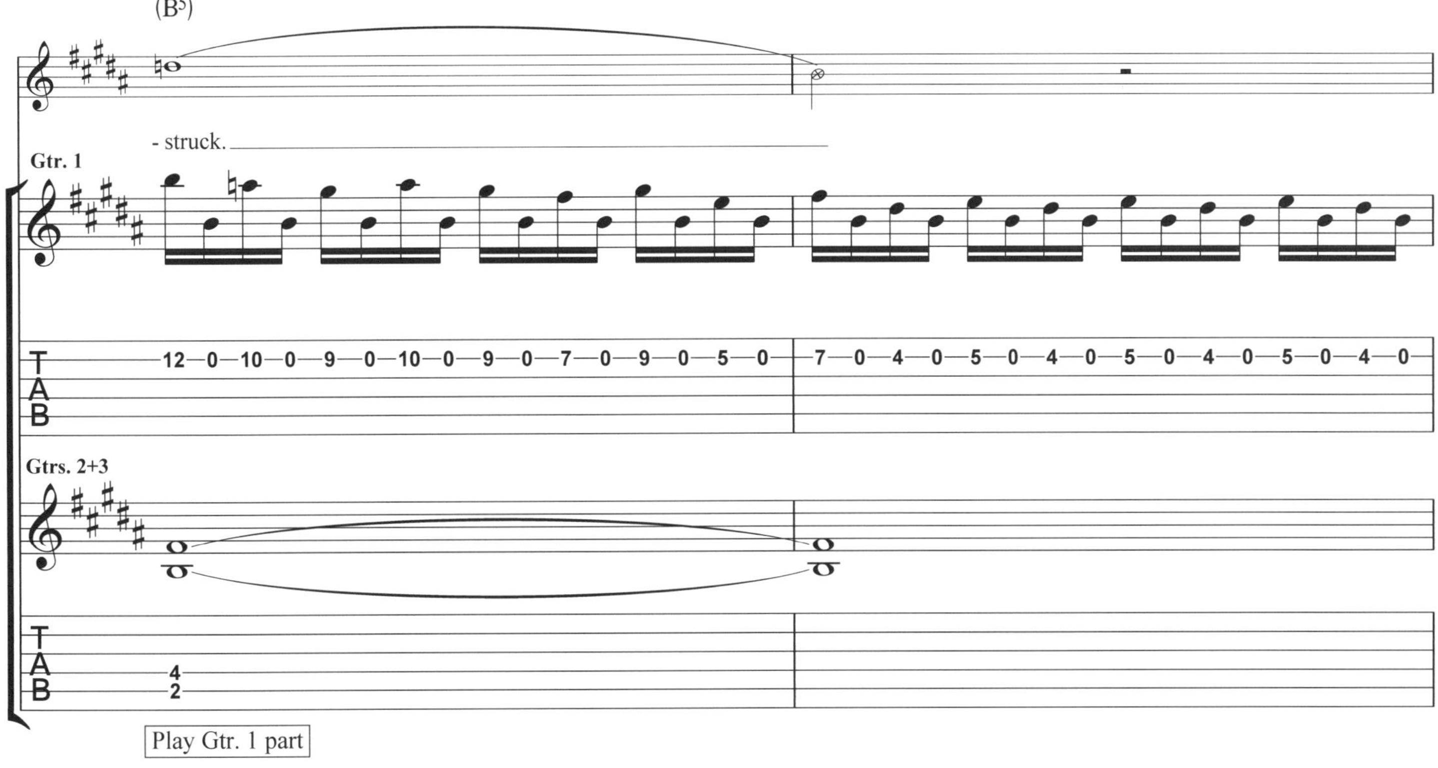

rall.
(B5)
- struck.
Gtr. 1
Gtrs. 2+3
Play Gtr. 1 part


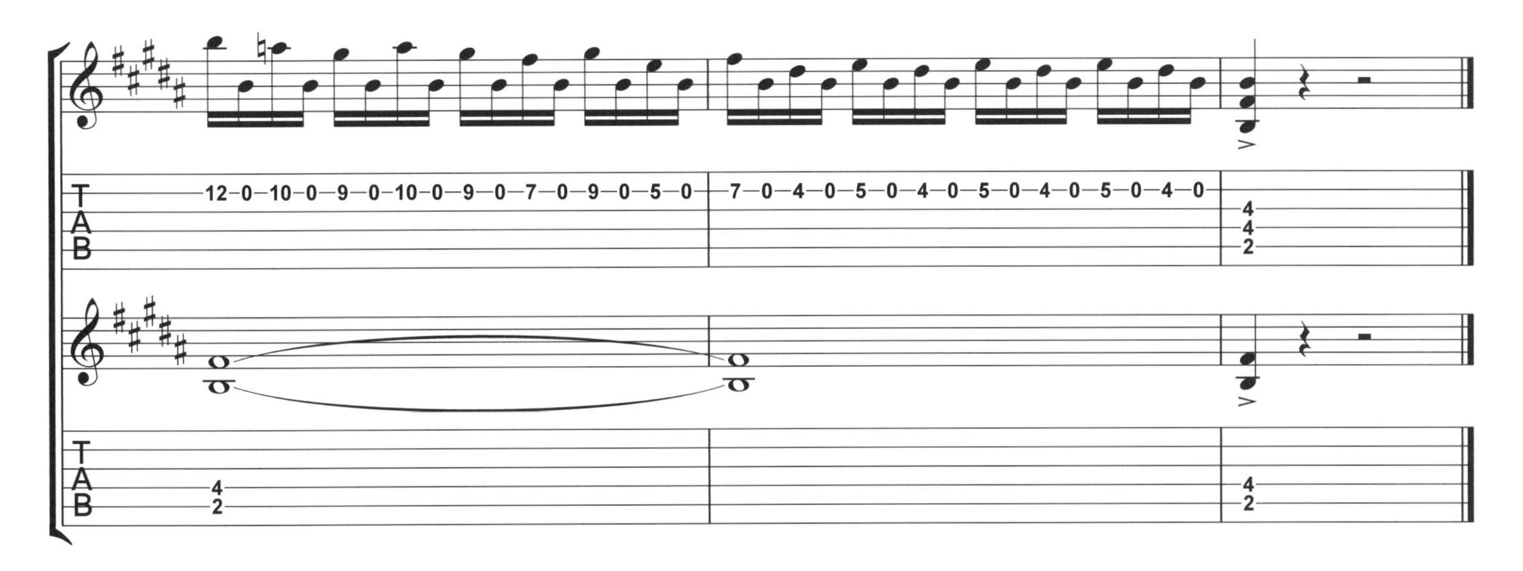

# t.n.t.

**Words & Music by**
**Angus Young, Malcolm Young & Bon Scott**



***Full performance demo: CD 1 track 11***
***Backing only: CD 2 track 11***

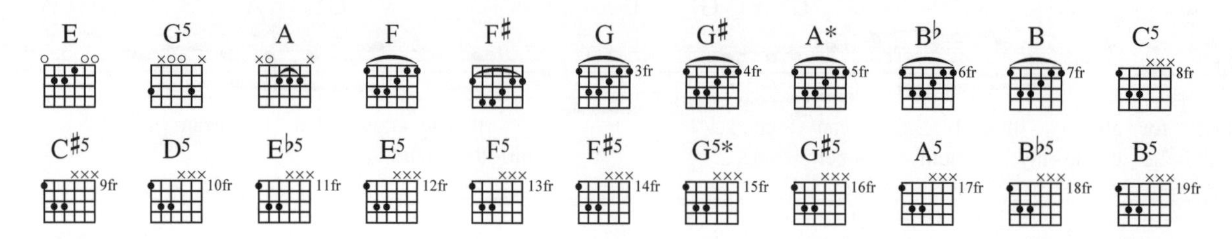


**Intro**
**2 bar count in:**

♩ = 126

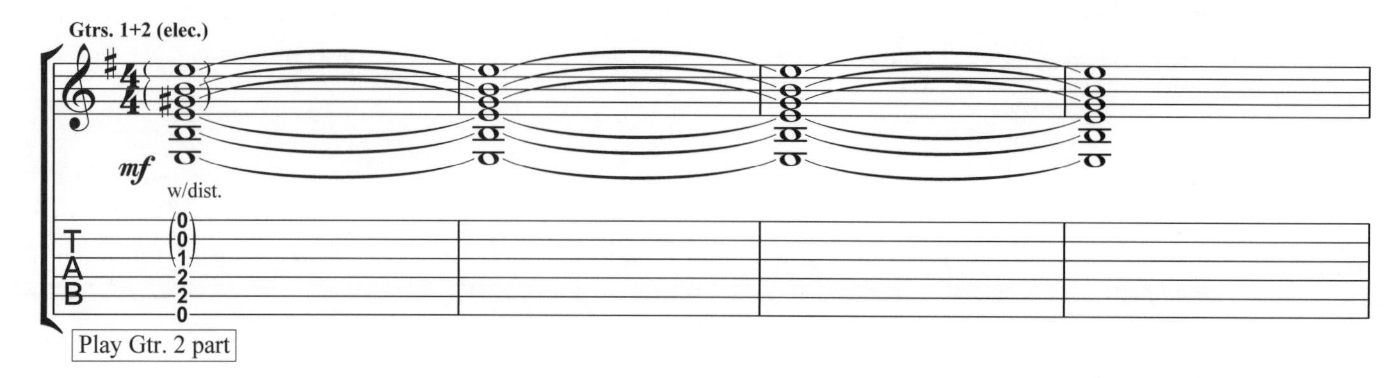


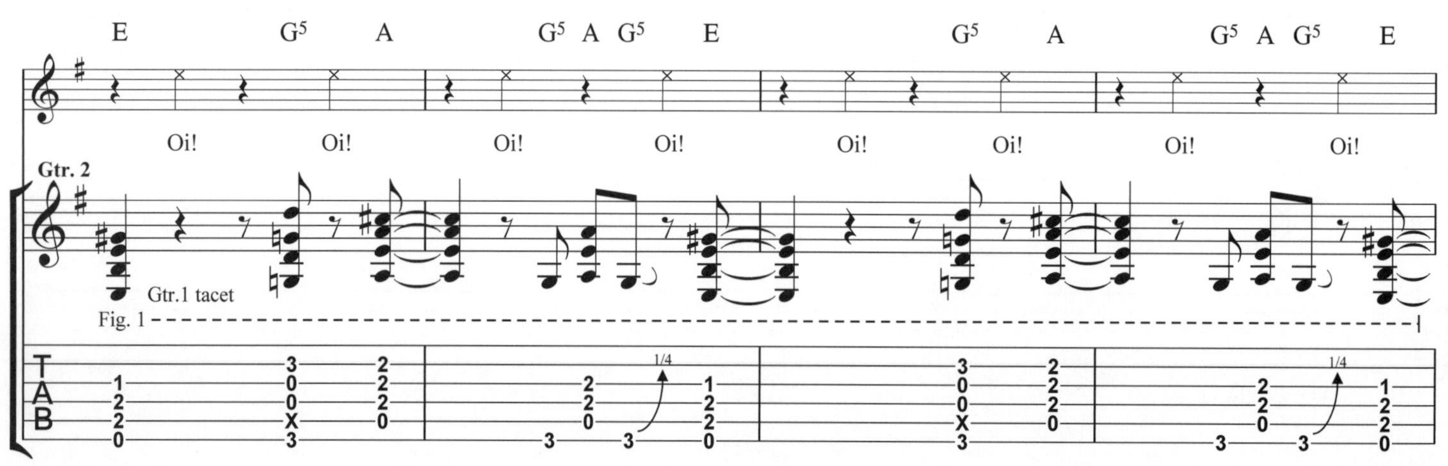


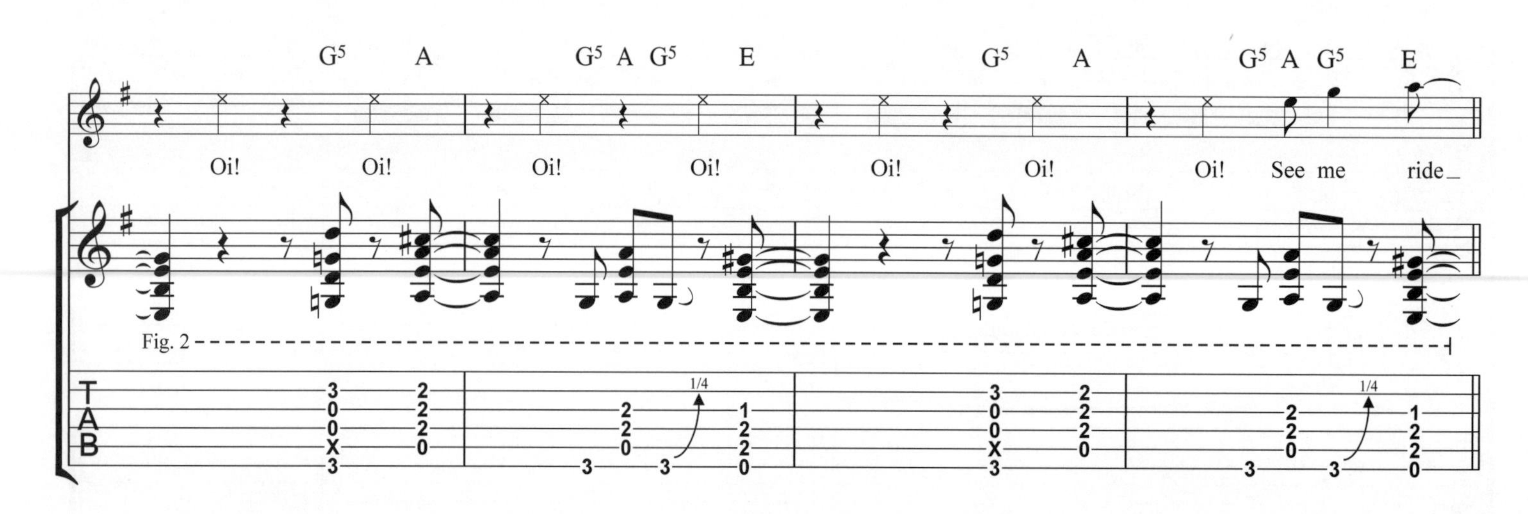

Verse
G5 A G5 A G5 E G5 A G5 A G5 E
out of that sun - set on your co - lour T. V. screen,
dir - ty, mean and migh - ty un - clean, I'm a wan - ted man.
Gtr. 2 w/Fig. 2 (x3)
2° w/Gtr. 1

G5 A G5 A G5 E G5 A G5 A G5 E
Out for all that I can get, if you know what I mean.
Pub - lic e - ne - my num - ber one, un - der - stand? So

G5 A G5 A G5 E G5 A
Wo - men to the left of me and wo - men to the right,
lock up your daugh - ter and lock up your wife, lock up your back door and

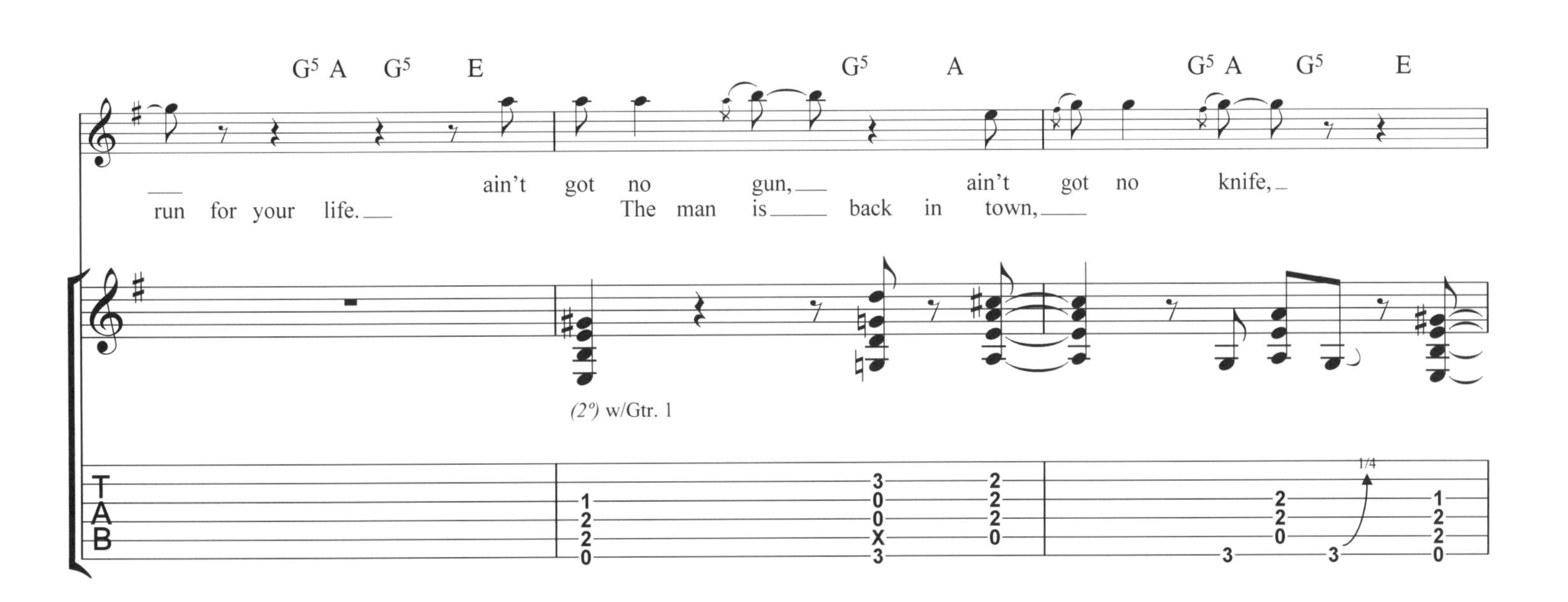
G5 A G5 E G5 A G5 A G5 E
ain't got no gun, ain't got no knife,
run for your life. The man is back in town,
(2°) w/Gtr. 1
TAB
1/4

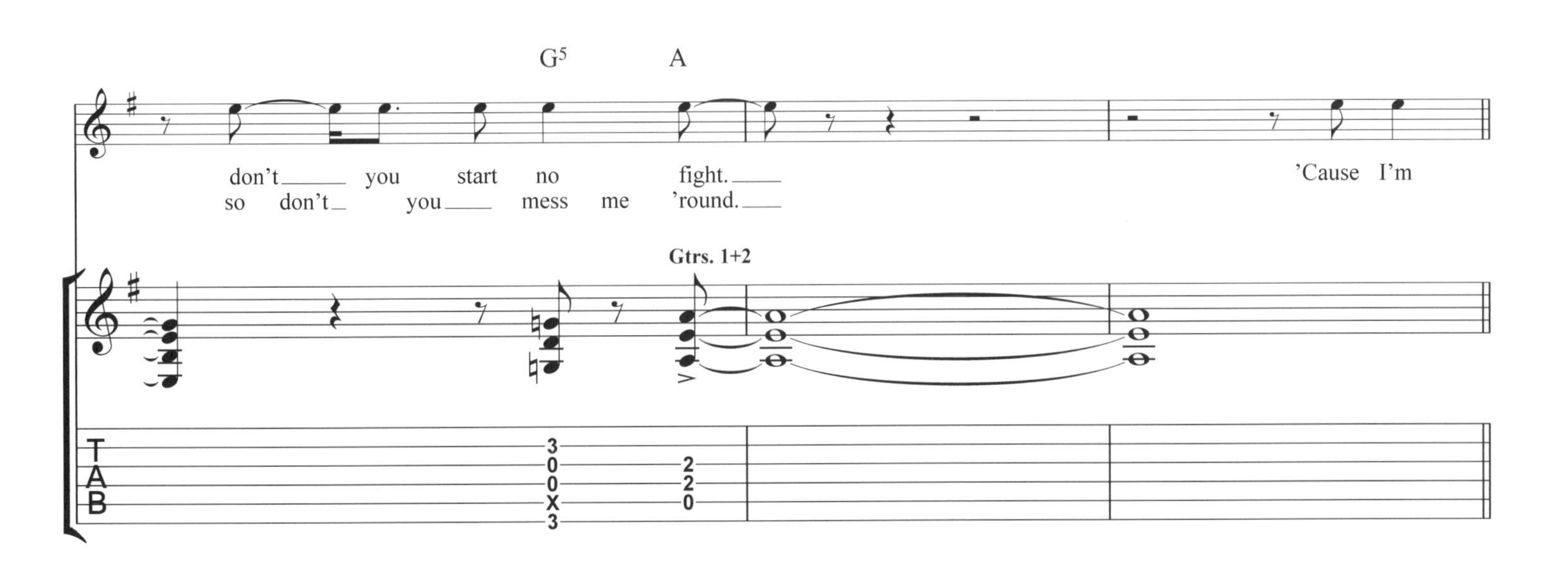
G5 A
don't you start no fight. 'Cause I'm
so don't you mess me 'round.
Gtrs. 1+2
TAB

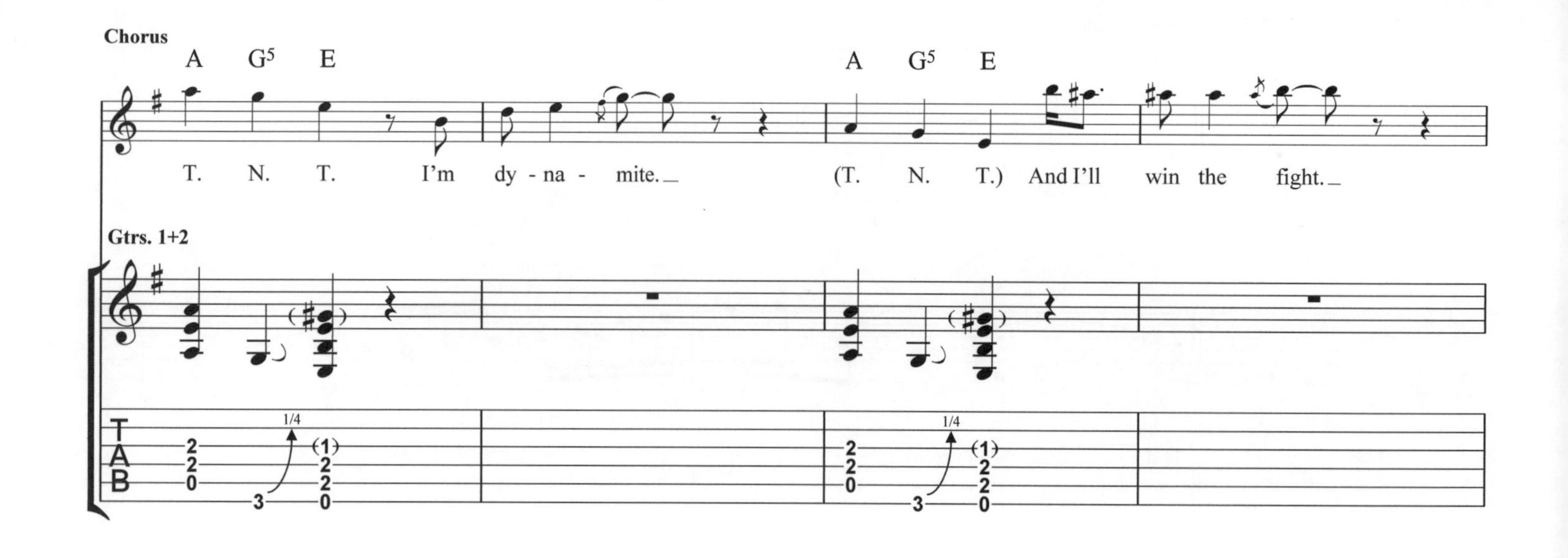
Chorus
A G5 E
A G5 E
T. N. T. I'm dy - na - mite.
(T. N. T.) And I'll win the fight.
Gtrs. 1+2
1/4
1/4

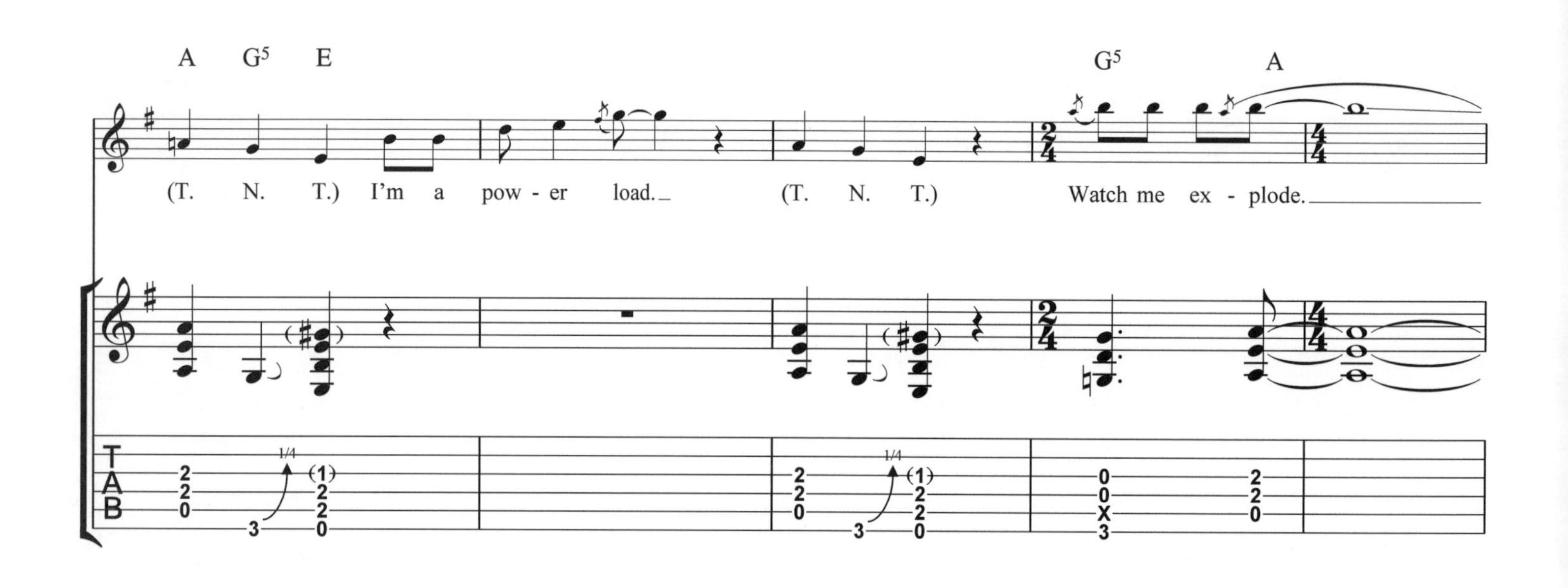
A G5 E
G5 A
(T. N. T.) I'm a pow - er load.
(T. N. T.) Watch me ex - plode.
1/4
1/4

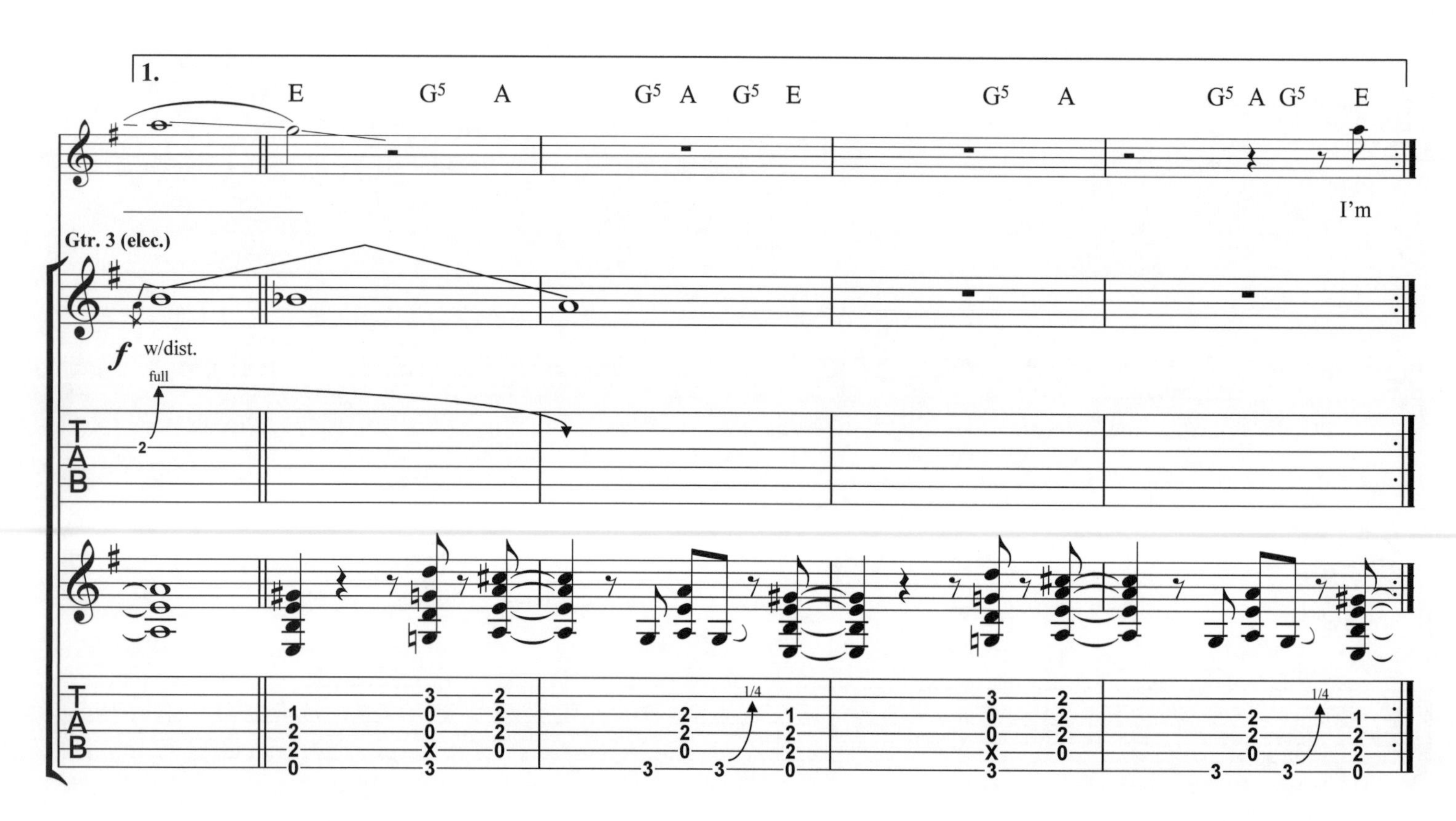
1.
E G5 A G5 A G5 E G5 A G5 A G5 E
I'm
Gtr. 3 (elec.)
f w/dist.
full
1/4
1/4

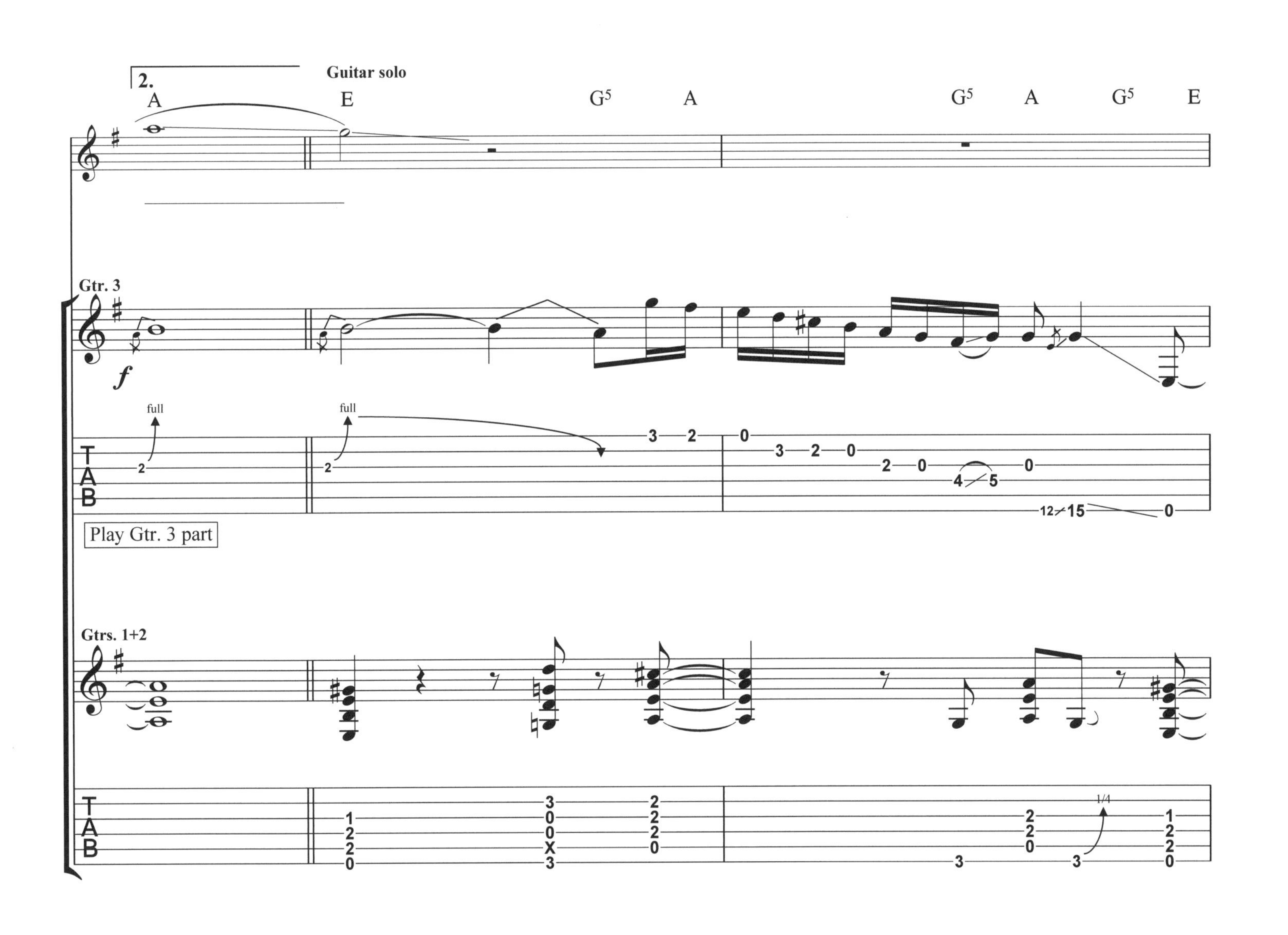
2.
Guitar solo
A
E
G5
A
G5
A
G5
E
Gtr. 3
f
full
full
Play Gtr. 3 part
Gtrs. 1+2
1/4

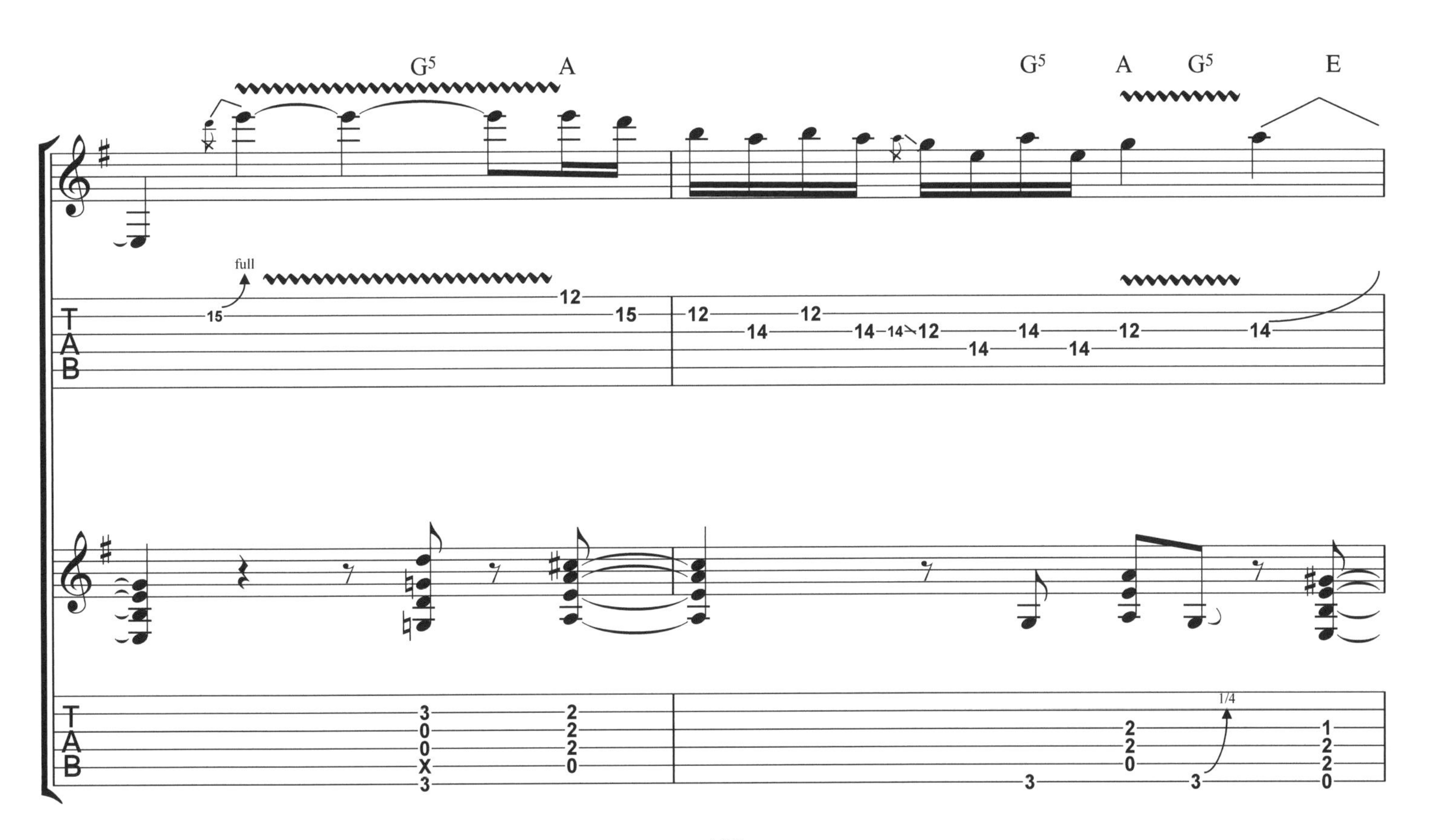
G5
A
G5
A
G5
E
full
1/4

G5
A
E
full
1/4
1/2
8va
Chorus
T. N. T. Oi! Oi! Oi!
Play written part

A G5 E
A G5 E
T. N. T. I'm dy - na - mite.
(T. N. T.) And I'll win the fight.
1/4
1/4

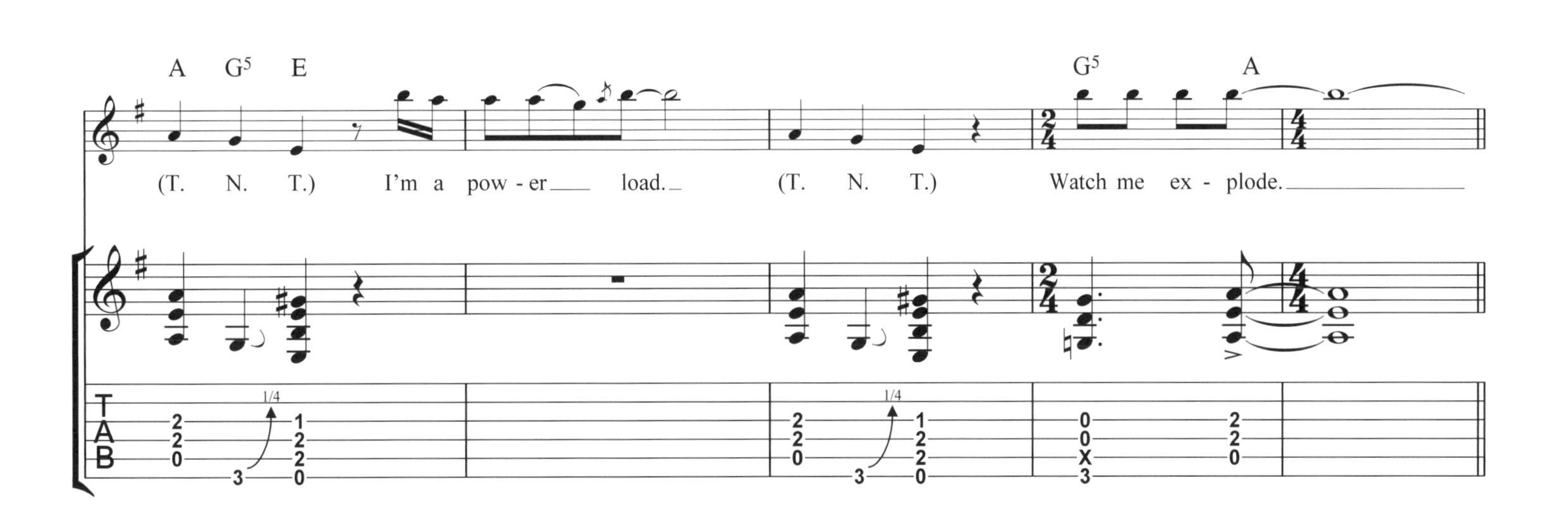
A G5 E
G5 A
(T. N. T.) I'm a pow - er load.
(T. N. T.) Watch me ex - plode.
1/4
1/4

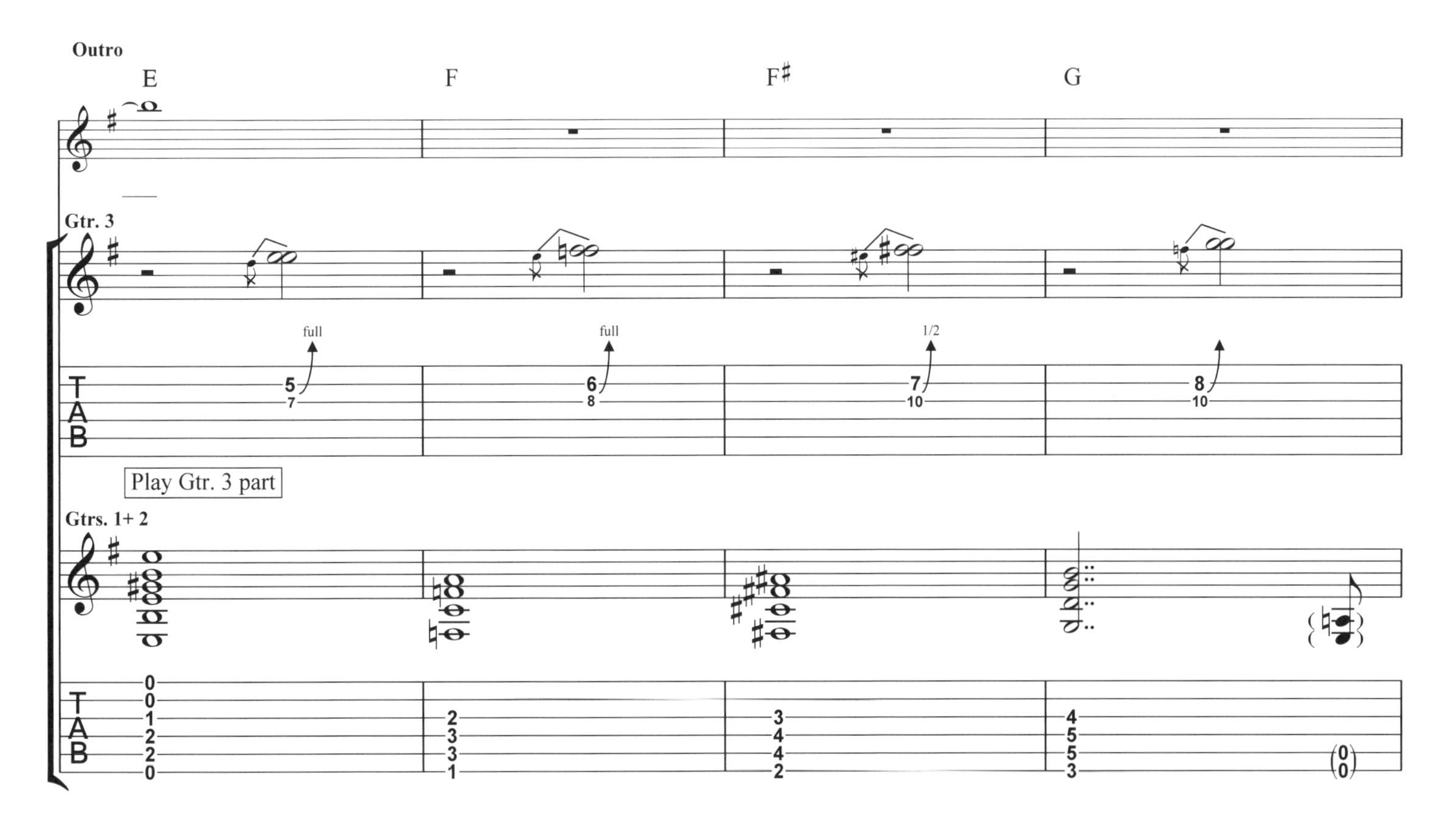
Outro
E F F♯ G
Gtr. 3
full
full
1/2
Play Gtr. 3 part
Gtrs. 1+ 2

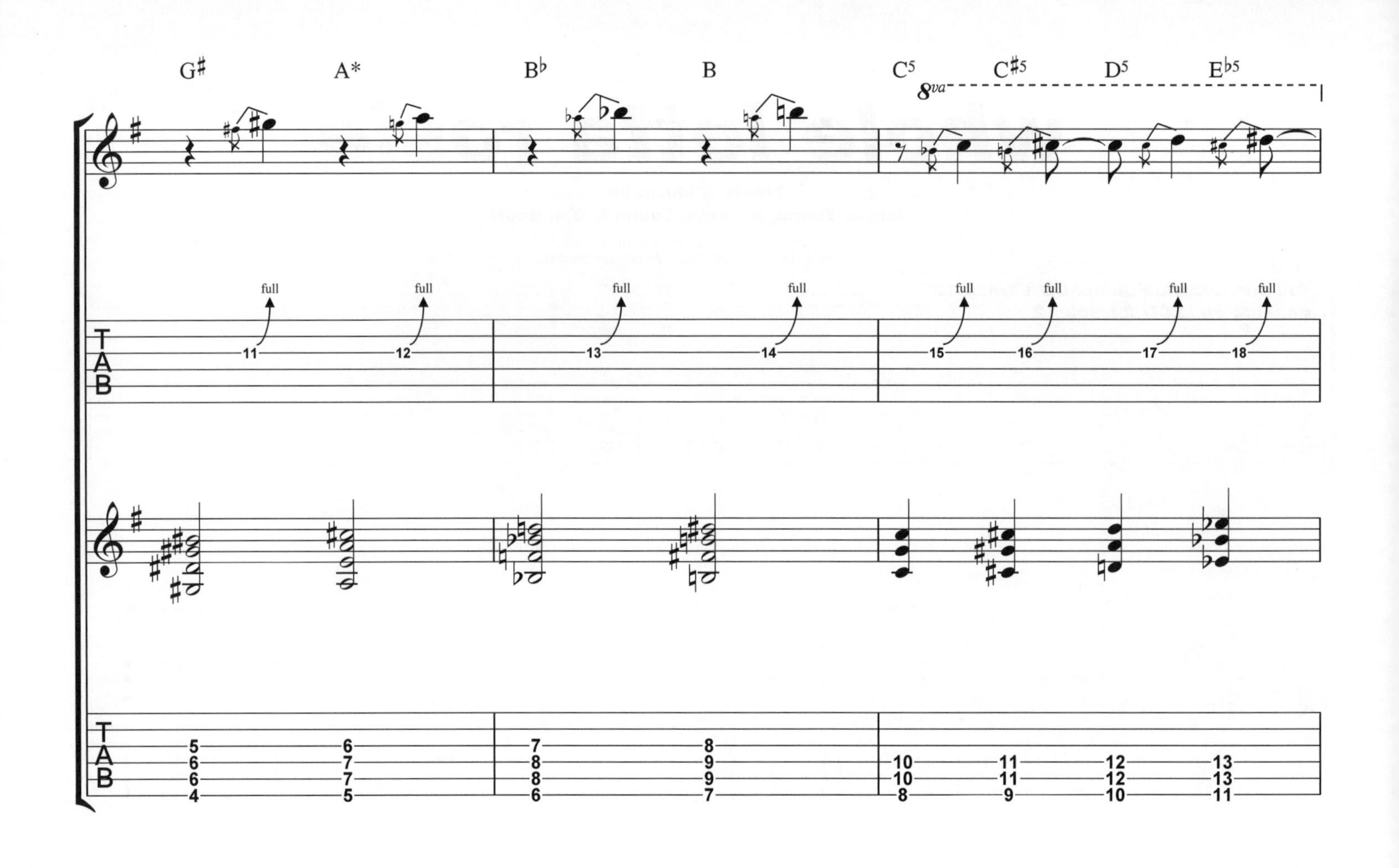
G♯ A* B♭ B C5 C♯5 D5 E♭5
8va
full full full full full full full full
TAB

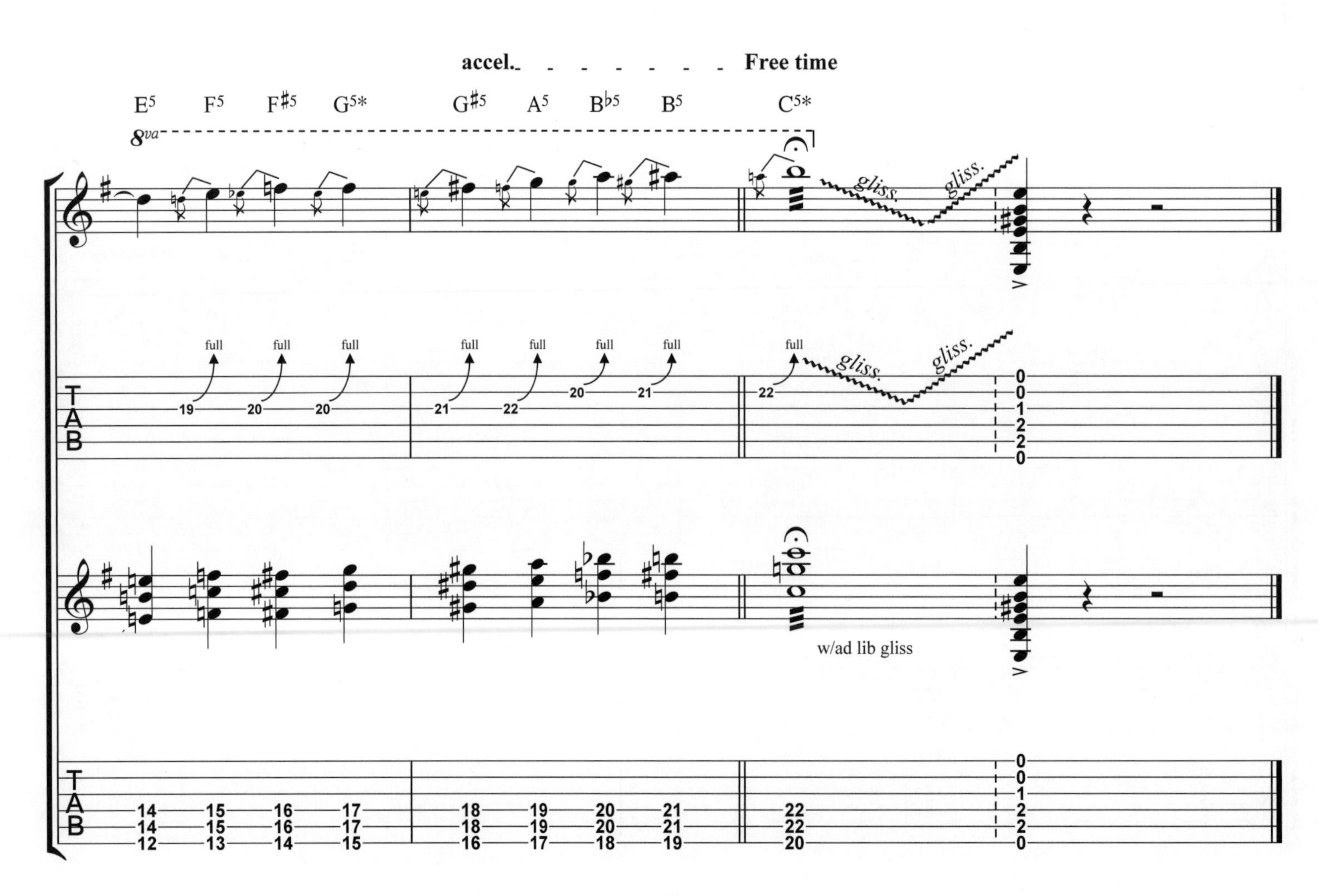
accel. Free time
E5 F5 F♯5 G5* G♯5 A5 B♭5 B5 C5*
8va
gliss. gliss.
full full full full full full full full
w/ad lib gliss
TAB

# whole lotta rosie

Words & Music by
Angus Young, Malcolm Young & Bon Scott



***Full performance demo: CD 1 track 12***
***Backing only: CD 2 track 12***

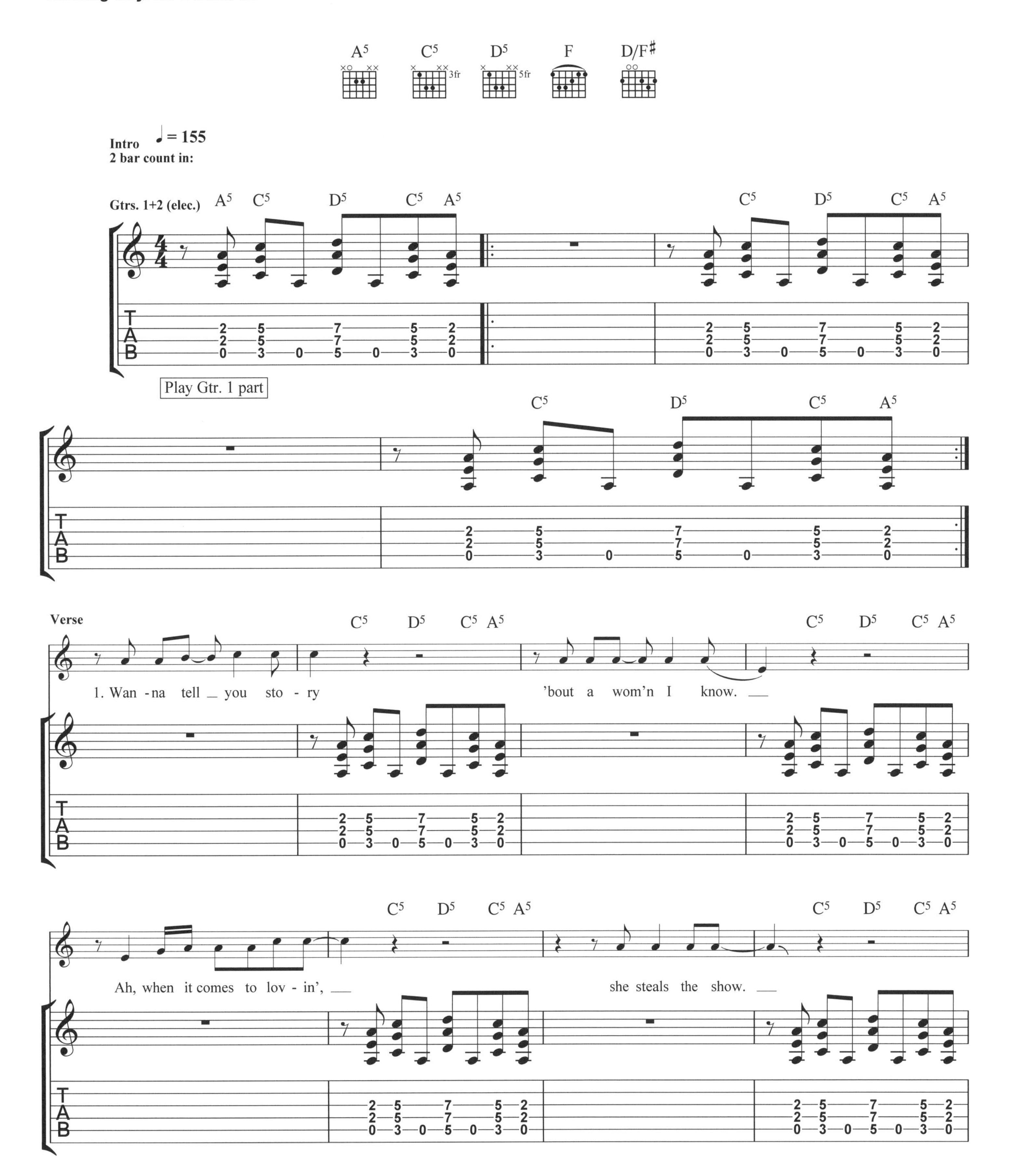

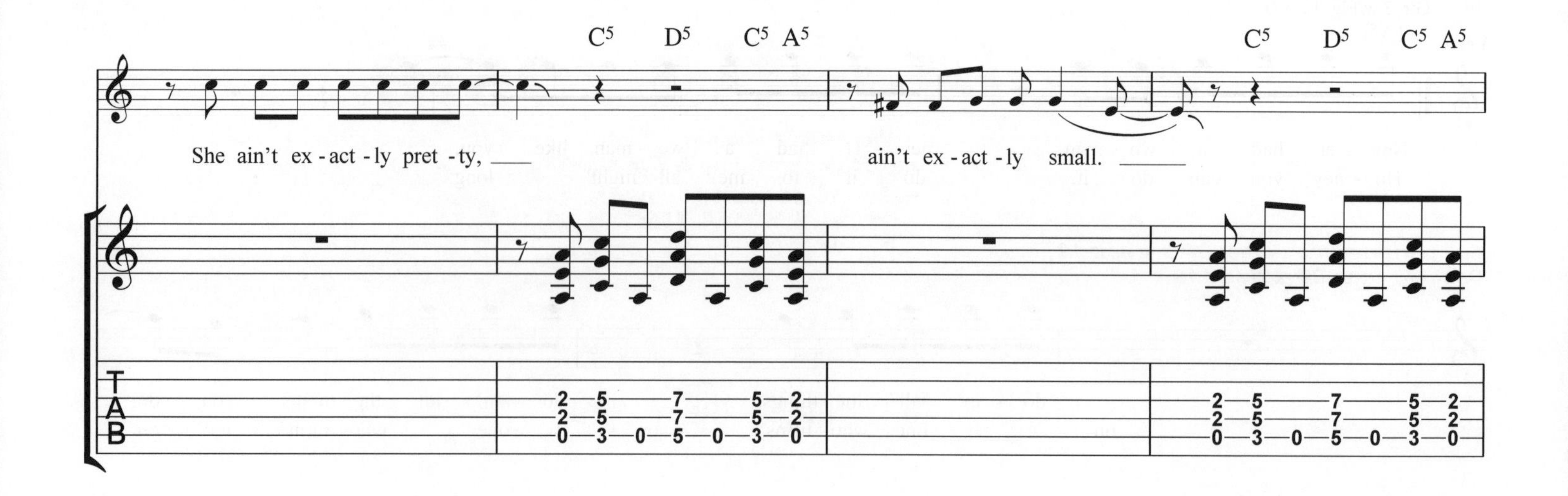
C5 D5 C5 A5
C5 D5 C5 A5
She ain't ex - act - ly pret - ty, ___
ain't ex - act - ly small. ______
T
A
B

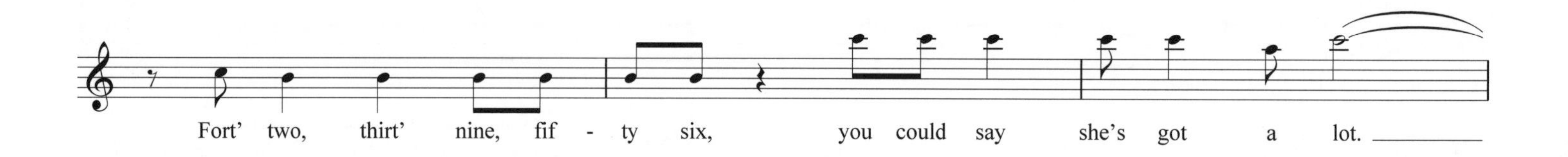
Fort' two, thirt' nine, fif - ty six, you could say she's got a lot. ________

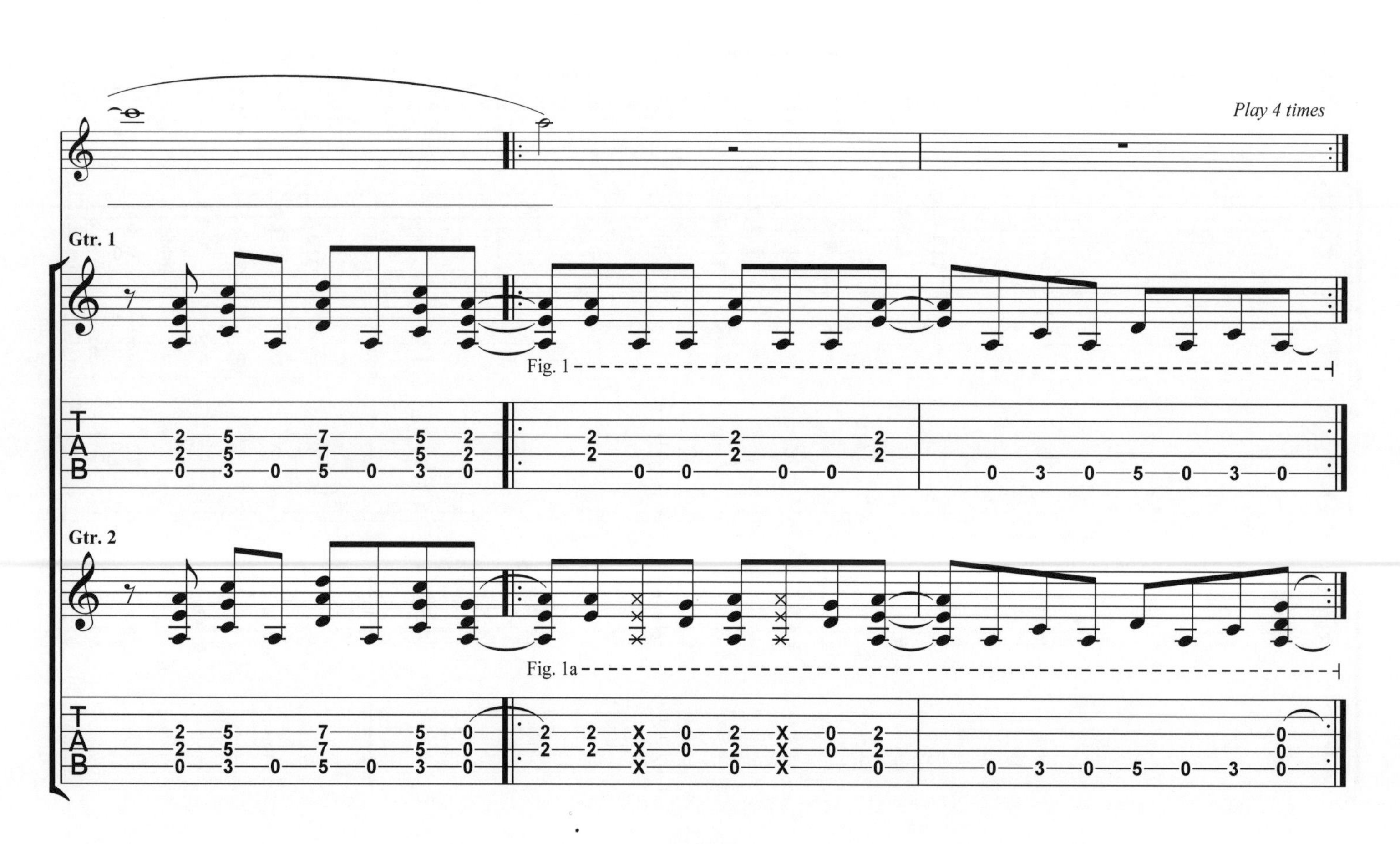
Play 4 times
Gtr. 1
Fig. 1
Gtr. 2
Fig. 1a
T
A
B

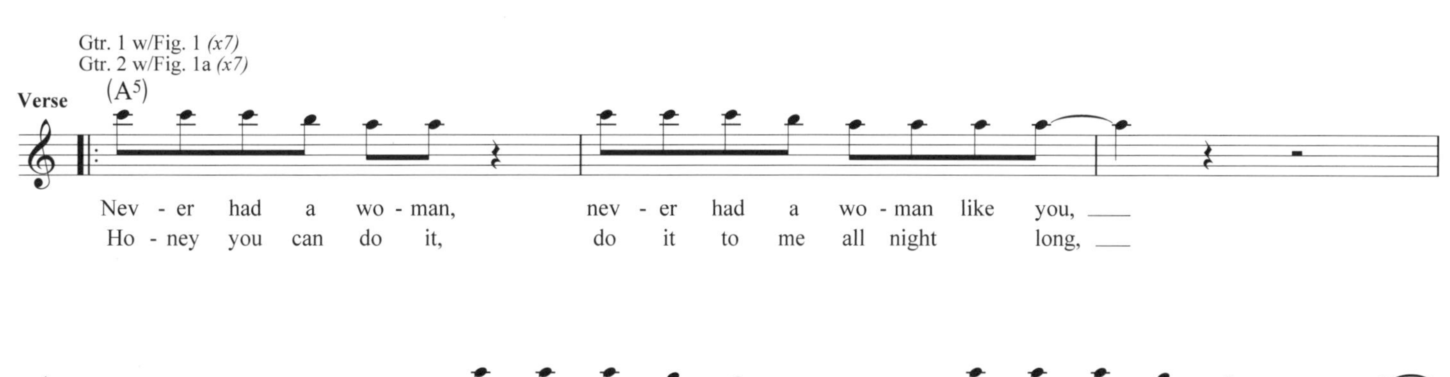
Gtr. 1 w/Fig. 1 (x7)
Gtr. 2 w/Fig. 1a (x7)
Verse
(A5)
Nev - er had a wo - man, nev - er had a wo - man like you,
Ho - ney you can do it, do it to me all night long,

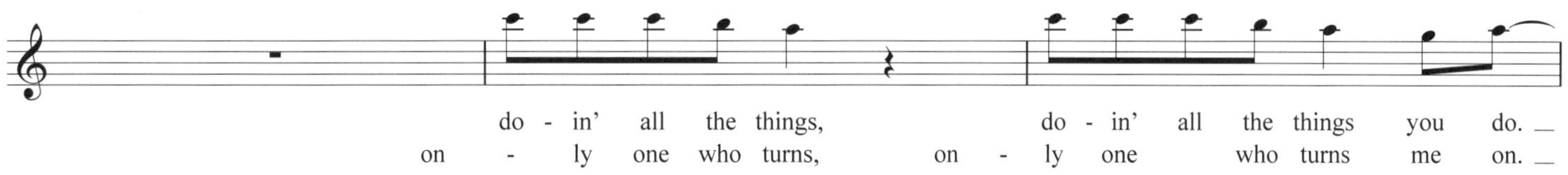
do - in' all the things, do - in' all the things you do.
on - ly one who turns, on - ly one who turns me on.

Ain't no fair - y sto - ry,
All through the night - time

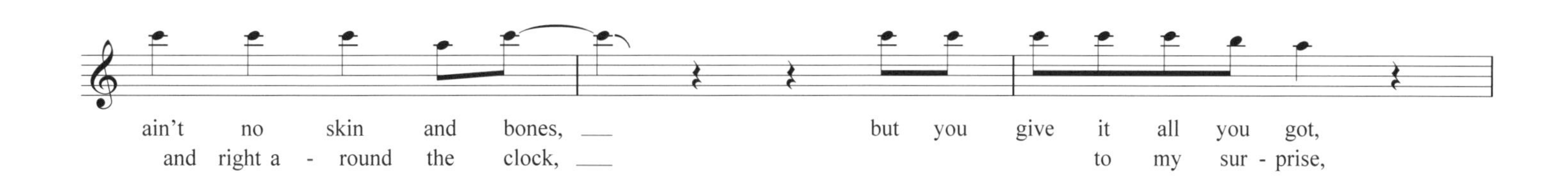
ain't no skin and bones, but you give it all you got,
and right a - round the clock, to my sur - prise,

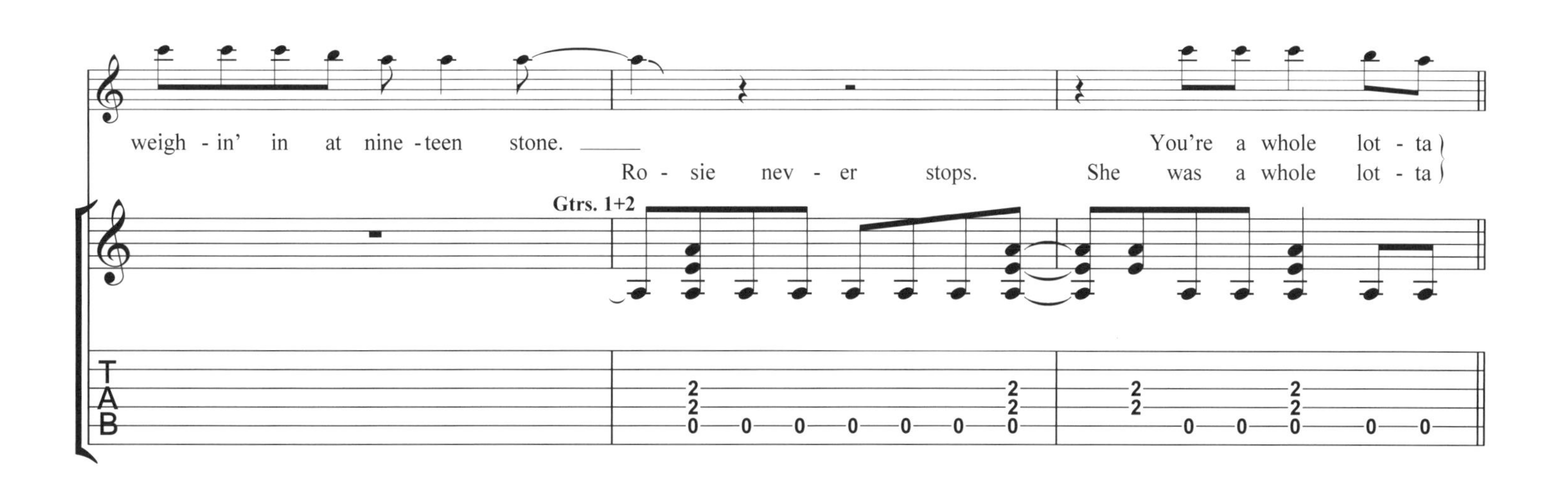
weigh - in' in at nine - teen stone. You're a whole lot - ta
Ro - sie nev - er stops. She was a whole lot - ta
Gtrs. 1+2

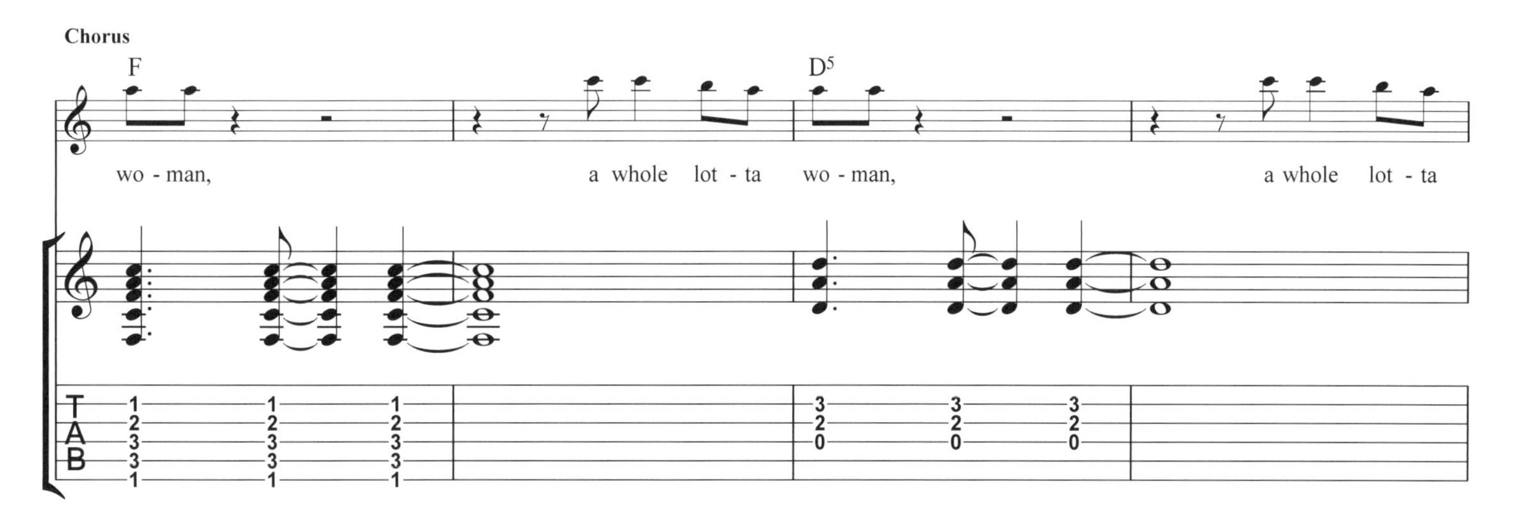
Chorus
F
D5
wo - man, a whole lot - ta wo - man, a whole lot - ta

A5
G5
Ros - ie,
whole lot - ta
Ros - ie,
whole lot - ta
Ros - ie,
and you're a whole lot - ta
(1° only)
1.
D/F♯
wo - man.
Oh,
T
A
B

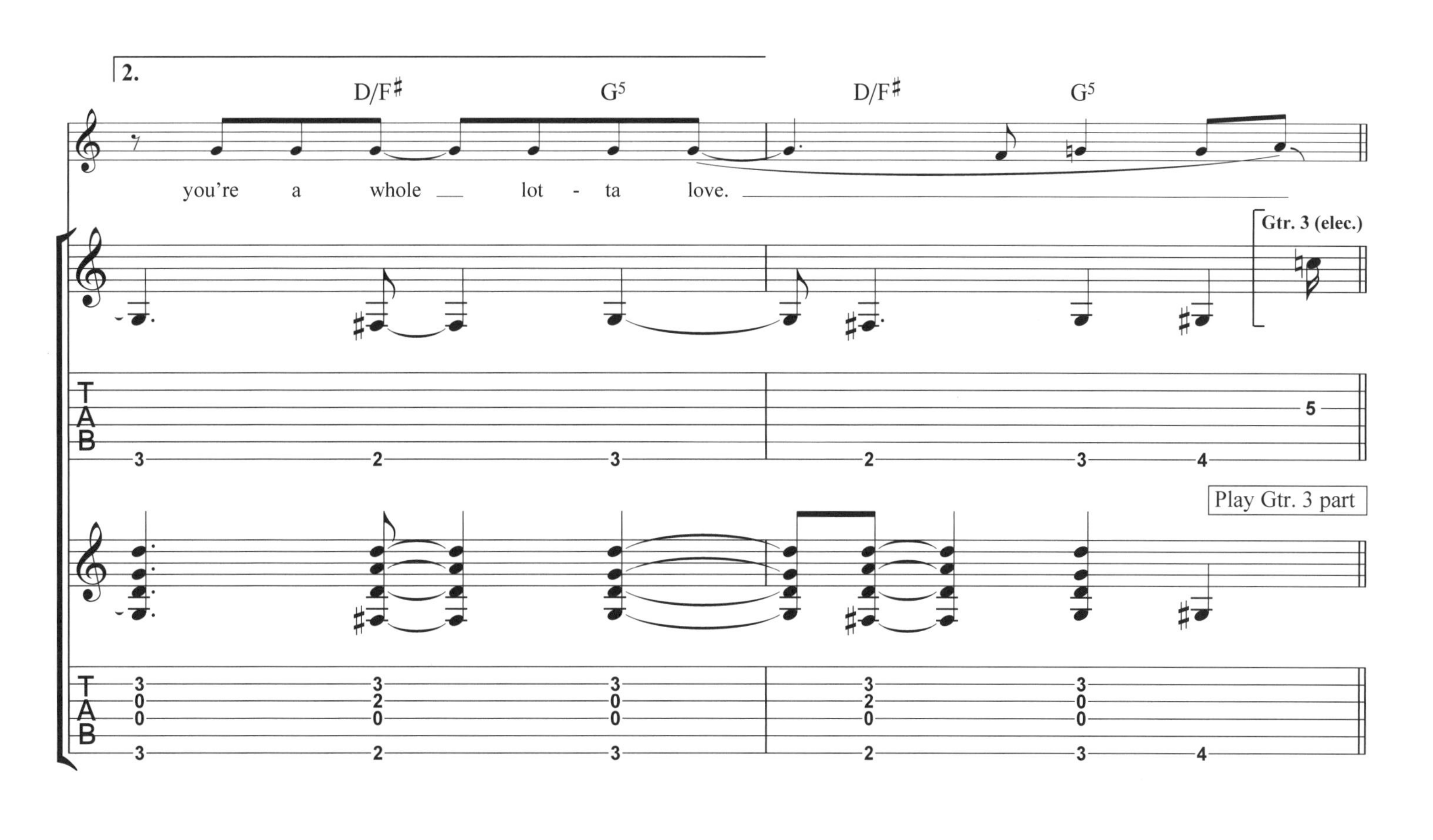
2.
D/F♯
G5
D/F♯
G5
you're a whole lot - ta love.
Gtr. 3 (elec.)
Play Gtr. 3 part

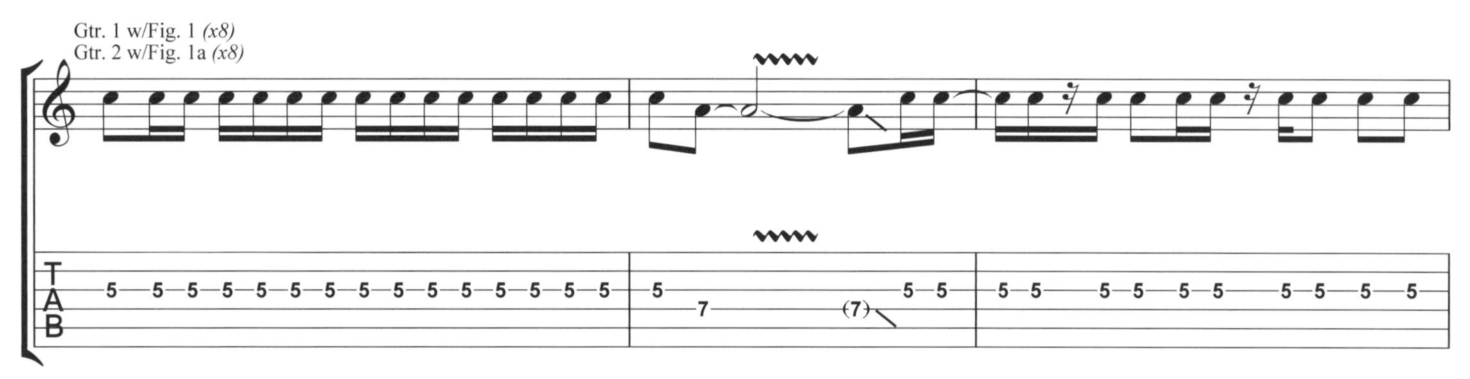
Gtr. 1 w/Fig. 1 (x8)
Gtr. 2 w/Fig. 1a (x8)

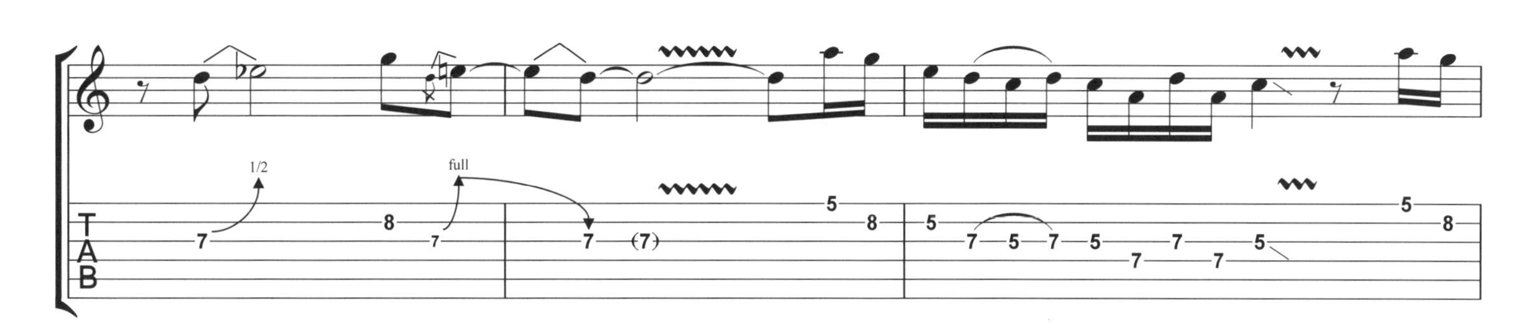
1/2
full

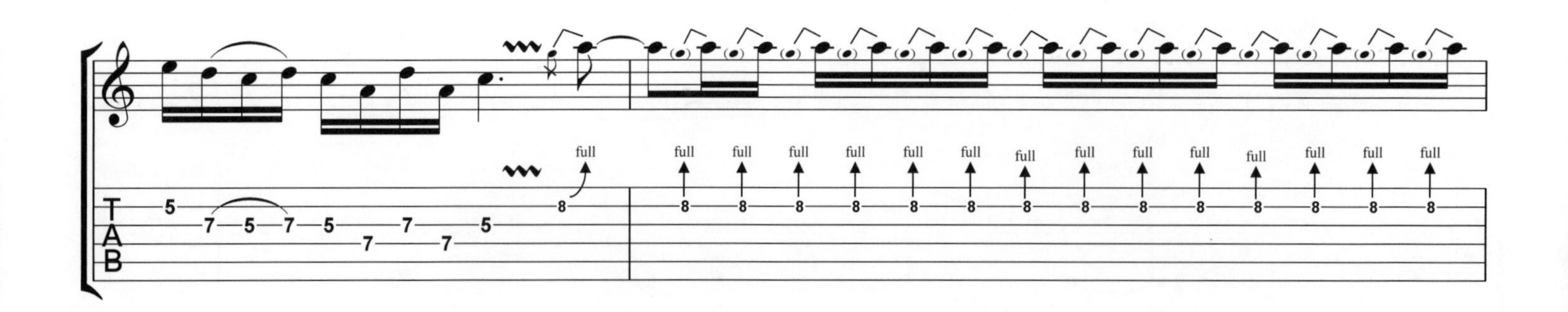

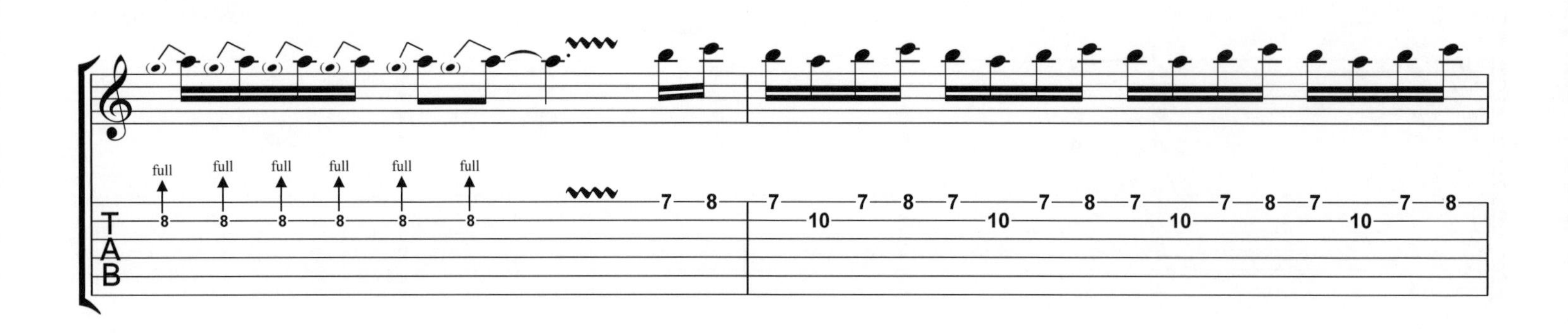

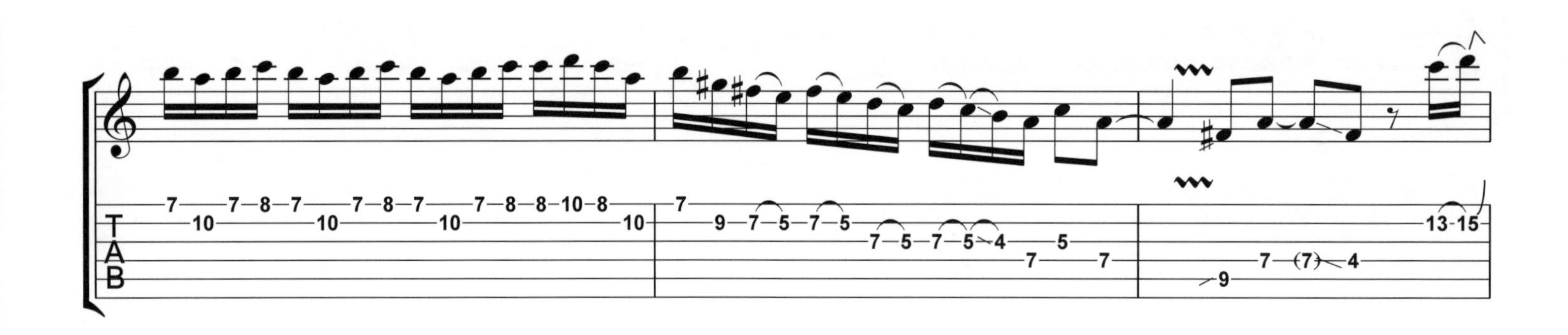

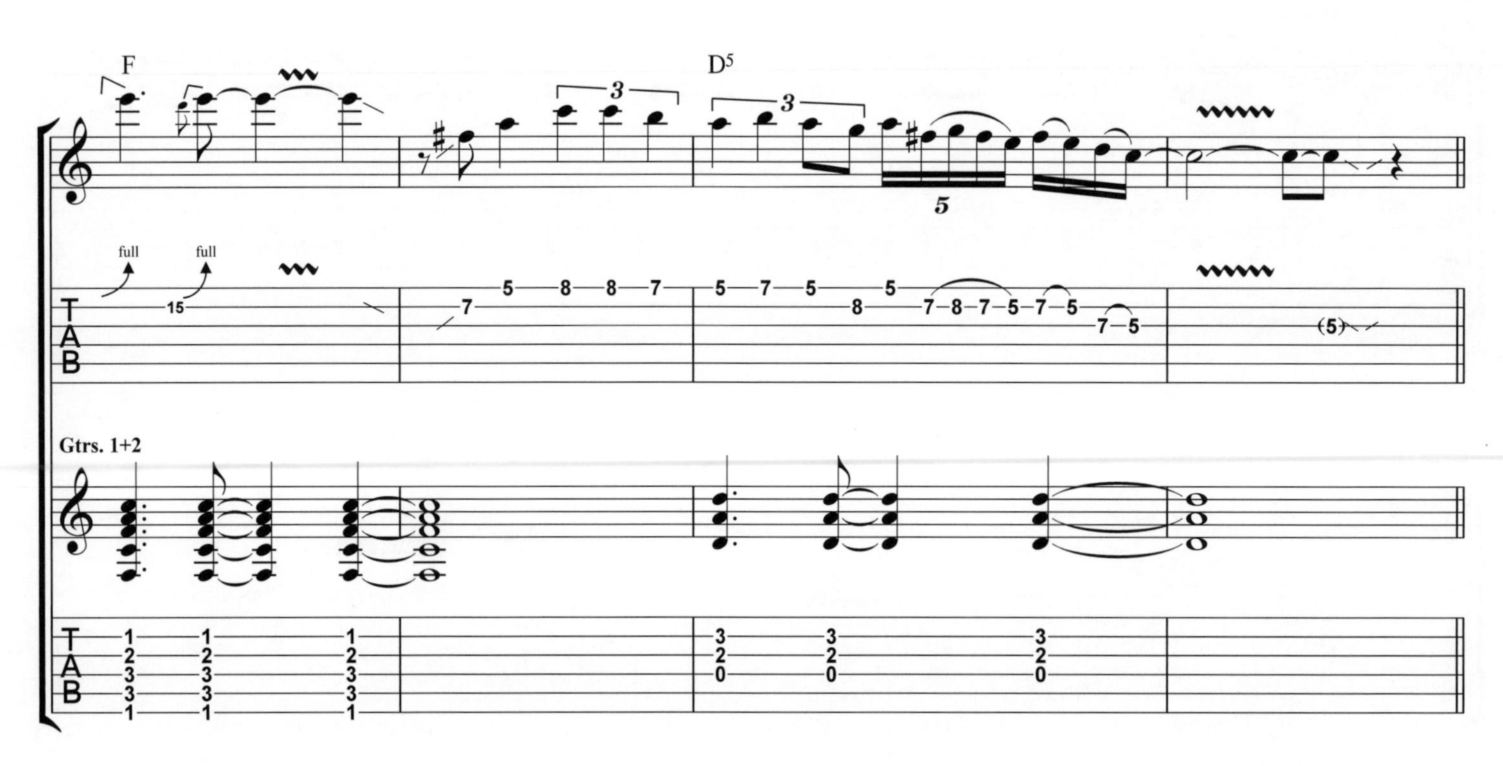
F
D5
Gtrs. 1+2

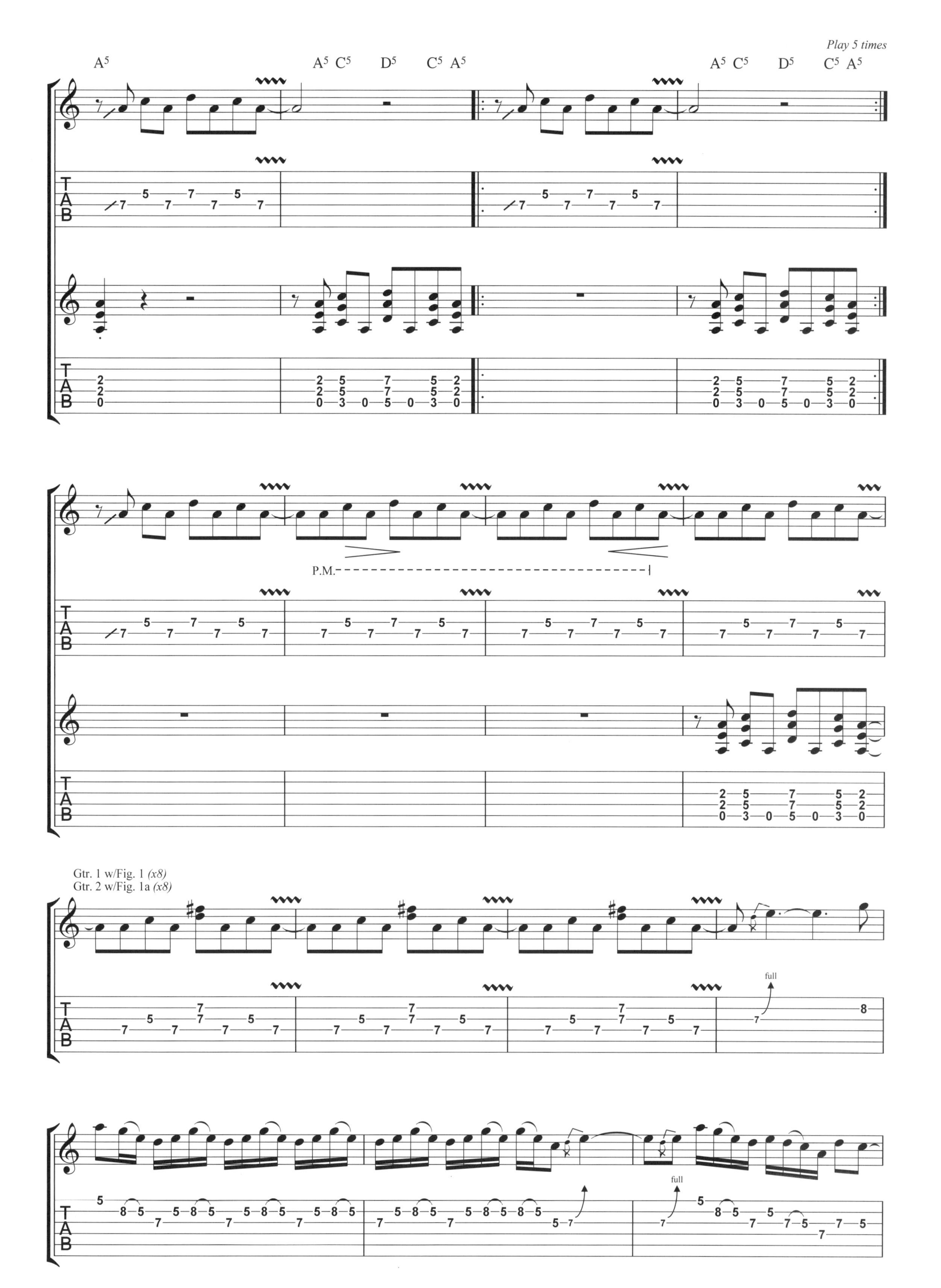
Play 5 times
A5
A5 C5
D5
C5 A5
P.M.
Gtr. 1 w/Fig. 1 (x8)
Gtr. 2 w/Fig. 1a (x8)
full
TAB

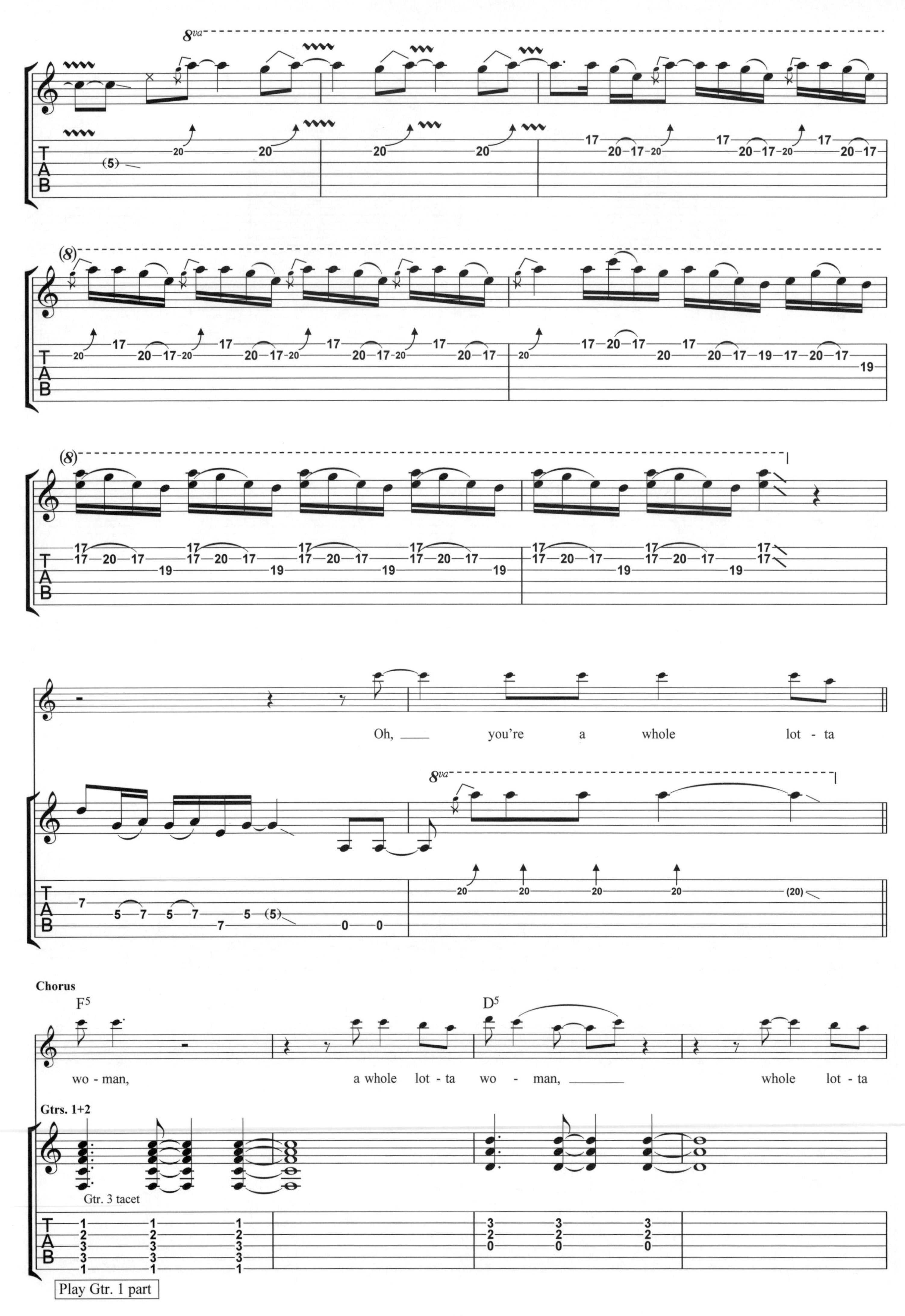

8va
(8)
(8)
Oh, you're a whole lot - ta
8va
Chorus
F5
D5
wo - man, a whole lot - ta wo - man, whole lot - ta
Gtrs. 1+2
Gtr. 3 tacet
Play Gtr. 1 part

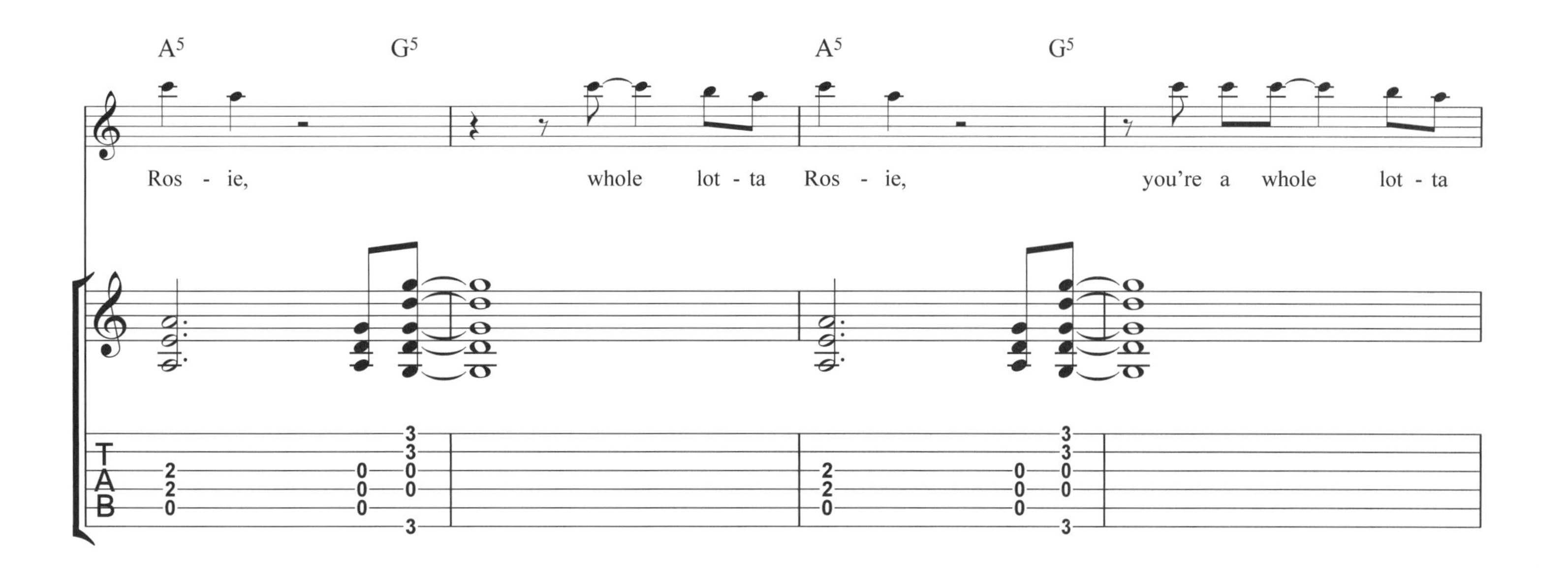
A5
G5
A5
G5
Ros - ie,
whole
lot - ta
Ros - ie,
you're a
whole
lot - ta
T
A
B

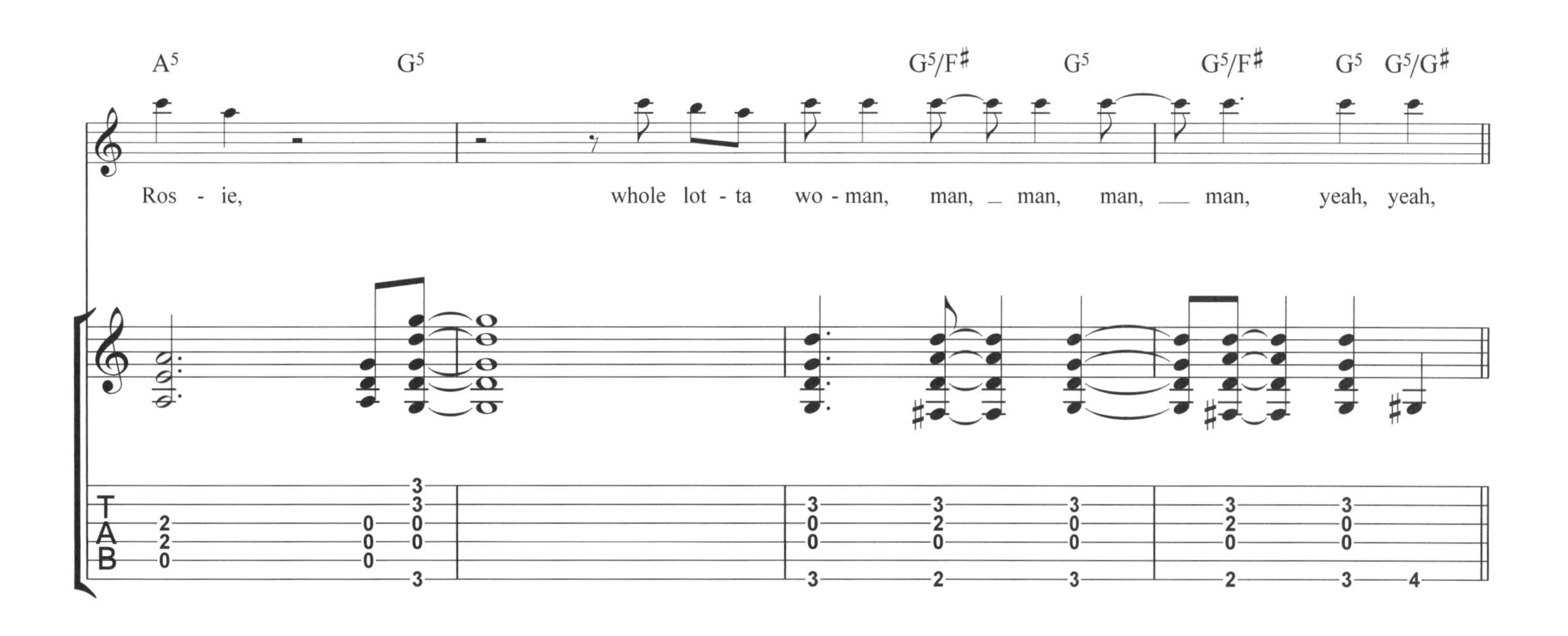
A5
G5
G5/F♯
G5
G5/F♯
G5
G5/G♯
Ros - ie,
whole lot - ta
wo - man,
man, _ man,
man, ___ man,
yeah, yeah,
T
A
B

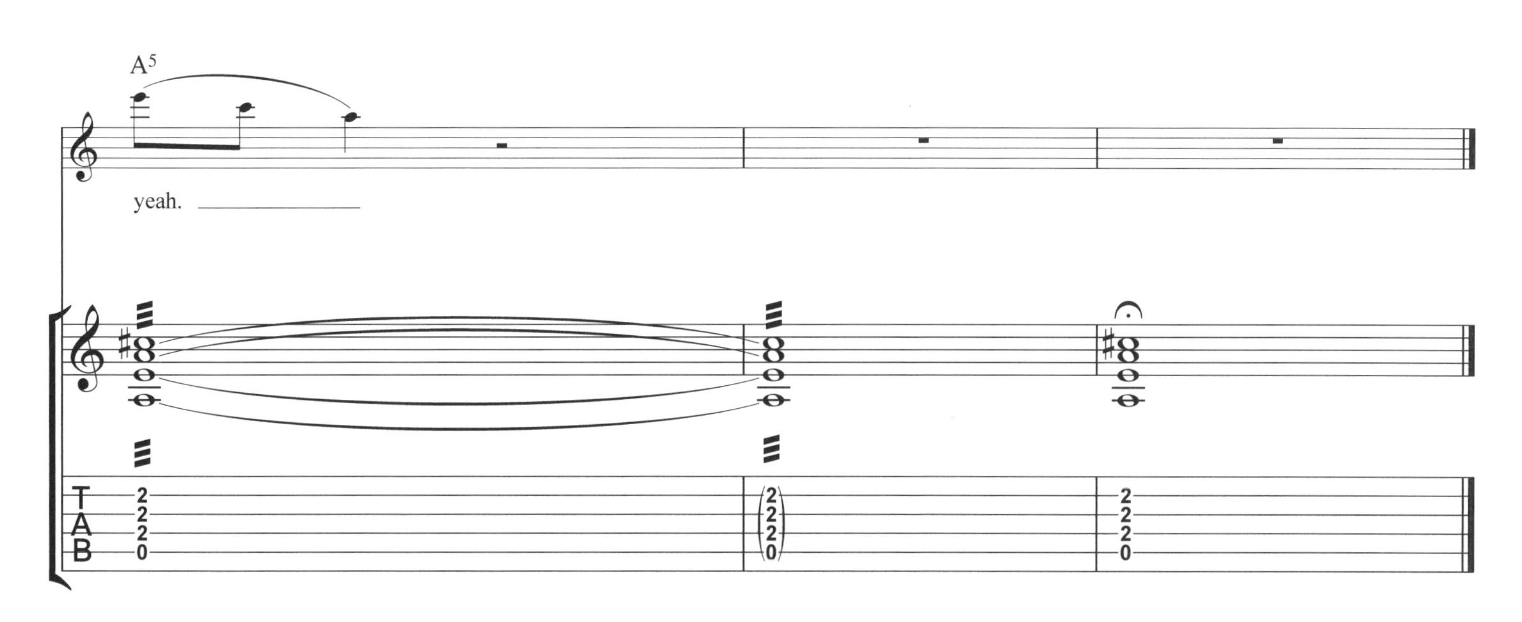
A5
yeah.
T
A
B

# you shook me all night long

Words & Music by
Angus Young, Malcolm Young & Brian Johnson

**Full performance demo: CD 1 track 13**
**Backing only: CD 2 track 13**



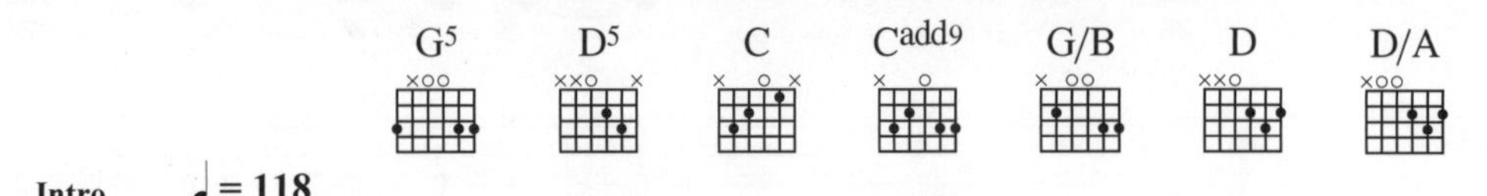


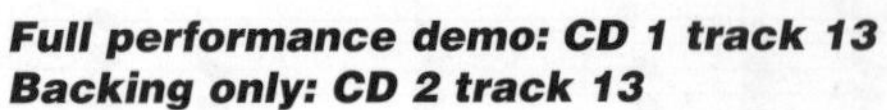


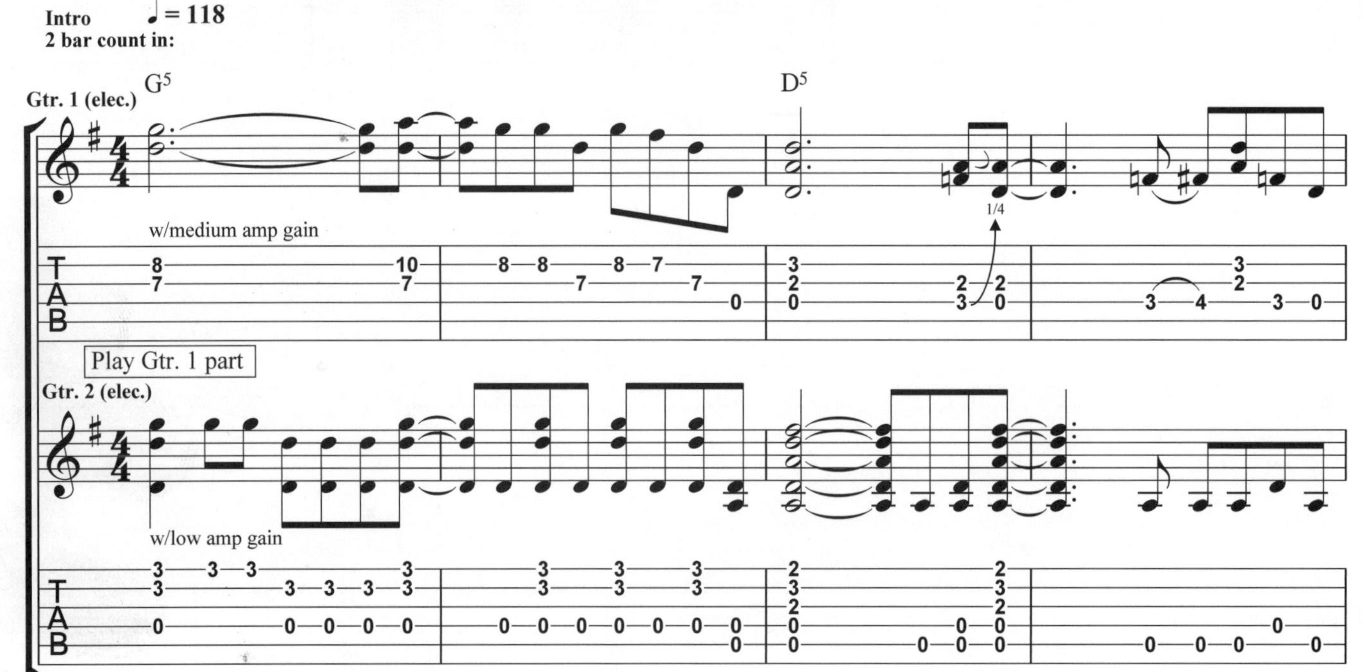


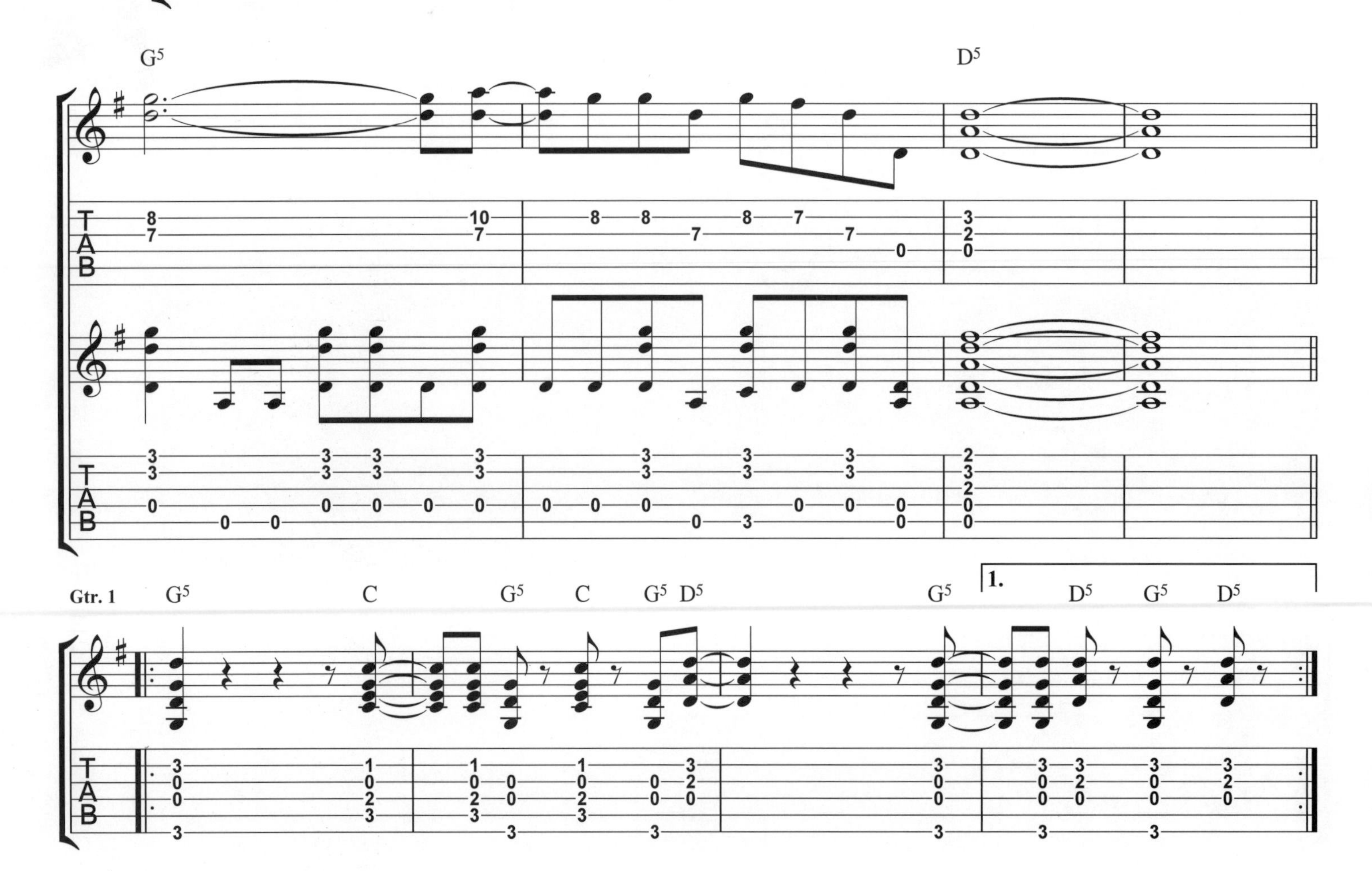

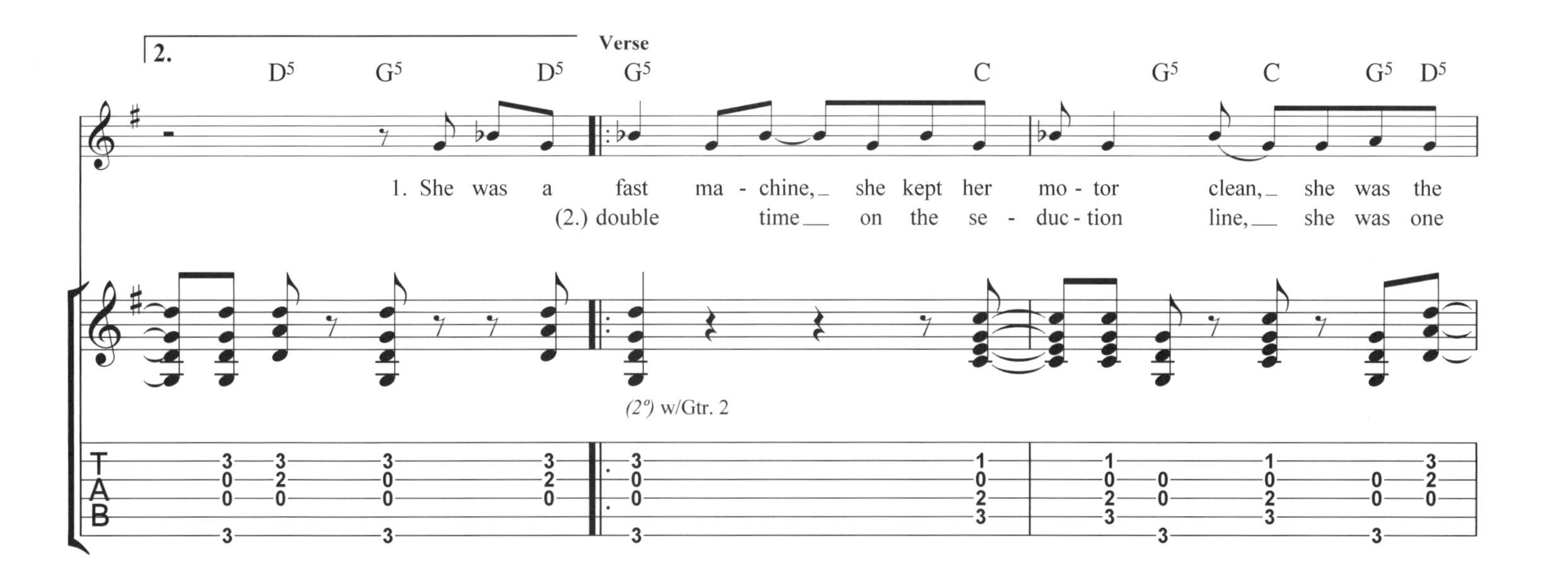
2.
Verse
D5 G5 D5 G5 C G5 C G5 D5
1. She was a fast ma - chine, she kept her mo - tor clean, she was the
(2.) double time on the se - duc - tion line, she was one
(2°) w/Gtr. 2
TAB

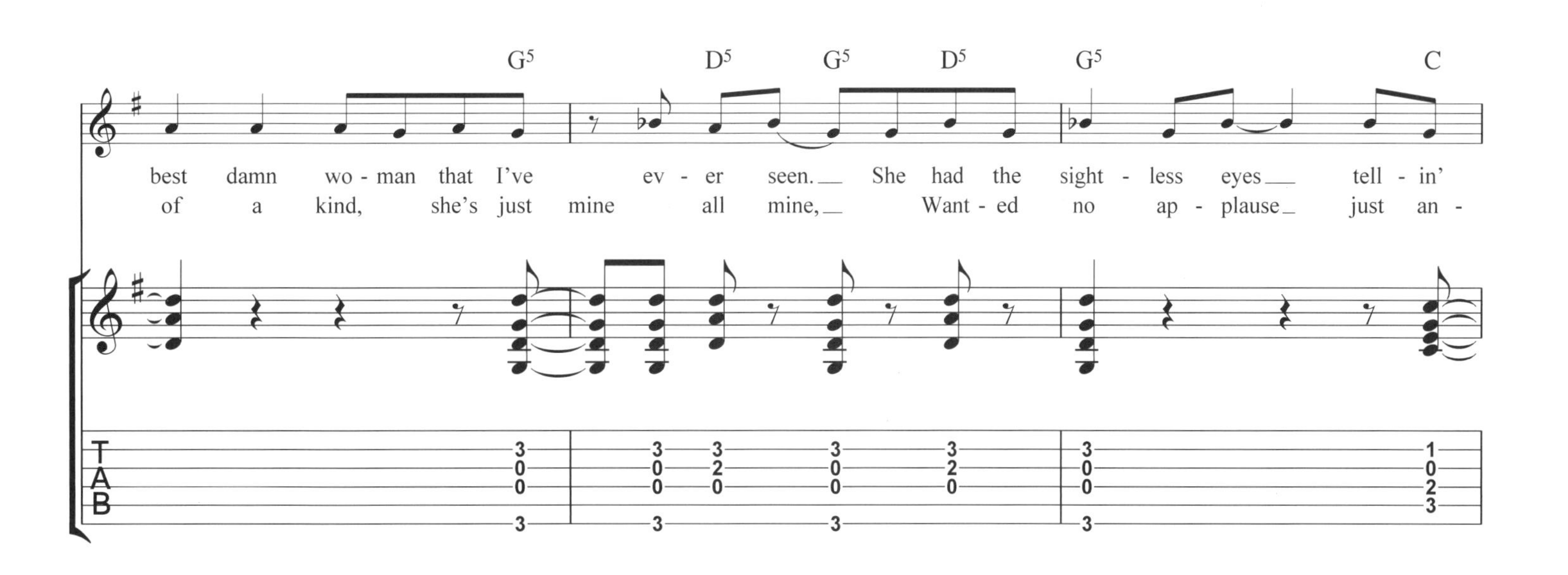
G5 D5 G5 D5 G5 C
best damn wo - man that I've ev - er seen. She had the sight - less eyes tell - in'
of a kind, she's just mine all mine, Want - ed no ap - plause just an -
TAB

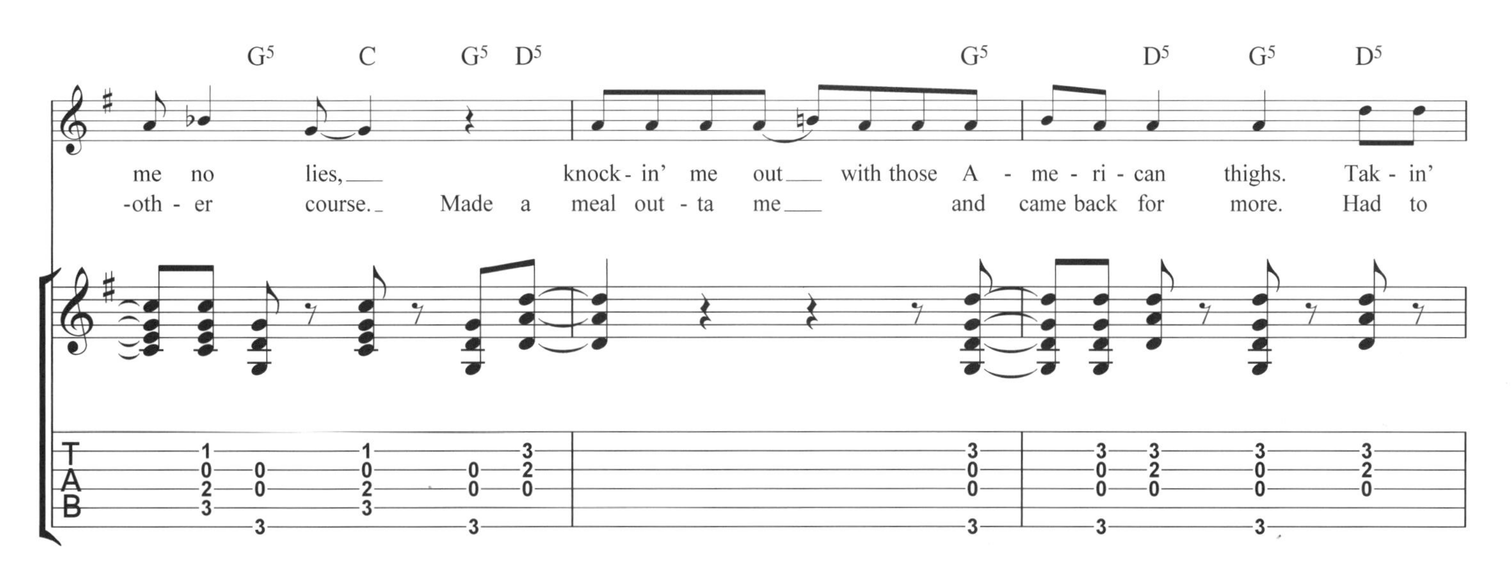
G5 C G5 D5 G5 D5 G5 D5
me no lies, knock - in' me out with those A - me - ri - can thighs. Tak - in'
-oth - er course. Made a meal out - ta me and came back for more. Had to
TAB

G5 C G5 C G5 D5 G5
more that her share had me fight - in' for air. she told me to come but I was
cool me down to take an - oth - er round, now I'm back in the ring to take an -
Gtr. 2 (1°)


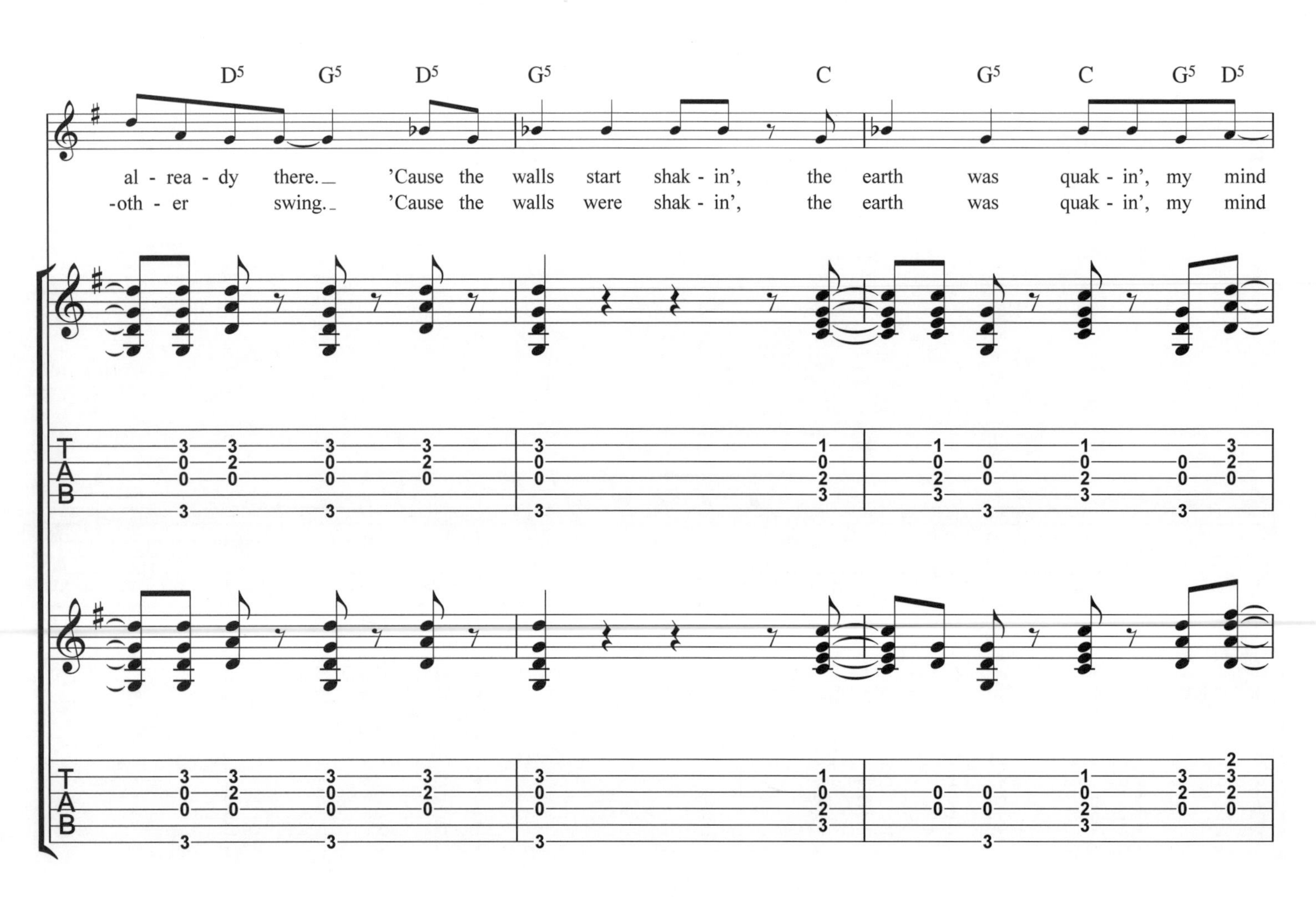

D5 G5 D5 G5 C G5 C G5 D5
al - rea - dy there. 'Cause the walls start shak - in', the earth was quak - in', my mind
-oth - er swing. 'Cause the walls were shak - in', the earth was quak - in', my mind

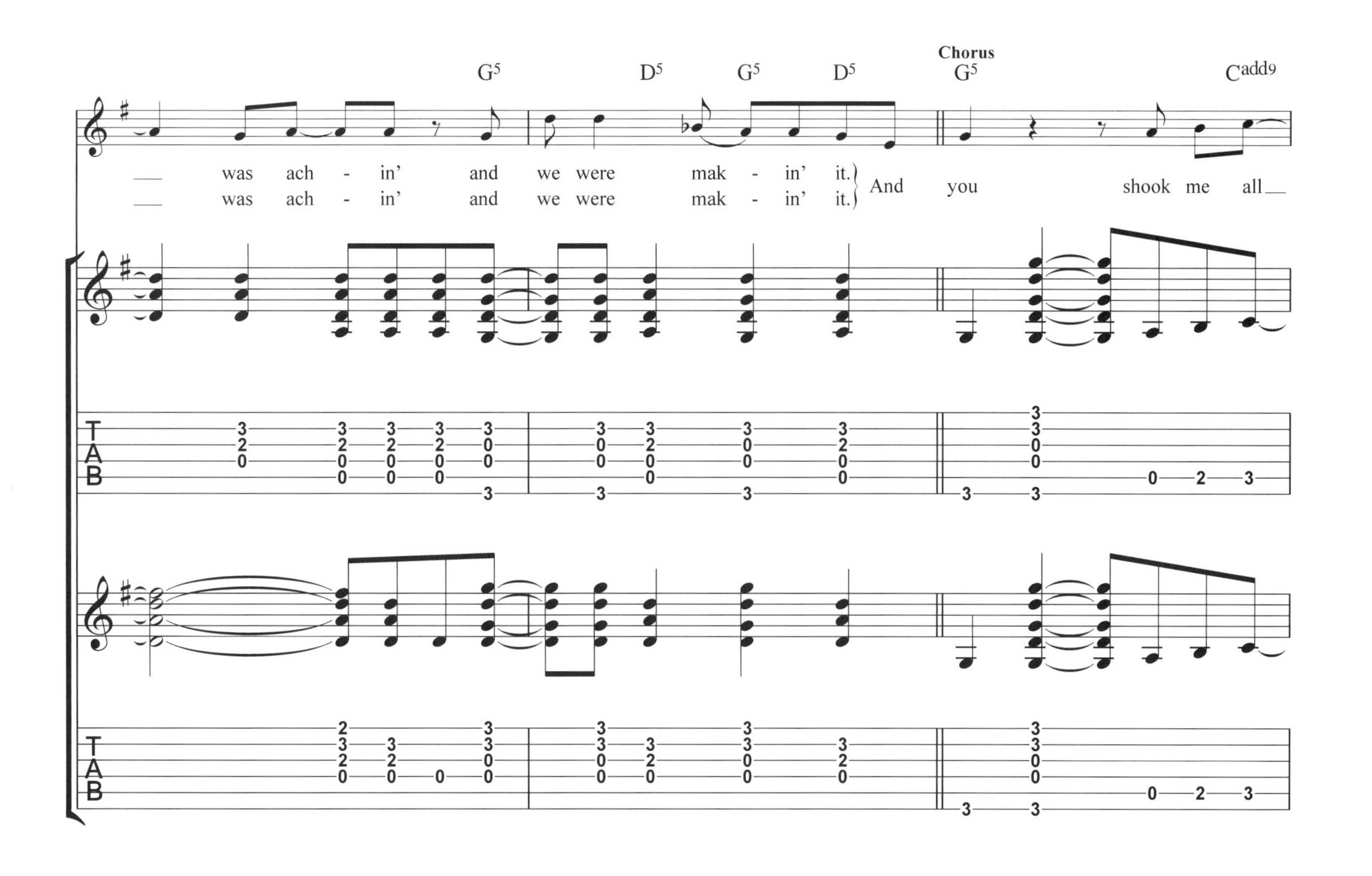
Chorus
G5 D5 G5 D5 G5 Cadd9
was ach - in' and we were mak - in' it.
was ach - in' and we were mak - in' it.
And you shook me all
TAB

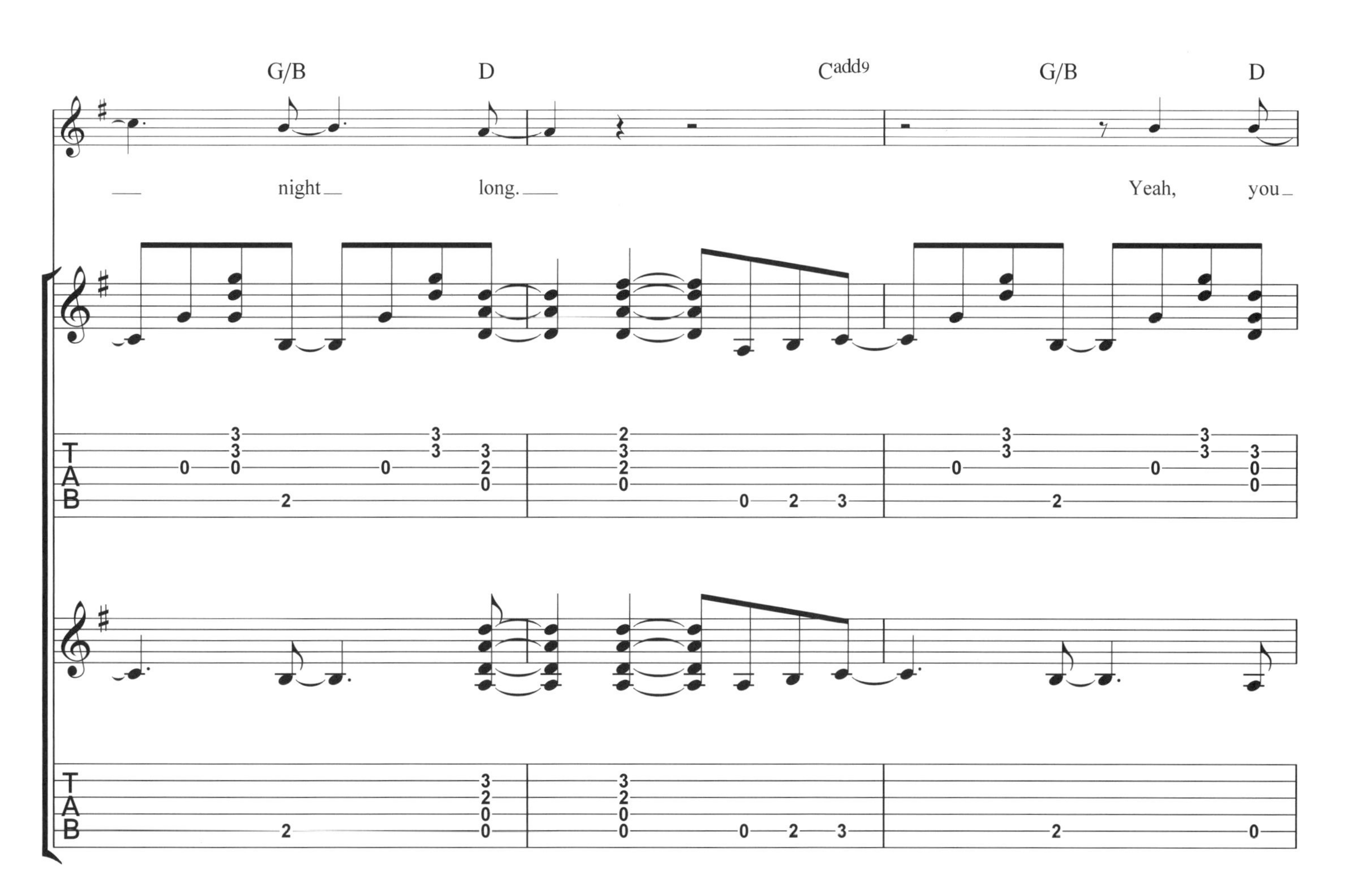
G/B D Cadd9 G/B D
night long. Yeah, you
TAB

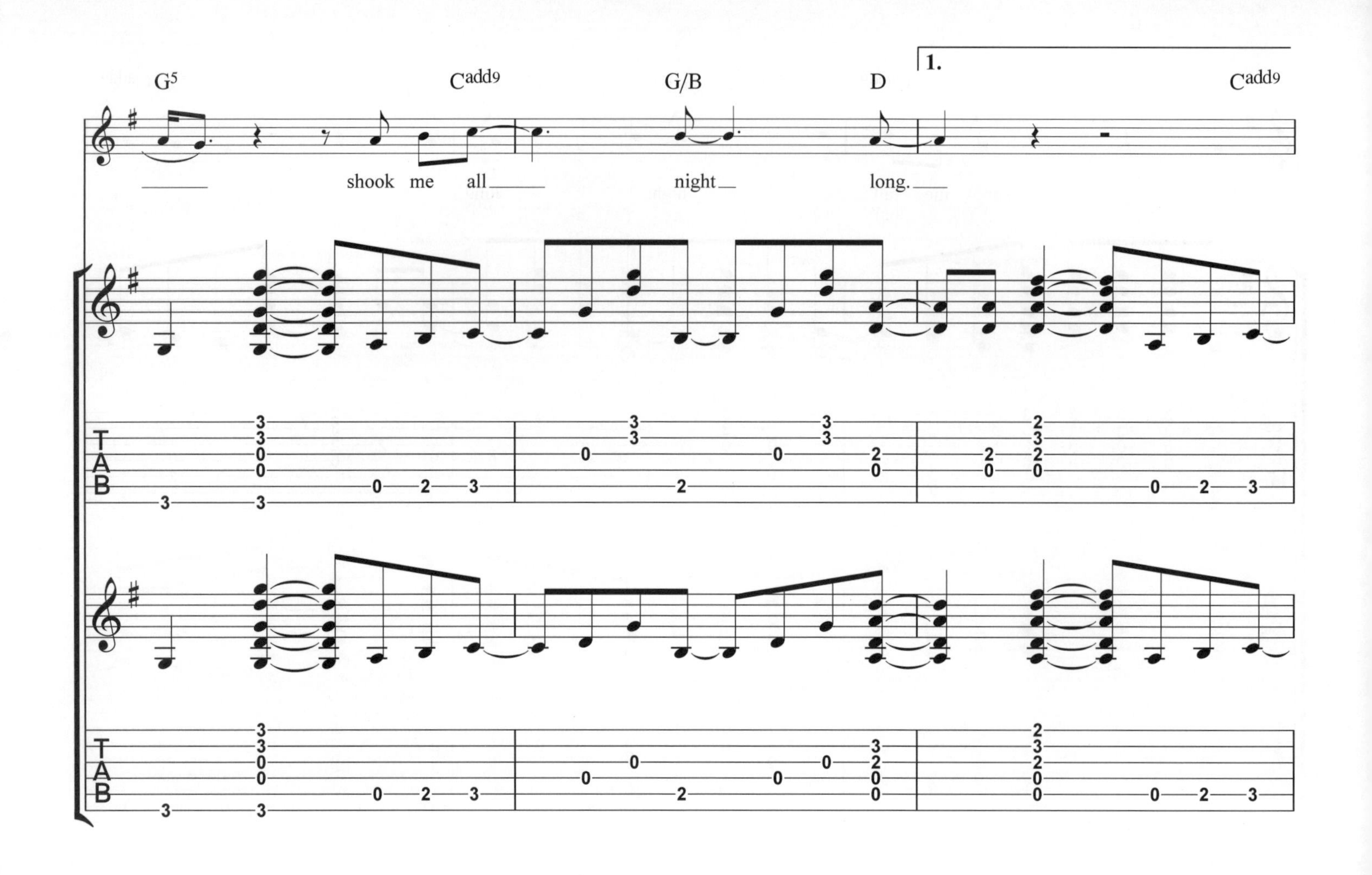
1.
G5
Cadd9
G/B
D
Cadd9
shook me all
night
long.
T
A
B

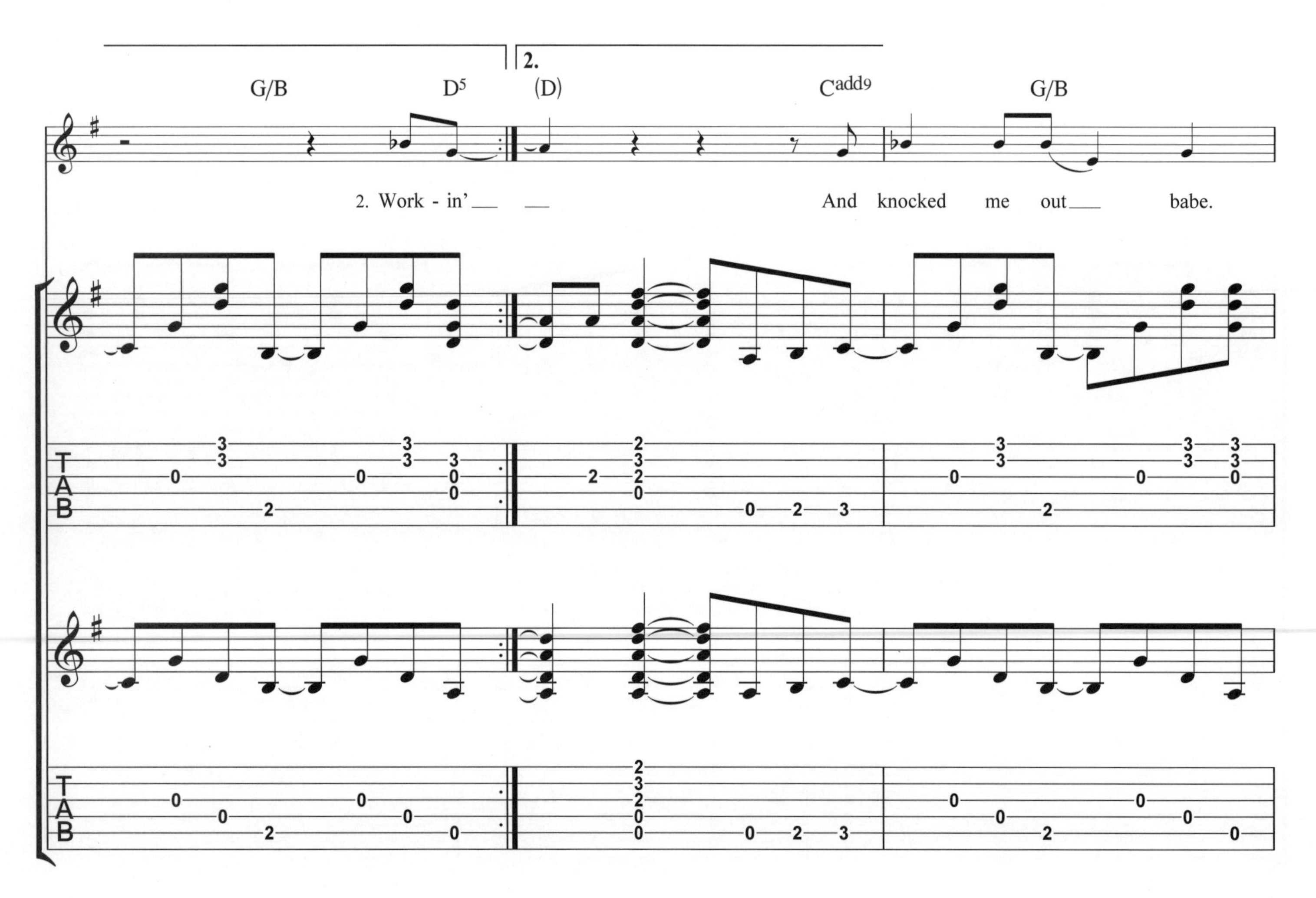
2.
G/B
D5
(D)
Cadd9
G/B
2. Work - in'
And knocked me out
babe.
T
A
B

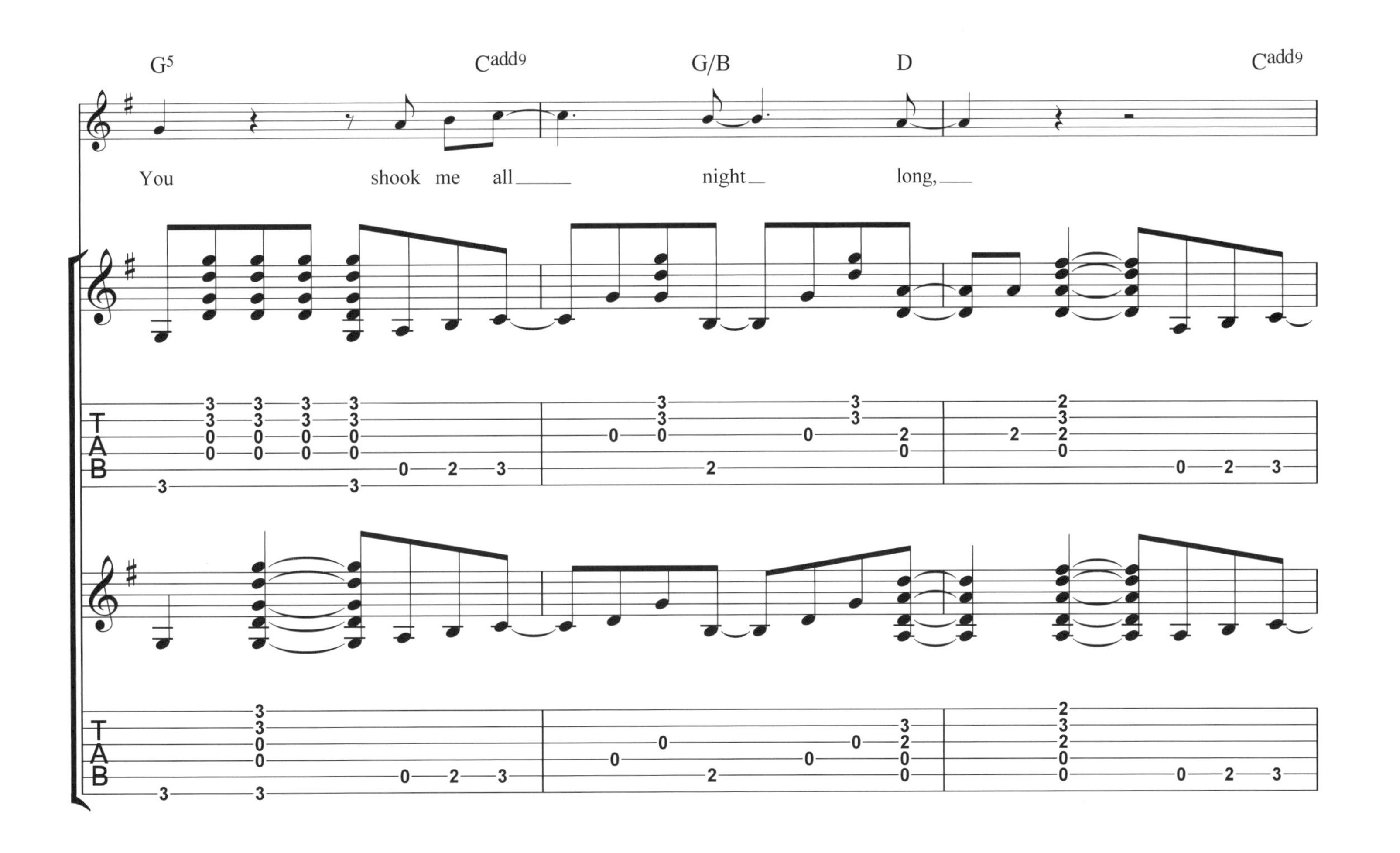
G5
Cadd9
G/B
D
Cadd9
You shook me all night long,

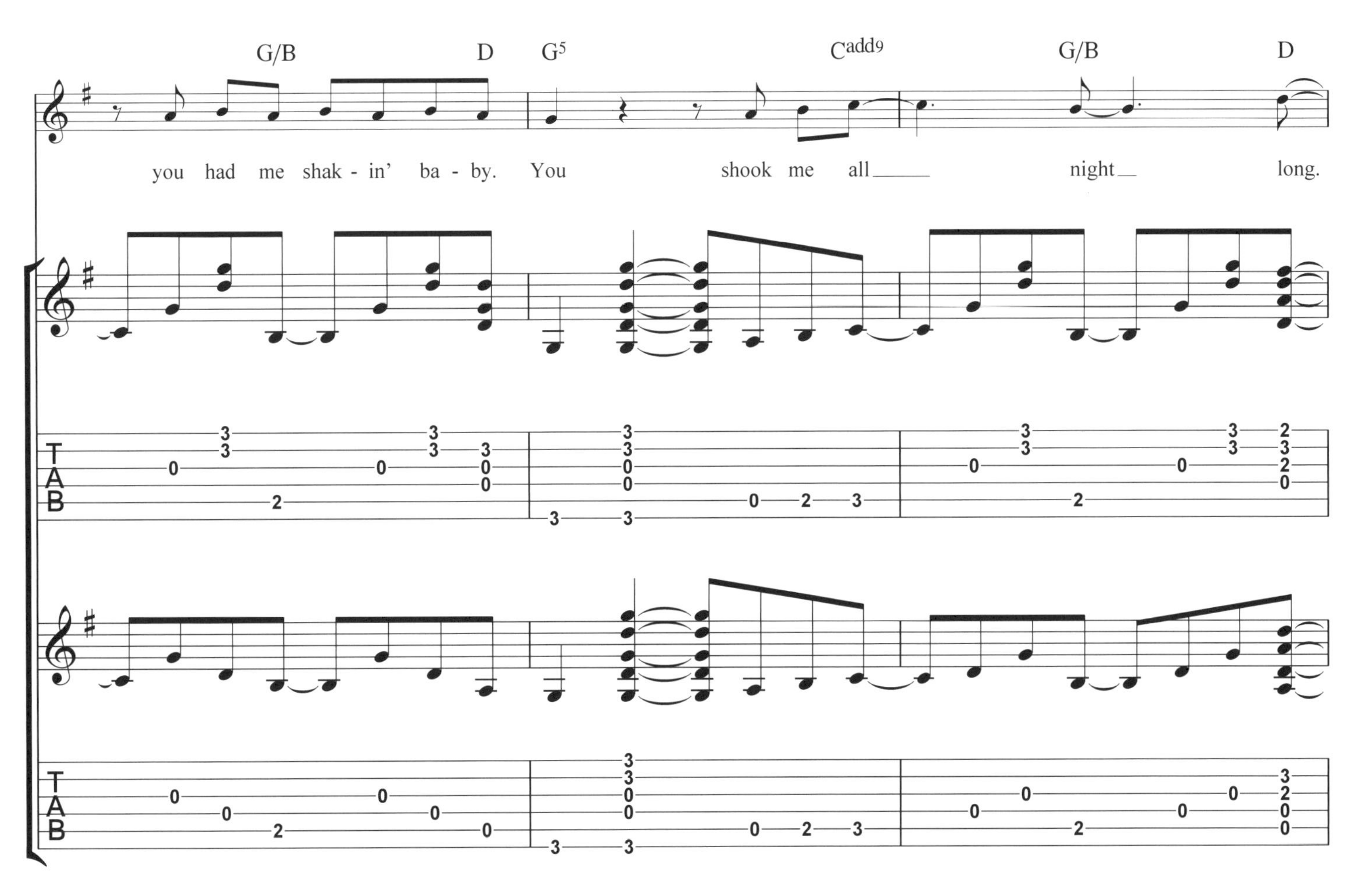
G/B
D
G5
Cadd9
G/B
D
you had me shak - in' ba - by. You shook me all night long.

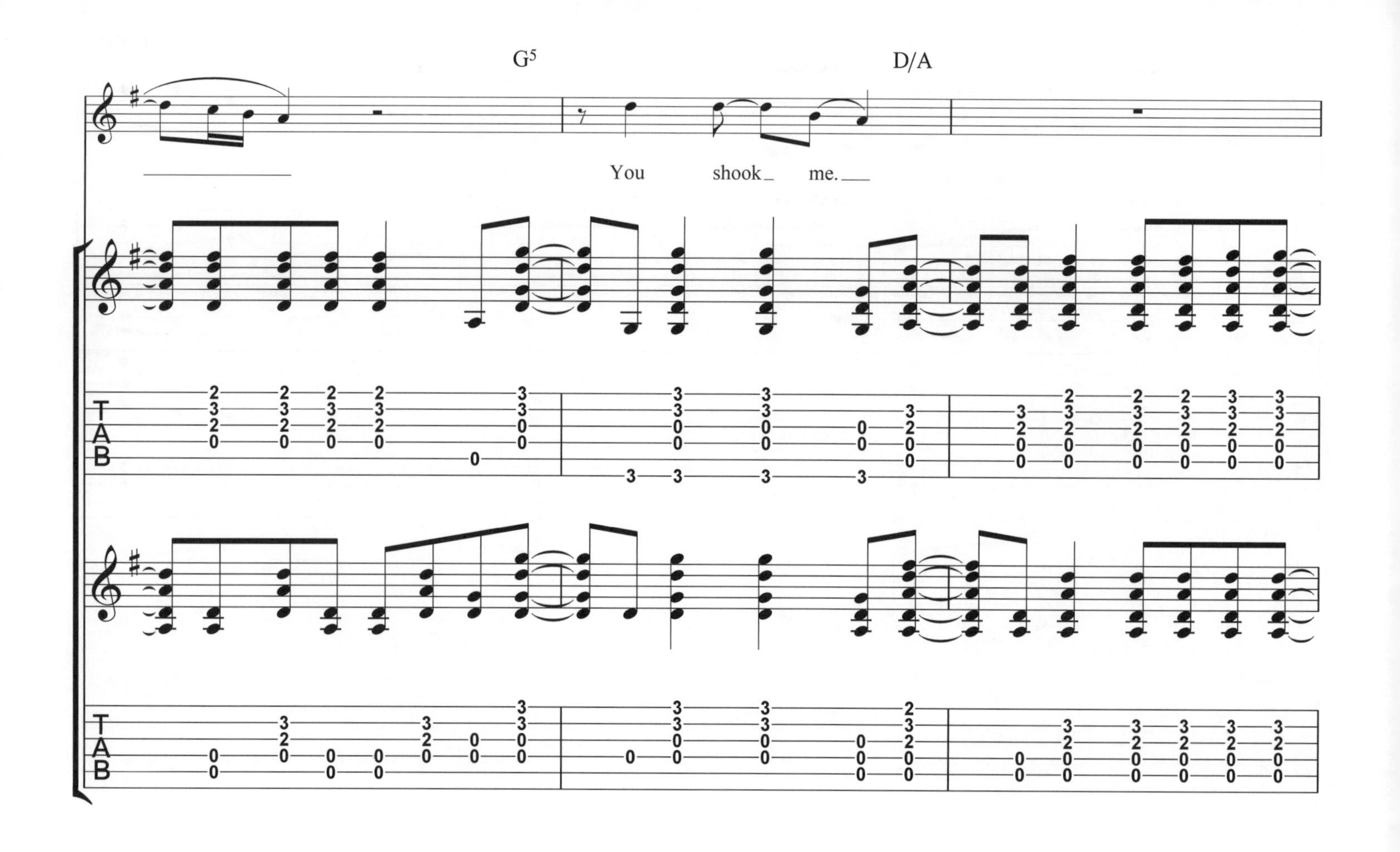
G5
D/A
You shook me.

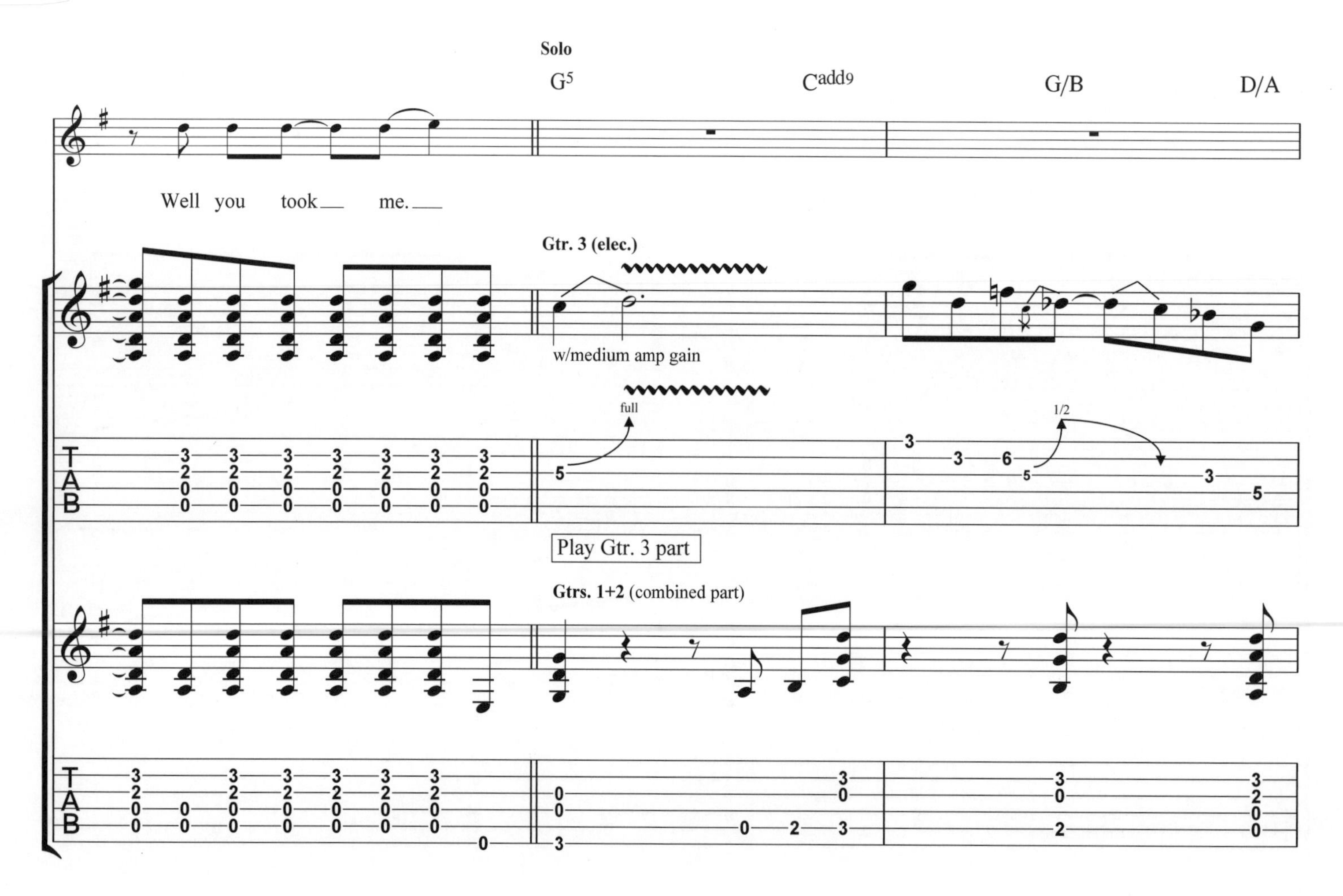
Solo
G5
Cadd9
G/B
D/A
Well you took me.
Gtr. 3 (elec.)
w/medium amp gain
full
1/2
Play Gtr. 3 part
Gtrs. 1+2 (combined part)

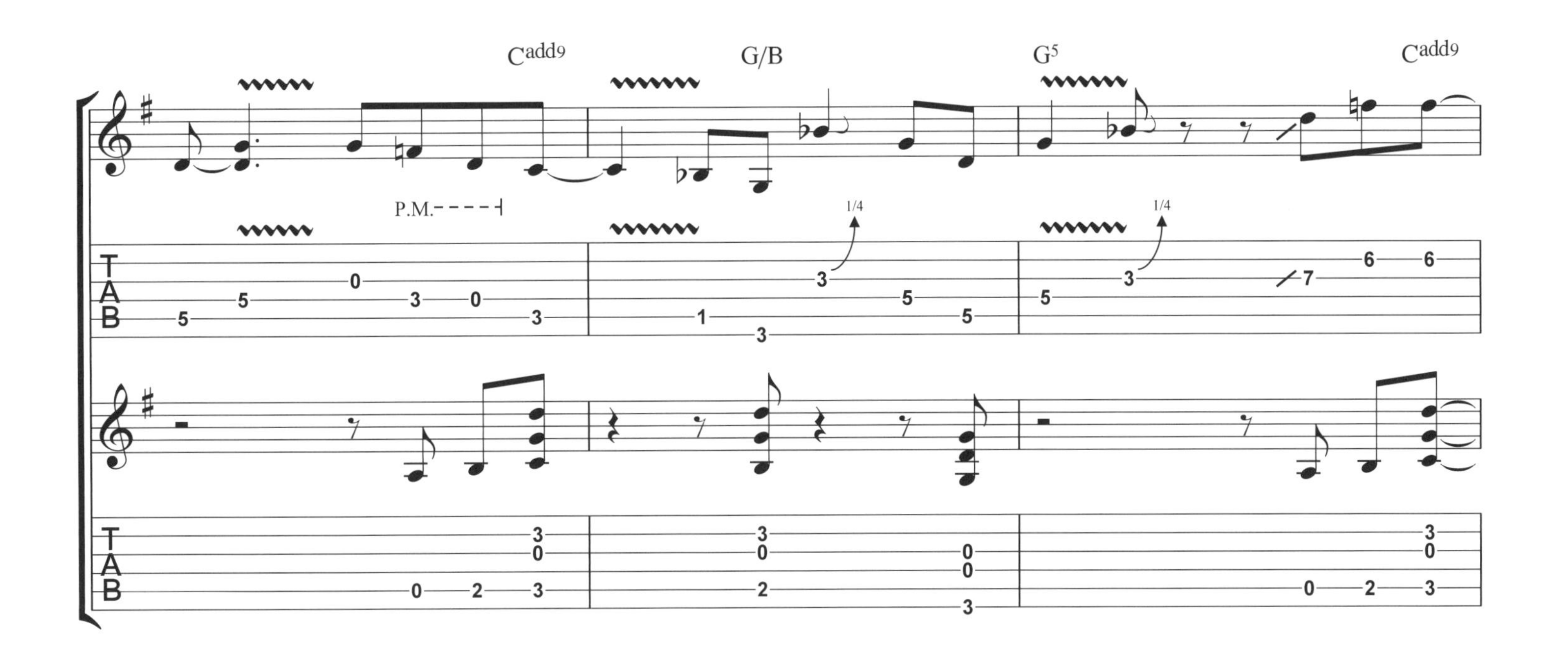
Cadd9
G/B
G5
Cadd9
P.M.
1/4
1/4

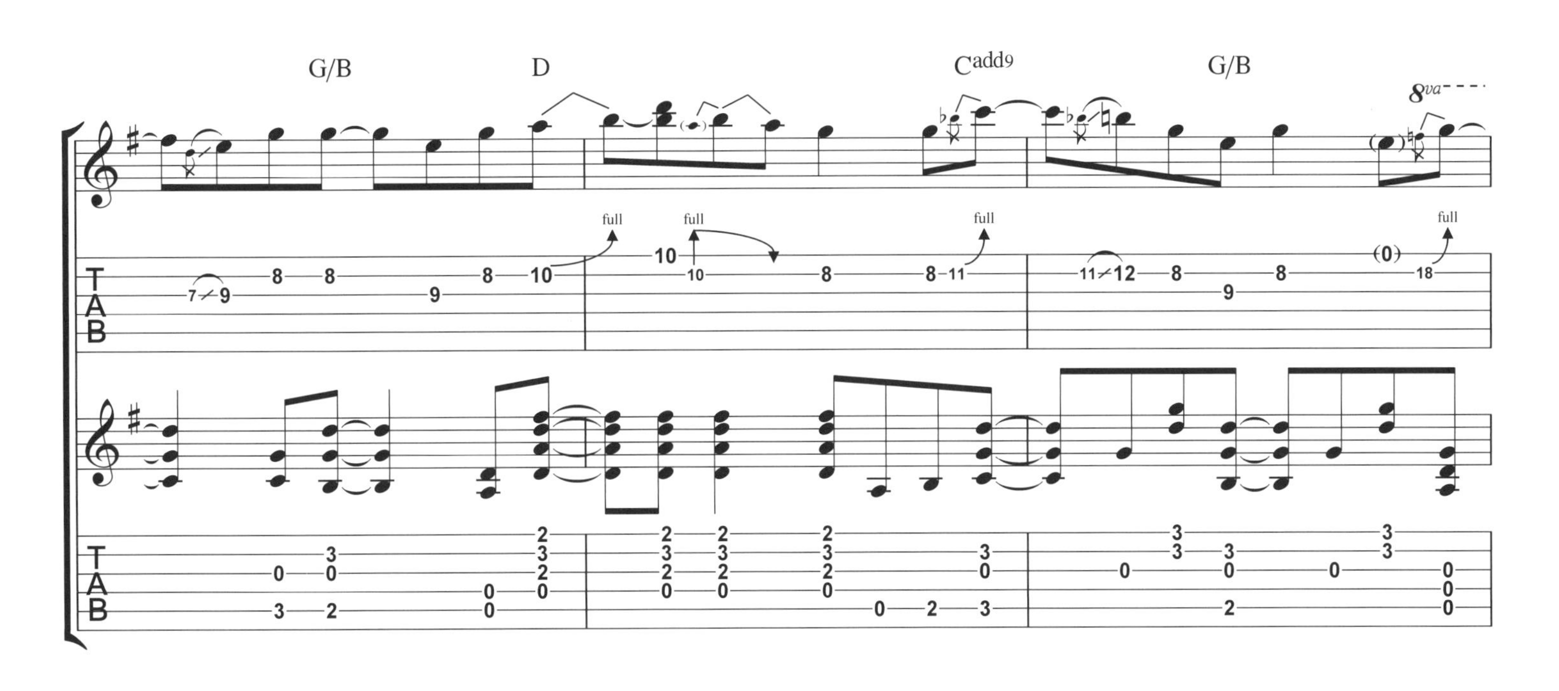
G/B
D
Cadd9
G/B
8va
full
full
full
full

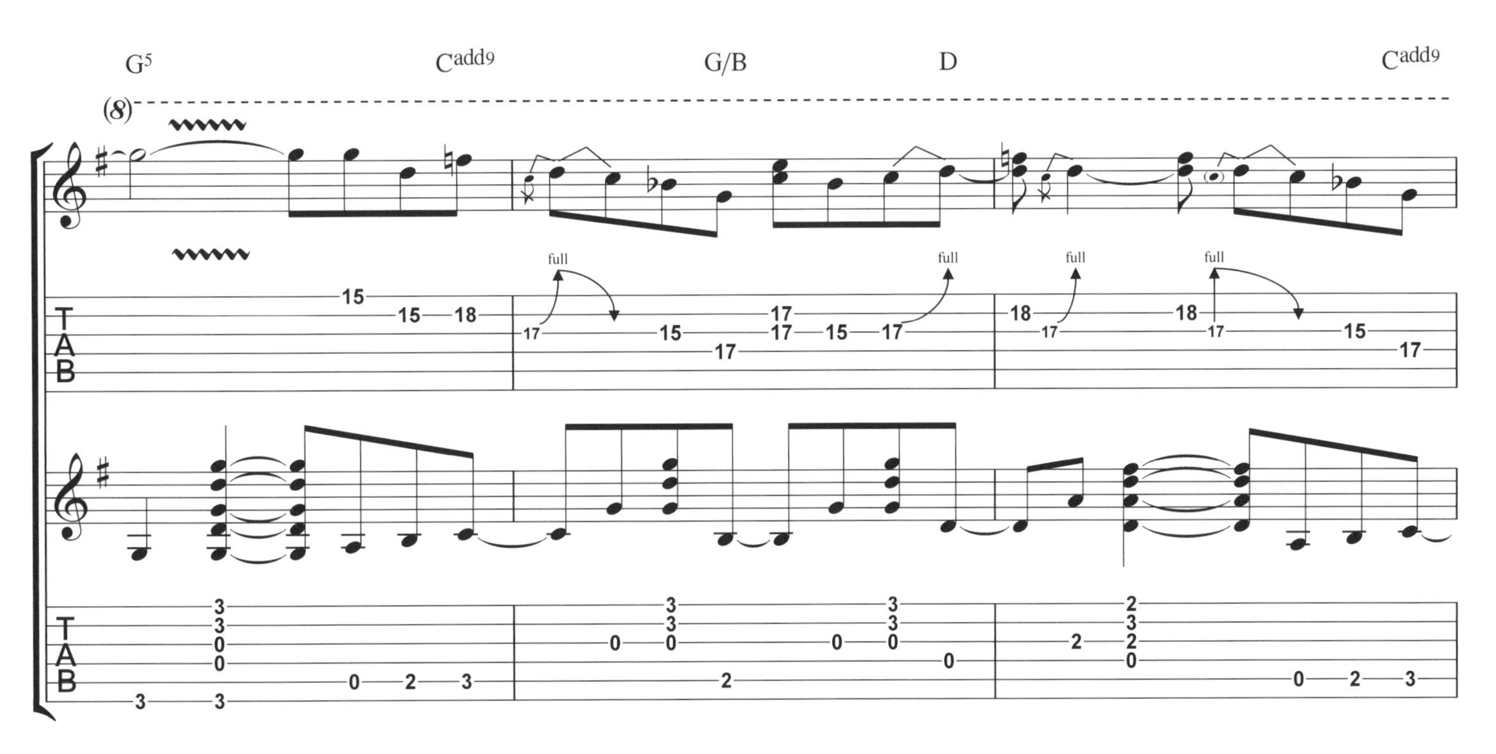
G5
Cadd9
G/B
D
Cadd9
full
full
full
full

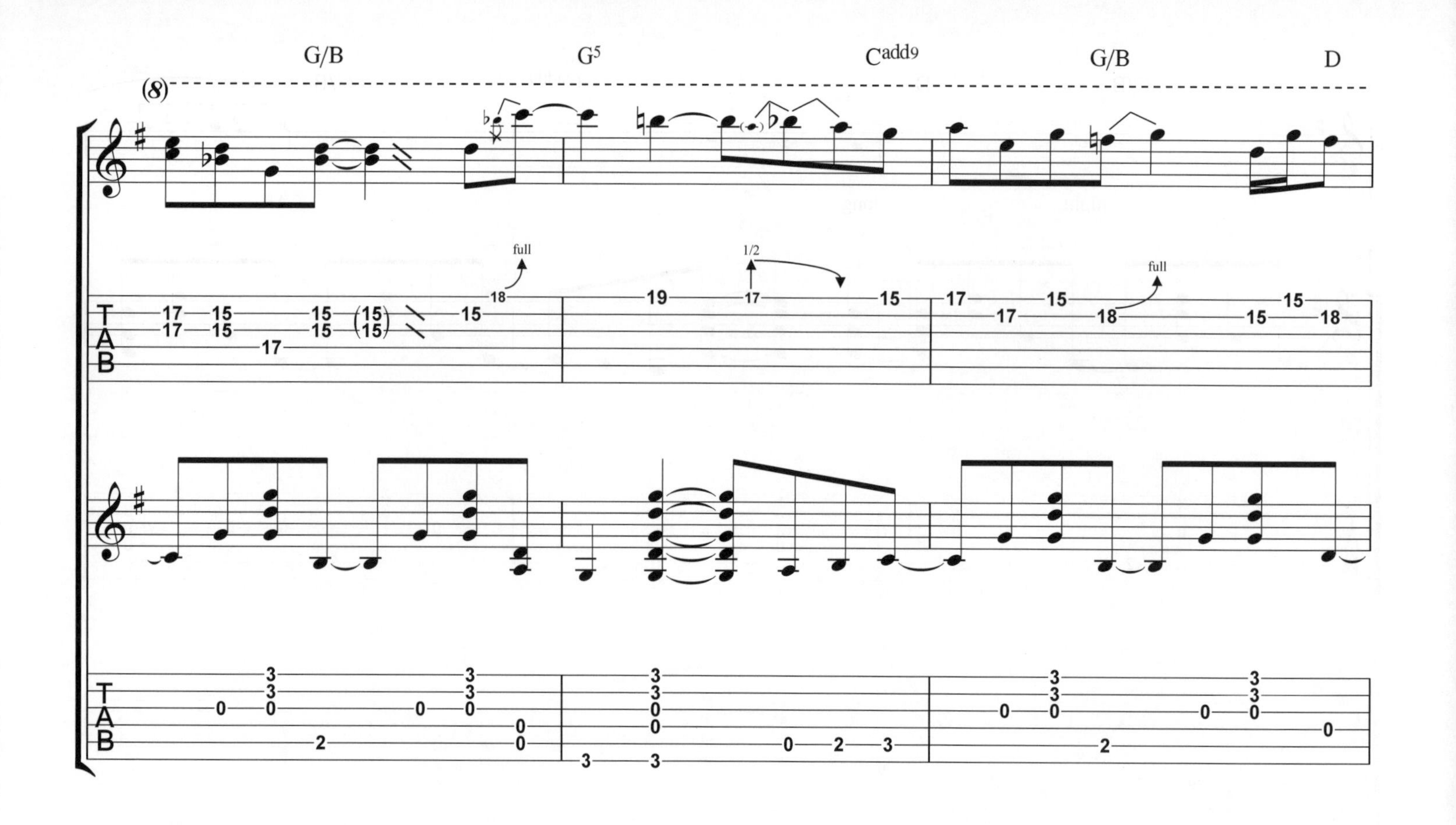
G/B
G5
Cadd9
G/B
D
(8)
full
1/2
full
T
A
B

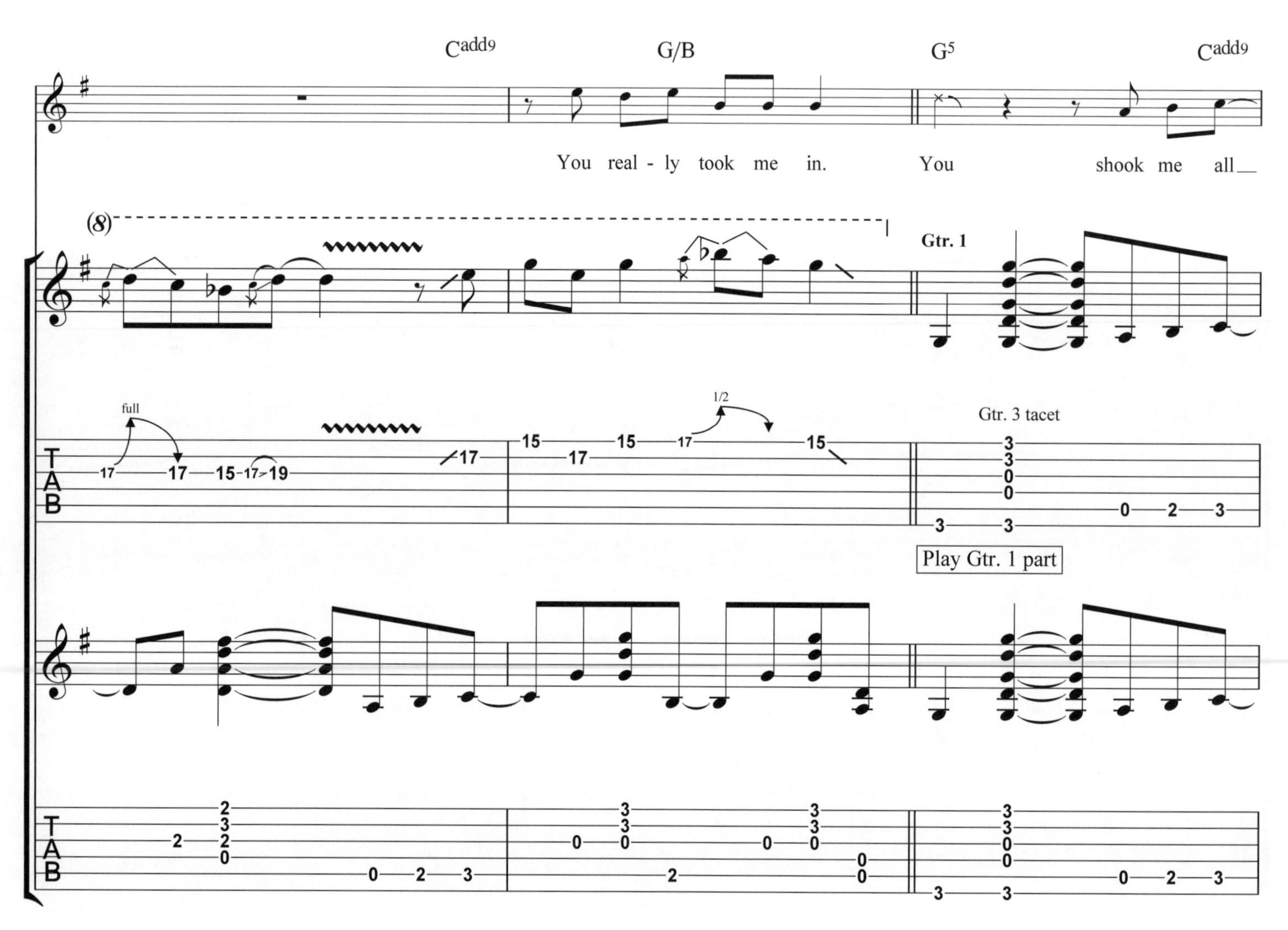
Cadd9
G/B
G5
Cadd9
You real - ly took me in.
You shook me all
(8)
Gtr. 1
full
1/2
Gtr. 3 tacet
Play Gtr. 1 part
T
A
B

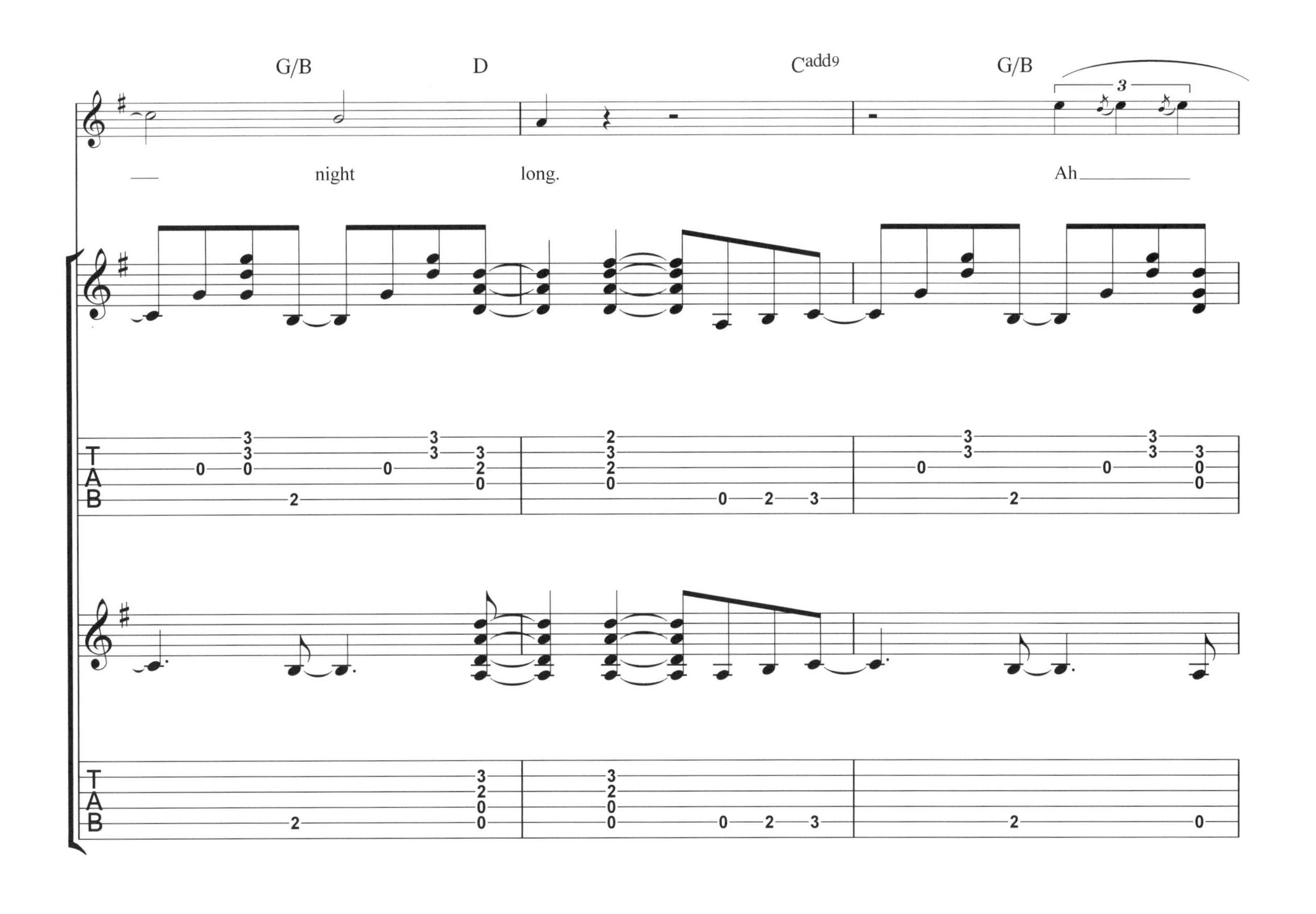
G/B
D
Cadd9
G/B
3
night
long.
Ah
T
A
B

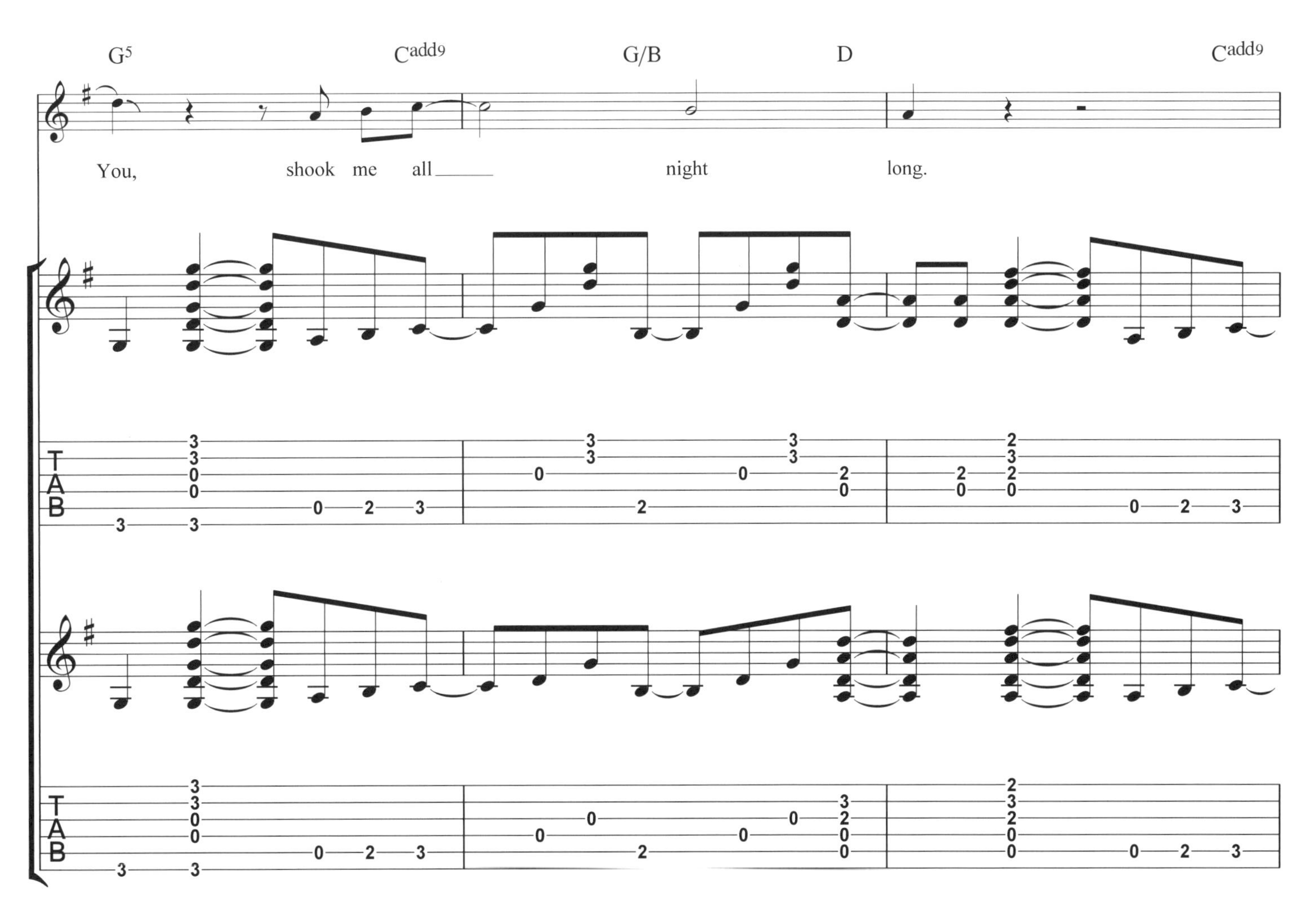
G5
Cadd9
G/B
D
Cadd9
You,
shook me all
night
long.
T
A
B

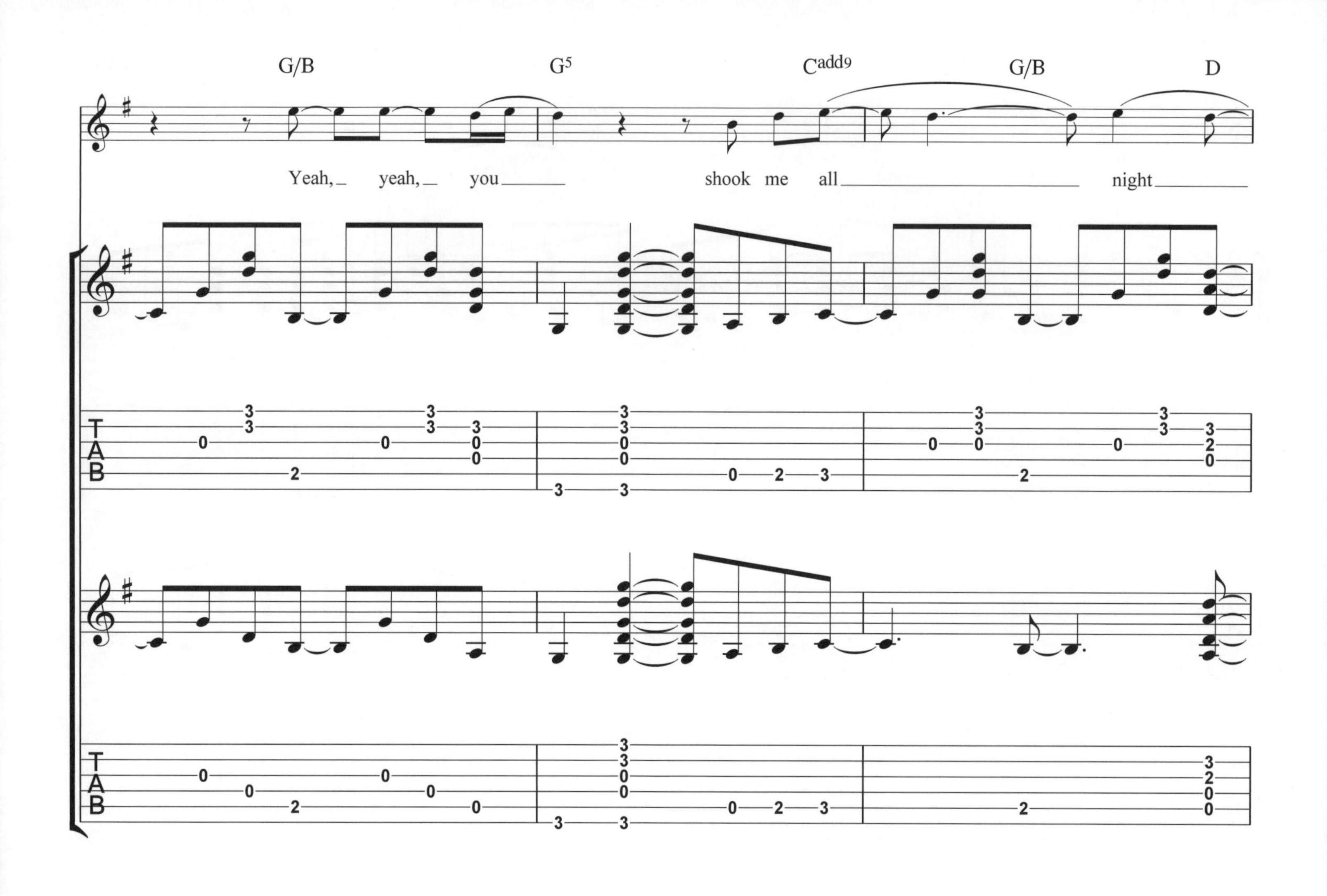
G/B
G5
Cadd9
G/B
D
Yeah, yeah, you shook me all night

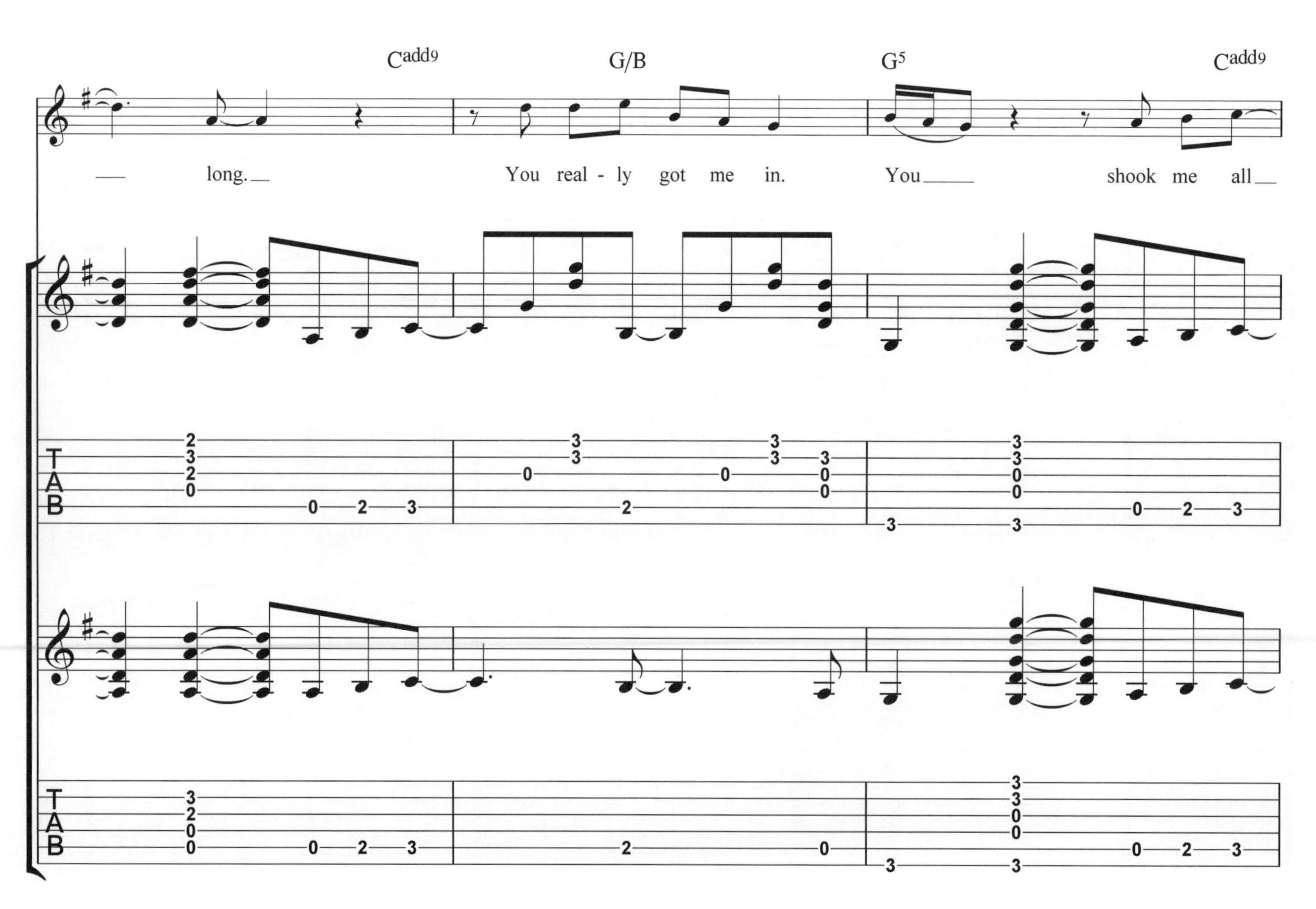
Cadd9
G/B
G5
Cadd9
long. You real - ly got me in. You shook me all

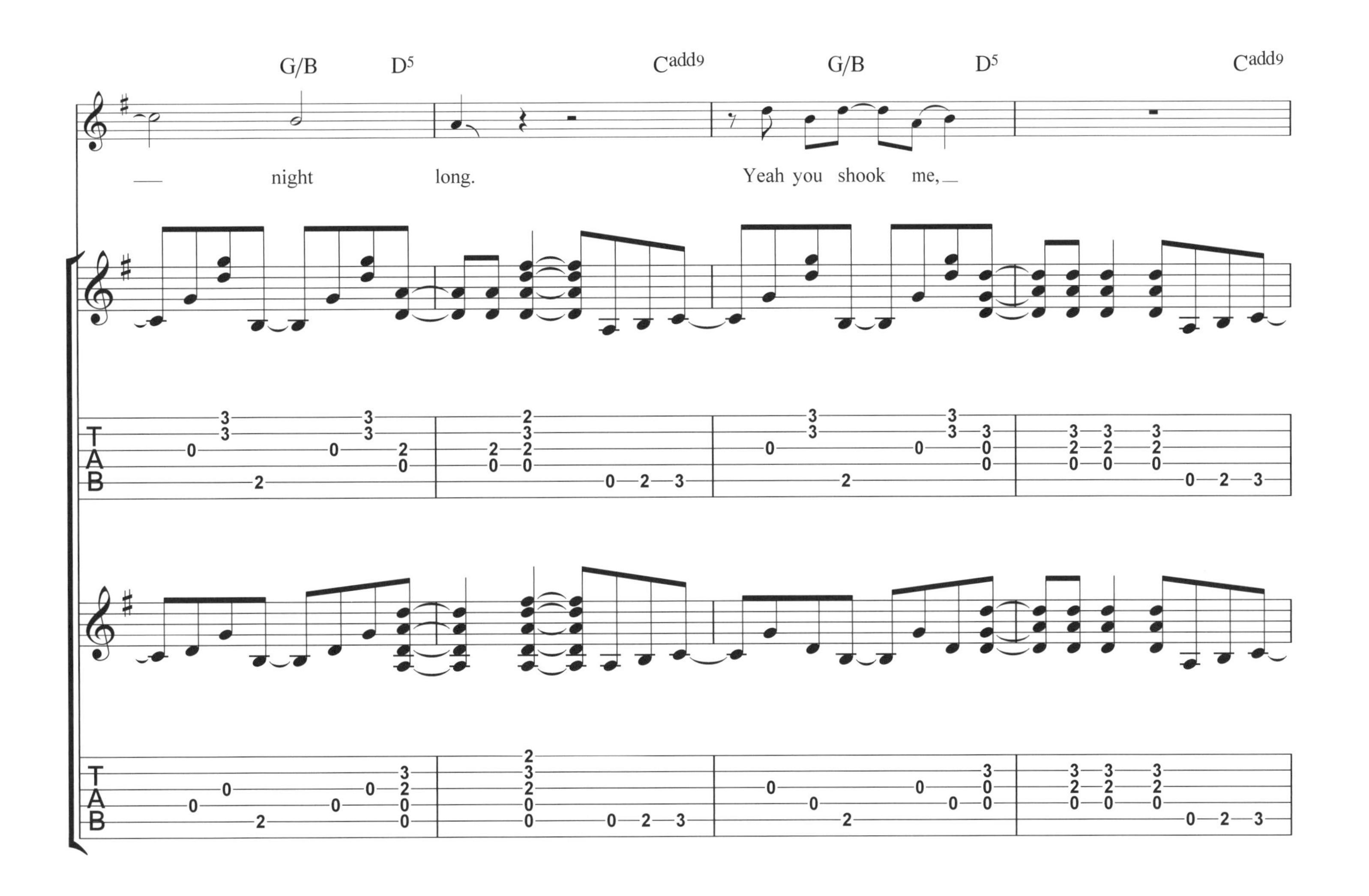
G/B
D5
Cadd9
G/B
D5
Cadd9
night
long.
Yeah you shook me,

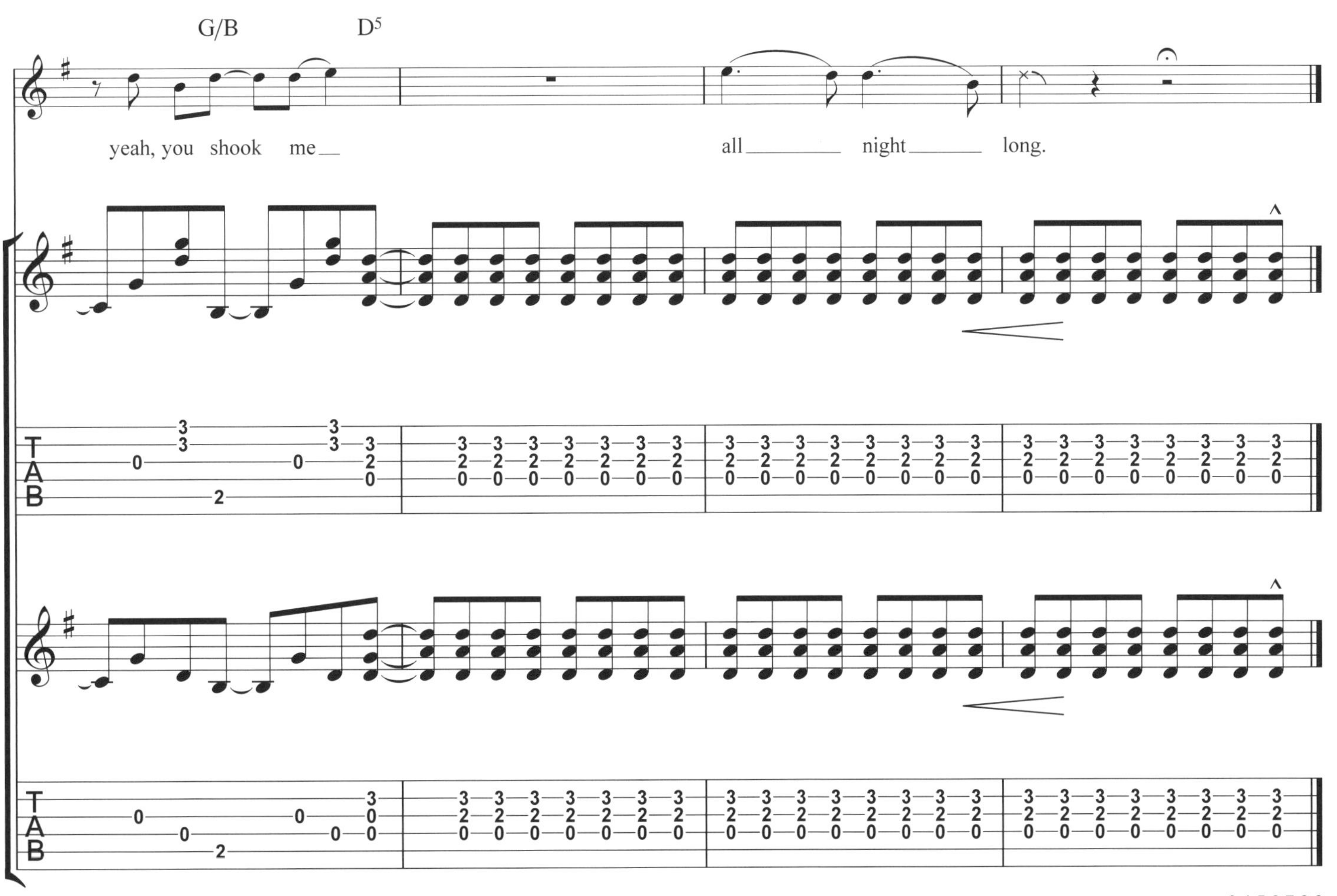
G/B
D5
yeah, you shook me
all
night
long.

3 4 5 6 7 8 9

**CD track listing**

**Disc 1**
**Full instrumental performances (with guitar)...**

1 ***back in black***
(A. Young/M. Young/B. Johnson) J. Albert & Son Pty. Ltd

2 ***dirty deeds done dirt cheap***
(A. Young/M. Young/B. Scott) J. Albert & Son Pty. Ltd.

3 ***for those about to rock (we salute you)***
(A. Young/M. Young/B. Johnson) J. Albert & Son Pty. Ltd.

4 ***hells bells***
(A. Young/M. Young/B. Johnson) J. Albert & Son Pty. Ltd.

5 ***highway to hell***
(A. Young/M. Young/B. Scott) J. Albert & Son Pty. Ltd.

6 ***it's a long way to the top (if you wanna rock 'n' roll)***
(A. Young/M. Young/B. Scott) J. Albert & Son Pty. Ltd.

7 ***let there be rock***
(A. Young/M. Young/B. Scott) J. Albert & Son Pty. Ltd.

8 ***rock and roll ain't noise pollution***
(A. Young/M. Young/B. Johnson) J. Albert & Son Pty. Ltd

9 ***rock 'n' roll train***
(A. Young/M. Young) Leidseplein Presse B.V.
Administered by J. Albert & Son Pty. Ltd.

10 ***thunderstruck***
(A. Young/M. Young) J. Albert & Son Pty. Ltd.

11 ***t.n.t.***
(A. Young/M. Young/B. Scott) J. Albert & Son Pty. Ltd.

12 ***whole lotta rosie***
(A. Young/M. Young/B. Scott) J. Albert & Son Pty. Ltd.

13 ***you shook me all night long***
(A. Young/M. Young/B. Johnson) J. Albert & Son Pty. Ltd.

**Disc 2**
**Backing tracks (without guitar)...**

1 ***back in black***

2 ***dirty deeds done dirt cheap***

3 ***for those about to rock (we salute you)***

4 ***hells bells***

5 ***highway to hell***

6 ***it's a long way to the top (if you wanna rock 'n' roll)***

7 ***let there be rock***

8 ***rock and roll ain't noise pollution***

9 ***rock 'n' roll train***

10 ***thunderstruck***

11 ***t.n.t.***

12 ***whole lotta rosie***

13 ***you shook me all night long***

**To remove your CD from the plastic sleeve, lift the small lip to break the perforations. Replace the disc after use for convenient storage.**